THE

CENTENARY EDITION

OF THE WORKS OF

NATHANIEL HAWTHORNE

Volume VII

A WONDER BOOK

and

TANGLEWOOD TALES

EDITORS

General Editors

WILLIAM CHARVAT, 1905–1966

ROY HARVEY PEARCE

CLAUDE M. SIMPSON

FREDSON BOWERS, *Textual Editor*

L. NEAL SMITH, *Associate Textual Editor*

JOHN MANNING, *Associate Textual Editor*

A PUBLICATION OF
THE OHIO STATE UNIVERSITY CENTER
FOR TEXTUAL STUDIES

NATHANIEL HAWTHORNE

A WONDER BOOK

and

TANGLEWOOD TALES

Ohio State University Press

CENTER FOR EDITIONS OF
AMERICAN AUTHORS
AN APPROVED TEXT
MODERN LANGUAGE
ASSOCIATION OF AMERICA

®

*Editorial expenses for this volume have been supported by
grants from the National Endowment for the Humanities
administered through the
Center for Editions of American Authors of the
Modern Language Association*

Standard Book Number 8142-0158-X
Library of Congress Catalogue Card Number 77-150221
Copyright © 1972 by the Ohio State University Press

ACKNOWLEDGMENTS

THE EDITORS express their gratitude for the generous assist-
ance of C. Waller Barrett, of Charlottesville, Virginia;
Edmund Berkeley and Joan Crane, of the University of
Virginia; Douglas Ewing, the Pierpont Morgan Library;
Carolyn Jakeman, the Houghton Library of Harvard Uni-
versity; Norman Holmes Pearson, of Yale University; Lola
L. Szladits, the Berg Collection of the New York Public
Library; and the Committee on Research of the University
of California, San Diego.

Thanks for work in the preparation of *True Stories, A
Wonder Book,* and *Tanglewood Tales* go to F. Dean Altizer,
Philip A. H. Brown, David Clayton, Andrew Hilen, Richard
Jacobson, Via Jankovic, David Lane, Diane Darrow Maresca,
R. Mitra, Blake Nevius, Calvin Schorer, and Robert Ward,
in San Diego; and to Marianne Bailey, Peggy Bennington,
Frances Lappe, and Don Nigro, in Columbus.

Permission to transcribe and edit manuscript materials was
graciously given by the Henry W. and Albert A. Berg Collection of the New York Public Library, Astor, Lenox, and
Tilden foundations; the Pierpont Morgan Library; the Historical Society of Pennsylvania; the Philip H. and A. S. W.
Rosenbach Foundation; and the Barrett Collection of the
University of Virginia Library.

The project has been made possible through the support
of the Department of English, the Graduate School, the
University Libraries, and the Research Foundation of the
Ohio State University.

THE EDITORS

CONTENTS

A Wonder Book

Tanglewood Tales

The introduction by Roy Harvey Pearce to the two volumes of the Centenary Edition devoted to Hawthorne's books for children will be found on pages 287–311 of Volume VI.

ILLUSTRATIONS

Frontispiece to the 1852 first edition of *A Wonder Book.*
(page 2)

Illustration to "The Dragon's Teeth" in the 1853 first edition of *Tanglewood Tales.*
(page 174)

A WONDER BOOK

PREFACE

THE AUTHOR has long been of opinion, that many of the classical myths were capable of being rendered into very capital reading for children. In the little volume here offered to the Public, he has worked up half-a-dozen of them, with this end in view. A great freedom of treatment was necessary to his plan; but it will be observed by every one, who attempts to render these legends malleable in his intellectual furnace, that they are marvellously independent of all temporary modes and circumstances. They remain essentially the same, after changes that would affect the identity of almost anything else.

He does not, therefore, plead guilty to a sacrilege, in having sometimes shaped anew, as his fancy dictated, the forms that have been hallowed by an antiquity of two or three thousand years. No epoch of time can claim a copyright in these immortal fables. They seem never to have been made; and certainly, so long as man exists, they can never perish; but, by their indestructibility itself, they are legitimate subjects for every age to clothe with its own garniture of manners and sentiment, and to imbue with its own morality. In the present version, they may have lost much of their classical

---

Facing: Frontispiece to the 1852 first edition of *A Wonder Book.*

aspect, (or, at all events, the Author has not been careful to preserve it,) and have perhaps assumed a Gothic or romantic guise.

In performing this pleasant task—for it has been really a task fit for hot weather, and one of the most agreeable, of a literary kind, which he ever undertook—the Author has not always thought it necessary to write downward, in order to meet the comprehension of children. He has generally suffered the theme to soar, whenever such was its tendency, and when he himself was buoyant enough to follow without an effort. Children possess an unestimated sensibility to whatever is deep or high, in imagination or feeling, so long as it is simple, likewise. It is only the artificial and the complex that bewilders them.

Lenox, July 15th, 1851.

TANGLEWOOD PORCH

B ENEATH the porch of the country-seat called
Tanglewood, one fine autumnal morning, was assembled a merry party of little folks, with a tall youth in
the midst of them. They had planned a nutting expedition,
and were impatiently waiting for the mists to roll up the
hill-slopes, and for the sun to pour the warmth of the Indian
Summer over the fields and pastures, and into the nooks of
the many-colored woods. There was the prospect of as fine
a day as ever gladdened the aspect of this beautiful and
comfortable world. As yet, however, the morning mist filled
up the whole length and breadth of the valley, above which,
on a gently sloping eminence, the mansion stood.

This body of white vapor extended to within less than a
hundred yards of the house. It completely hid everything
beyond that distance, except a few ruddy or yellow tree-tops,
which here and there emerged, and were glorified by the
early sunshine, as was likewise the broad surface of the mist.
Four or five miles off, to the southward, rose the summit of
Monument Mountain, and seemed to be floating on a cloud.
Some fifteen miles farther away, in the same direction,

appeared the loftier Dome of Taconic, looking blue and indistinct, and hardly so substantial as the vapory sea that almost rolled over it. The nearer hills, which bordered the valley, were half submerged, and were specked with little cloud-wreaths all the way to their tops. On the whole, there was so much cloud, and so little solid earth, that it had the effect of a vision.

The children above-mentioned, being as full of life as they could hold, kept overflowing from the porch of Tanglewood, and scampering along the gravel-walk, or rushing across the dewy herbage of the lawn. I can hardly tell how many of these small people there were; not less than nine or ten, however, nor more than a dozen, of all sorts, sizes, and ages, whether girls or boys. They were brothers, sisters, and cousins, together with a few of their young acquaintances, who had been invited by Mr. and Mrs. Pringle to spend some of this delightful weather with their own children, at Tanglewood. I am afraid to tell you their names, or even to give them any names which other children have ever been called by; because, to my certain knowledge, authors sometimes get themselves into great trouble by accidentally giving the names of real persons to the characters in their books. For this reason, I mean to call them Primrose, Periwinkle, Sweet Fern, Dandelion, Blue Eye, Clover, Huckleberry, Cowslip, Squash Blossom, Milkweed, Plantain, and Butter-cup; although, to be sure, such titles might better suit a group of fairies than a company of earthly children.

It is not to be supposed that these little folks were to be permitted by their careful fathers and mothers, uncles, aunts, or grandparents, to stray abroad into the woods and fields, without the guardianship of some particularly grave and elderly person. Oh, no, indeed! In the first sentence of my book, you will recollect that I spoke of a tall youth, standing in the midst of the children. His name—(and I shall let you know his real name, because he considers it a great honor to have told the stories that are here to be printed)—his name was Eustace Bright. He was a student at Williams College, and had reached, I think, at this period, the venerable age of eighteen years; so that he felt quite like a grandfather towards Periwinkle, Dandelion, Huckleberry, Squash Blossom, Milkweed, and the rest, who were only half or a third as venerable as he. A trouble in his eyesight (such as many students think it necessary to have, now-a-days, in order to prove their diligence at their books) had kept him from college a week or two after the beginning of the term. But, for my part, I have seldom met with a pair of eyes that looked as if they could see farther or better, than those of Eustace Bright.

This learned student was slender, and rather pale, as all Yankee students are, but yet of a healthy aspect, and as light and active as if he had wings to his shoes. By-the-by, being much addicted to wading through streamlets and across meadows, he had put on cow-hide boots for the expedition. He wore a linen blouse, a cloth cap, and a pair of green spectacles, which he had assumed, probably, less for the preservation of his eyes, than for the dignity that they imparted to his countenance. In either case, however, he might as well have let them alone; for Huckleberry, a mischievous little elf, crept behind Eustace as he sat on the steps of the porch; snatched the spectacles from his nose, and clapt them on her own; and, as the student forgot to take them back, they fell off into the grass, and lay there till the next spring.

Now, Eustace Bright, you must know, had won great fame among the children as a narrator of wonderful stories; and though he sometimes pretended to be annoyed, when they teazed him for more, and more, and always for more, yet I really doubt whether he liked anything quite so well as to tell them. You might have seen his eyes twinkle, therefore, when Clover, Sweet Fern, Cowslip, Butter-cup, and most of their playmates, besought him to relate one of his stories, while they were waiting for the mist to clear up.

"Yes, Cousin Eustace," said Primrose, who was a bright girl of twelve, with laughing eyes, and a nose that turned up a little, "the morning is certainly the best time for the stories, with which you so often tire out our patience. We shall be in less danger of hurting your feelings by falling asleep at the most interesting points—as little Cowslip and I did, last night!"

"Naughty Primrose," cried Cowslip, a child of six years old, "I did not fall asleep, and I only shut my eyes, so as to see a picture of what Cousin Eustace was telling about. His stories are good to hear at night, because we can dream about them, asleep;—and good in the morning, too, because then we can dream about them, awake. So I hope he will tell us one, this very minute!"

"Thank you, my little Cowslip," said Eustace. "Certainly, you shall have the best story I can think of, if it were only for defending me so well from that naughty Primrose. But, children, I have already told you so many fairy tales, that I doubt whether there is a single one which you have not heard at least twice over. I am afraid you will fall asleep, in reality, if I repeat any of them again."

"No, no, no!" cried Blue Eye, Periwinkle, Plantain, and half-a-dozen others. "We like a story all the better for having heard it two or three times before."

And it is a truth, as regards children, that a story seems often to deepen its mark in their interest, not merely by two or three, but by numberless repetitions. But Eustace Bright, in the exuberance of his resources, scorned to avail himself of an advantage, which an older story-teller would have been glad to grasp at.

"It would be a great pity," said he, "if a man of my learning (to say nothing of original fancy) could not find a new story, every day, year in and year out, for children such as you. I will tell you one of the nursery-tales that were made for the amusement of our great, old grandmother, the Earth, when she was a child in frock and pin-a-fore. There are a hundred such; and it is a wonder to me, that they have not long ago been put into picture-books for little girls and boys. But, instead of that, old gray-bearded grandsires pore over them, in musty volumes of Greek, and puzzle themselves with trying to find out when, and how, and for what, they were made."

"Well, well, well, well, Cousin Eustace!" cried all the children at once. "Talk no more about your stories, but begin!"

"Sit down, then, every soul of you," said Eustace Bright, "and be all as still as so many mice. At the slightest interruption, whether from great, naughty Primrose, little Dandelion, or any other, I shall bite the story short off between my teeth, and swallow the untold part. But, in the first place, do any of you know what a Gorgon is?"

"I do," said Primrose.

"Then hold your tongue!" rejoined Eustace, who had rather she would have known nothing about the matter. "Hold all your tongues; and I shall tell you a sweet-pretty story of a Gorgon's Head."

And so he did, as you may begin to read on the next page. Working up his sophomorical erudition, with a good deal of tact, and incurring great obligations to Professor Anthon, he, nevertheless, disregarded all classical authorities, whenever the vagrant audacity of his imagination impelled him to do so.

THE GORGON'S HEAD

PERSEUS was the son of Danaë, who was the daughter of a king. And when Perseus was a very little boy, some wicked people put his mother and himself into a chest, and set them afloat upon the sea. The wind blew freshly, and drove the chest away from the shore, and the uneasy billows tossed it up and down; while Danaë clasped her child closely to her bosom, and dreaded that some big wave would dash its foamy crest over them both. The chest sailed on, however, and neither sank nor was upset; until, when night was coming, it floated so near an island that it got entangled in a fisherman's nets, and was drawn out high and dry upon the sand. The island was called Seriphus, and it was reigned over by King Polydectes, who happened to be the fisherman's brother.

This fisherman, I am glad to tell you, was an exceedingly humane and upright man. He showed great kindness to Danaë and her little boy, and continued to befriend them, until Perseus had grown to be a handsome youth, very strong and active, and skilful in the use of arms. Long before this time, King Polydectes had seen the two strangers—the mother and her child—who had come to his dominions in a floating chest. As he was not good and kind, like his brother the fisherman, but extremely wicked, he resolved to send Perseus on a dangerous enterprise, in which he would probably be killed, and then to do some great mischief to Danaë herself. So this bad-hearted king spent a long while in considering what was the most dangerous thing that a young man could possibly undertake to perform. At last, having hit upon an enterprise that promised to turn out as fatally as he desired, he sent for the youthful Perseus.

The young man came to the palace, and found the king sitting upon his throne.

"Perseus," said King Polydectes, smiling craftily upon him, "you are grown up a fine young man. You and your good mother have received a great deal of kindness from myself, as well as from my worthy brother, the fisherman, and I suppose you would not be sorry to repay some of it!"

"Please your majesty," answered Perseus, "I would willingly risk my life to do so."

"Well, then," continued the king, still with a cunning smile on his lips, "I have a little adventure to propose to you; and, as you are a brave and enterprising youth, you will doubtless look upon it as a great piece of good luck to have so rare an opportunity of distinguishing yourself. You must know, my good Perseus, I think of getting married to the beautiful Princess Hippodamia; and it is customary, on these occasions, to make the bride a present of some far-fetched and elegant curiosity. I have been a little perplexed, I must honestly confess, where to obtain anything likely to please a princess of her exquisite taste. But, this morning, I flatter myself, I have thought of precisely the article."

"And can I assist your majesty in obtaining it?" cried Perseus eagerly.

"You can, if you are as brave a youth as I believe you to be," replied King Polydectes, with the utmost graciousness of manner. "The bridal gift, which I have set my heart on presenting to the beautiful Hippodamia, is the head of the Gorgon Medusa, with the snaky locks; and I depend on you, my dear Perseus, to bring it to me. So, as I am anxious to settle affairs with the princess, the sooner you go in quest of the Gorgon, the better I shall be pleased."

"I will set out tomorrow morning," answered Perseus.

"Pray do so, my gallant youth!" rejoined the king. "And, Perseus, in cutting off the Gorgon's head, be careful to make a clean stroke, so as not to injure its appearance. You must bring it home in the very best condition, in order to suit the exquisite taste of the beautiful Princess Hippodamia."

Perseus left the palace, but was scarcely out of hearing before Polydectes burst into a laugh; being greatly amused, wicked king that he was, to find how readily the young man fell into the snare. The news quickly spread abroad, that Perseus had undertaken to cut off the head of Medusa with the snaky locks. Everybody was rejoiced; for most of the inhabitants of the island were as wicked as the king himself, and would have liked nothing better than to see some enormous mischief happen to Danaë and her son. The only good man, in this unfortunate island of Seriphus, appears to have been the fisherman. As Perseus walked along, therefore, the people pointed after him, and made mouths, and winked to one another, and ridiculed him as loudly as they dared.

"Ho, ho!" cried they. "Medusa's snakes will sting him soundly!"

Now, there were three Gorgons alive, at that period; and they were the most strange and terrible monsters that had ever been seen, since the world was made, or that have been seen in after days, or that are likely to be seen, in all time to come. I hardly know what sort of creature or hobgoblin to call them. They were three sisters, and seem to have borne some distant resemblance to women, but were really a very frightful and mischievous species of dragon. It is indeed difficult to imagine what hideous beings these three sisters were. Why, instead of locks of hair, if you can believe me, they had each of them a hundred enormous snakes growing on their heads, all alive, twisting, wriggling, curling, and thrusting out their venomous tongues, with forked stings at the end! The teeth of the Gorgons were terribly long tusks; their hands were made of brass; and their bodies were all over scales, which, if not iron, were something as hard and impenetrable. They had wings, too, and exceedingly splendid ones, I can assure you; for every feather in them was pure, bright, glittering, burnished gold, and they looked very dazzlingly, no doubt, when the Gorgons were flying about in the sunshine.

But, when people happened to catch a glimpse of their glittering brightness, aloft in the air, they seldom stopt to gaze, but ran and hid themselves as speedily as they could. You will think, perhaps, that they were afraid of being stung by the serpents that served the Gorgons instead of hair—or of having their heads bitten off by their ugly tusks—or of being torn all to pieces by their brazen claws. Well, to be sure, these were some of the dangers, but by no means the greatest, nor the most difficult to avoid. For the worst thing about these abominable Gorgons was, that, if once a poor mortal fixed his eyes full upon one of their faces, he was certain, that very instant, to be changed from warm flesh and blood into cold and lifeless stone!

Thus, as you will easily perceive, it was a very dangerous adventure that the wicked King Polydectes had contrived for this innocent young man. Perseus himself, when he had thought over the matter, could not help seeing that he had very little chance of coming safely through it, and that he was far more likely to become a stone image, than to bring back the head of Medusa with the snaky locks. For, not to speak of other difficulties, there was one which it would have puzzled an older man than Perseus to get over. Not only must he fight with and slay this golden-winged, iron-scaled, long-tusked, brazen-clawed, snaky-haired monster, but he must do it with his eyes shut, or, at least, without so much as a glance at the enemy with whom he was contending. Else, while his arm was lifted to strike, he would stiffen into stone, and stand with that uplifted arm for centuries, until time, and the wind and weather, should crumble him quite away. This would be a very sad thing to befal a young man, who wanted to perform a great many brave deeds, and to enjoy a great deal of happiness, in this bright and beautiful world.

So disconsolate did these thoughts make him, that Perseus could not bear to tell his mother what he had undertaken to do. He therefore took his shield, girded on his sword, and crossed over from the island to the mainland, where he sat down in a solitary place, and hardly refrained from shedding tears.

But while he was in this sorrowful mood, he heard a voice close beside him.

"Perseus," said the voice, "why are you sad?"

He lifted his head from his hands, in which he had hidden it; and, behold! all alone as Perseus had supposed himself to be, there was a stranger in the solitary place. It was a brisk, intelligent, and remarkably shrewd-looking young man, with a cloak over his shoulders, an odd sort of cap on his head, a strangely twisted staff in his hand, and a short and very crooked sword hanging by his side. He was exceedingly light and active in his figure, like a person much accustomed to gymnastic exercises, and well able to leap or run. Above all, the stranger had such a cheerful, knowing, and helpful aspect, (though it was certainly a little mischievous, into the bargain,) that Perseus could not help feeling his spirits grow livelier, as he gazed at him. Besides, being really a courageous youth, he felt greatly ashamed that anybody should have found him with tears in his eyes, like a timid little schoolboy, when, after all, there might be no occasion for despair. So Perseus wiped his eyes, and answered the stranger pretty briskly, putting on as brave a look as he could.

"I am not so very sad," said he—"only thoughtful about an adventure that I have undertaken."

"Oho!" answered the stranger. "Well; tell me all about it, and possibly I may be of service to you. I have helped a good many young men through adventures that looked difficult enough beforehand. Perhaps you may have heard of me. I have more names than one; but the name of Quicksilver suits me as well as any other. Tell me what your trouble is; and we will talk the matter over, and see what can be done."

The stranger's words and manner put Perseus into quite a different mood from his former one. He resolved to tell Quicksilver all his difficulties; since he could not easily be worse off than he already was, and, very possibly, his new friend might give him some advice that would turn out well in the end. So he let the stranger know, in few words, pre- cisely what the case was;—how that King Polydectes wanted the head of Medusa with the snaky locks, as a bridal gift for the beautiful Princess Hippodamia, and how that he had undertaken to get it for him, but was afraid of being turned into stone.

"And that would be a great pity," said Quicksilver, with his mischievous smile. "You would make a very handsome marble statue, it is true; and it would be a considerable num- ber of centuries before you crumbled away. But, on the whole, one would rather be a young man for a few years, than a stone image for a great many."

"Oh, far rather!" exclaimed Perseus, with the tears again standing in his eyes. "And, besides, what would my dear mother do, if her beloved son were turned into a stone!"

"Well, well, let us hope that the affair will not turn out so very badly," replied Quicksilver, in an encouraging tone. "I am the very person to help you, if anybody can. My sister and myself will do our utmost to bring you safe through the adventure, ugly as it now looks."

"Your sister?" repeated Perseus.

"Yes; my sister," said the stranger. "She is very wise, I promise you; and as for myself, I generally have all my wits about me, such as they are. If you show yourself bold and cautious, and follow our advice, you need not fear being a stone image yet awhile. But, first of all, you must polish your shield till you can see your face in it as distinctly as in a mirror."

This seemed to Perseus rather an odd beginning of the adventure; for he thought it of far more consequence that the shield should be strong enough to defend him from the Gorgon's brazen claws, than that it should be bright enough to show him the reflection of his face. However, concluding that Quicksilver knew better than himself, he immediately set to work, and scrubbed the shield with so much diligence and good-will, that it very quickly shone like the moon at harvest-time. Quicksilver looked at it with a smile, and nodded his approbation. Then, taking off his own short and crooked sword, he girded it about Perseus, instead of the one which he had before worn.

"No sword but mine will answer your purpose," observed he. "The blade has a most excellent temper, and will cut through iron and brass as easily as through the slenderest twig. And now we will set out. The next thing is to find the Three Gray Women, who will tell us where to find the Nymphs."

"The Three Gray Women!" cried Perseus, to whom this seemed only a new difficulty in the path of his adventure. "Pray, who may the Three Gray Women be? I never heard of them before."

"They are three very strange old ladies," said Quicksilver, laughing. "They have but one eye among them, and only one tooth! Moreover, you must find them out by starlight, or in the dusk of the evening; for they never show themselves by the light either of the sun or moon."

"But," said Perseus, "why should I waste my time with these Three Gray Women? Would it not be better to set out at once in search of the terrible Gorgons?"

"No, no," answered his friend. "There are other things to be done, before you can find your way to the Gorgons. There is nothing for it, but to hunt up these old ladies; and when we meet with them, you may be sure that the Gorgons are not a great way off. Come; let us be stirring!"

Perseus, by this time, felt so much confidence in his companion's sagacity, that he made no more objections, and professed himself ready to begin the adventure immediately. They accordingly set out, and walked at a pretty brisk pace; so brisk, indeed, that Perseus found it rather difficult to keep up with his nimble friend Quicksilver. To say the truth, he had a singular idea that Quicksilver was furnished with a pair of winged shoes, which, of course, helped him along marvellously. And then, too, when Perseus looked sideways at him, out of the corner of his eye, he seemed to see wings on the side of his head; although, if he turned a full gaze, there were no such things to be perceived, but only an odd kind of cap. But, at all events, the twisted staff was evidently a great convenience to Quicksilver, and enabled him to proceed so fast, that Perseus, though a remarkably active young man, began to be out of breath.

"Here!" cried Quicksilver, at last—for he knew well enough, rogue that he was, how hard Perseus found it to keep pace with him—"Take you the staff, for you need it a great deal more than I. Are there no better walkers than yourself, in the island of Seriphus?"

"I could walk pretty well," said Perseus, glancing slily at his companion's feet, "if I had only a pair of winged shoes."

"We must see about getting you a pair," answered Quicksilver.

But the staff helped Perseus along so bravely, that he no longer felt the slightest weariness. In fact, the stick seemed to be alive in his hand, and to lend some of its life to Perseus.

He and Quicksilver now walked onward, at their ease, talking very sociably together; and Quicksilver told so many pleasant stories about his former adventures, and how well his wits had served him on various occasions, that Perseus began to think him a very wonderful person. He evidently knew the world; and nobody is so charming to a young man, as a friend who has that kind of knowledge. Perseus listened the more eagerly, in the hope of brightening his own wits by what he heard.

At last, he happened to recollect that Quicksilver had spoken of a sister, who was to lend her assistance in the adventure which they were now bound upon.

"Where is she?" he inquired. "Shall we not meet her soon?"

"All at the proper time," said his companion. "But this sister of mine, you must understand, is quite a different sort of character from myself. She is very grave and prudent, seldom smiles, never laughs, and makes it a rule not to utter a word, unless she has something particularly profound to say. Neither will she listen to any but the wisest conversation."

"Dear me!" ejaculated Perseus. "I shall be afraid to say a syllable."

"She is a very accomplished person, I assure you," continued Quicksilver, "and has all the arts and sciences at her fingers' ends. In short, she is so immoderately wise, that many people call her Wisdom personified. But, to tell you the truth, she has hardly vivacity enough for my taste; and I think you would scarcely find her so pleasant a travelling companion as myself. She has her good points, nevertheless, and you will find the benefit of them in your encounter with the Gorgons."

By this time, it had grown quite dusk. They were now come to a very wild and desert place, overgrown with shaggy bushes, and so silent and solitary that nobody seemed ever to have dwelt or journeyed there. All was waste and desolate, in the gray twilight, which grew every moment more obscure. Perseus looked about him, rather disconsolately, and asked Quicksilver whether they had a great deal farther to go.

"Hist! Hist!" whispered his companion. "Make no noise! This is just the time and place to meet the Three Gray Women. Be careful that they do not see you before you see them; for though they have but a single eye among the three, it is as sharp-sighted as half-a-dozen common eyes."

"But what must I do," asked Perseus, "when we meet them?"

Quicksilver explained to Perseus how the Three Gray Women managed with their one eye. They were in the habit, it seems, of changing it from one to another, as if it had been a pair of spectacles, or—which would have suited them better—a quizzing-glass. When one of the three had kept the eye a certain time, she took it out of the socket and passed it to one of her sisters, whose turn it might happen to be, and who immediately clapt it into her own head, and enjoyed a peep at the visible world. Thus it will easily be understood, that only one of the Three Gray Women could see, while the other two were in utter darkness; and, moreover, at the instant when the eye was passing from hand to hand, neither of the poor old ladies was able to see a wink. I have heard of a great many strange things, in my day, and have witnessed not a few, but none, it seems to me, that can compare with the oddity of these Three Gray Women, all peeping through a single eye.

So thought Perseus, likewise, and was so astonished that he almost fancied his companion was joking with him, and that there were no such old women in the world.

"You will soon find whether I tell the truth or no," observed Quicksilver. "Hark! Hush! Hist! Hist! There they come, now!"

Perseus looked earnestly through the dusk of the evening, and there, sure enough, at no great distance off, he descried the Three Gray Women. The light being so faint, he could not well make out what sort of figures they were; only he discerned that they had long gray hair; and, as they came nearer, he saw that two of them had but the empty socket of an eye, in the middle of their foreheads. But, in the middle of the third sister's forehead, there was a very large, bright, and piercing eye, which sparkled like a great diamond in a ring; and so penetrating did it seem to be, that Perseus could not help thinking it must possess the gift of seeing in the darkest midnight, just as perfectly as at noon-day. The sight of three persons' eyes was melted and collected into that single one.

Thus the three old dames got along about as comfortably, upon the whole, as if they could all see at once. She, who chanced to have the eye in her forehead, led the other two by the hands, peeping sharply about her, all the while; insomuch that Perseus dreaded lest she should see right through the thick clump of bushes, behind which he and Quicksilver had hidden themselves. My stars! It was positively terrible to be within reach of so very sharp an eye!

But, before they reached the clump of bushes, one of the Three Gray Women spoke.

"Sister! Sister Scarecrow!" cried she. "You have had the eye long enough. It is my turn now!"

"Let me keep it a moment longer, Sister Nightmare," answered Scarecrow. "I thought I had a glimpse of something behind that thick bush."

"Well; and what of that?" retorted Nightmare, peevishly. "Can't I see into a thick bush as easily as yourself? The eye is mine as well as yours; and I know the use of it as well as you, or may be a little better. I insist upon taking a peep immediately!"

But here the third sister, whose name was Shake-joint, began to complain, and said that it was her turn to have the eye, and that Scarecrow and Nightmare wanted to keep it all to themselves. To end the dispute, old Dame Scarecrow took the eye out of her forehead, and held it forth in her hand.

"Take it, one of you," cried she, "and quit this foolish quarrelling. For my part, I shall be glad of a little thick darkness. Take it quickly, however; or I must clap it into my own head again!"

Accordingly, both Nightmare and Shake-joint stretched out their hands, groping eagerly to snatch the eye out of the hand of Scarecrow. But, being both alike blind, they could not easily find where Scarecrow's hand was; and Scarecrow, being now just as much in the dark as Shake-joint and Nightmare, could not at once meet either of their hands, in order to put the eye into it. Thus, (as you will see with half an eye, my wise little auditors,) these good old dames had fallen into a strange perplexity. For, though the eye shone and glistened like a star, as Scarecrow held it out, yet the Gray Women caught not the least glimpse of its light, and were all three in utter darkness, from too impatient a desire to see.

Quicksilver was so much tickled at beholding Shake-joint and Nightmare both groping for the eye, and each finding fault with Scarecrow and one another, that he could scarcely help laughing aloud.

"Now is your time!" he whispered to Perseus. "Quick, quick; before they can clap the eye into either of their heads! Rush out upon the old ladies, and snatch it from Scarecrow's hand!"

In an instant, while the Three Gray Women were still scolding each other, Perseus leaped from behind the clump of bushes, and made himself master of the prize. The marvellous eye, as he held it in his hand, shone very brightly, and seemed to look up into his face with a knowing air, and an expression as if it would have winked, had it been provided with a pair of eyelids for that purpose. But the Gray Women knew nothing of what had happened, and, each supposing that one of her sisters was in possession of the eye, they began their quarrel anew. At last, as Perseus did not wish to put these respectable dames to greater inconvenience than was really necessary, he thought it right to explain the matter.

"My good ladies," said he, "pray do not be angry with one another! If anybody is in fault, it is myself; for I have the honor to hold your very brilliant and excellent eye in my own hand!"

"You! You have our eye! And who are you?" screamed the Three Gray Women, all in a breath; for they were terribly frightened, of course, at hearing a strange voice, and discovering that their eyesight had got into the hands of they could not guess whom. "Oh, what shall we do, sisters, what shall we do! We are all in the dark! Give us our eye! Give us our one, precious, solitary eye! You have two of your own! Give us our eye!"

"Tell them," whispered Quicksilver to Perseus, "that they shall have back the eye, as soon as they direct you where to find the Nymphs, who have the flying slippers, the magic wallet, and the helmet of darkness."

"My dear, good, admirable old ladies," said Perseus, addressing the Gray Women, "there is no occasion for putting yourselves into such a fright. I am by no means a bad young man. You shall have back your eye, safe and sound, and as bright as ever, the moment you tell me where to find the Nymphs!"

"The Nymphs! Goodness me, sisters, what Nymphs does he mean?" screamed Scarecrow. "There are a great many Nymphs, people say:—some that go a-hunting in the woods, and some that live inside of trees, and some that have a comfortable home in fountains of water. We know nothing at all about them. We are three unfortunate old souls that go wandering about in the dusk, and never had but one eye

amongst us, and that one you have stolen away. Oh, give it
back, good stranger!—whoever you are—give it back!"

All this while, the Three Gray Women were groping with
their outstretched hands, and trying their utmost to get hold
of Perseus. But he took good care to keep out of their reach.

"My respectable dames," said he—for his mother had
taught him always to use the greatest civility—"I hold your
eye fast in my hand, and shall keep it safely for you, until
you please to tell me where to find these Nymphs. The
Nymphs, I mean, who keep the enchanted wallet, the flying
slippers, and the—what is it?—the helmet of invisibility!"

"Mercy on us, sisters, what is the young man talking
about?" exclaimed Scarecrow, Nightmare, and Shake-joint,
one to another, with great appearance of astonishment. "A
pair of flying slippers, quoth he! His heels would quickly
fly higher than his head, if he were silly enough to put them
on! And a helmet of invisibility! How could a helmet make
him invisible, unless it were big enough for him to hide under
it? And an enchanted wallet! What sort of a contrivance may
that be, I wonder? No, no, good stranger! We can tell you
nothing of these marvellous things. You have two eyes of
your own, and we but a single one amongst us three. You can
find out such wonders better than three blind old creatures,
like us!"

Perseus, hearing them talk in this way, began really to
think that the Gray Women knew nothing of the matter;
and, as it grieved him to have put them to so much trouble,
he was just on the point of restoring their eye, and asking
pardon for his rudeness in snatching it away. But Quicksilver
caught his hand.

"Don't let them make a fool of you!" said he. "These Three
Gray Women are the only persons in the world, that can
tell you where to find the Nymphs; and, unless you get that

information, you will never succeed in cutting off the head of Medusa with the snaky locks. Keep fast hold of the eye, and all will go well!"

As it turned out, Quicksilver was in the right. There are but few things that people prize so much as they do their eyesight; and the Gray Women valued their single eye as highly as if it had been half-a-dozen, which was the number they ought to have had. Finding that there was no other way of recovering it, they at last told Perseus what he wanted to know. No sooner had they done so, than he immediately, and with the utmost respect, clapt the eye into the vacant socket in one of their foreheads, thanked them for their kindness, and bade them farewell. Before the young man was out of hearing, however, they had got into a new dispute; because he happened to have given the eye to Scarecrow, who had already taken her turn of it, when their trouble with Perseus commenced.

It is greatly to be feared, that the Three Gray Women were very much in the habit of disturbing their mutual harmony by bickerings of this sort; which was the more pity, as they could not conveniently do without one another, and were evidently intended to be inseparable companions. As a general rule, I would advise all people, whether sisters or brothers, old or young, who chance to have but one eye amongst them, to cultivate forbearance, and not all insist upon peeping through it at once.

Quicksilver and Perseus, in the mean time, were making the best of their way in quest of the Nymphs. The old dames had given them such particular directions, that they were not long in finding them out. They proved to be very different persons from Nightmare, Shake-joint and Scarecrow; for instead of being old, they were young and beautiful; and instead of one eye amongst the sisterhood, each Nymph had two exceedingly bright eyes of her own, with which she looked very kindly at Perseus. They seemed to be acquainted with Quicksilver; and when he told them the adventure which Perseus had undertaken, they made no difficulty about giving him the valuable articles that were in their custody. In the first place, they brought out what appeared to be a small purse, made of deer-skin, and curiously embroidered, and bade him be sure and keep it safe. This was the magic wallet. The Nymphs next produced a pair of shoes, or slippers, or sandals, with a nice little pair of wings at the heel of each.

"Put them on, Perseus," said Quicksilver. "You will find yourself as light-heeled as you can desire, for the remainder of our journey."

So Perseus proceeded to put one of the slippers on, while he laid the other on the ground by his side. Unexpectedly, however, this other slipper spread its wings, fluttered up off the ground, and would probably have flown away, if Quicksilver had not made a leap, and luckily caught it in the air.

"Be more careful," said he, as he gave it back to Perseus. "It would frighten the birds, up aloft, if they should see a flying slipper amongst them!"

When Perseus had got on both of these wonderful slippers, he was altogether too buoyant to tread on earth. Making a step or two, lo and behold! upward he popt into the air, high above the heads of Quicksilver and the Nymphs, and found it very difficult to clamber down again. Winged slippers, and all such high-flying contrivances, are seldom quite easy to manage, until one grows a little accustomed to them. Quicksilver laughed at his companion's involuntary activity, and told him that he must not be in so desperate a hurry, but must wait for the invisible helmet.

The good-natured Nymphs had the helmet, with its dark tuft of waving plumes, all in readiness to put upon his head. And now there happened about as wonderful an incident as anything that I have yet told you. The instant before the helmet was put on, there stood Perseus, a beautiful young man, with golden ringlets and rosy cheeks, the crooked sword by his side, and the brightly polished shield upon his arm; a figure that seemed all made up of courage, sprightliness, and glorious light. But, when the helmet had descended over his white brow, there was no longer any Perseus to be seen! Nothing but empty air! Even the helmet, that covered him with its invisibility, had vanished!

"Where are you, Perseus?" asked Quicksilver.

"Why, here, to be sure!" answered Perseus, very quietly, although his voice seemed to come out of the transparent atmosphere. "Just where I was a moment ago. Don't you see me?"

"No indeed!" answered his friend. "You are hidden under the helmet. But if I cannot see you, neither can the Gorgons. Follow me, therefore, and we will try your dexterity in using the winged slippers."

With these words, Quicksilver's cap spread its wings, as if his head were about to fly away from his shoulders; but his whole figure rose lightly into the air, and Perseus followed. By the time they had ascended a few hundred feet, the young man began to feel what a delightful thing it was to leave the dull earth so far beneath him, and to be able to flit about like a bird.

It was now deep night. Perseus looked upward, and saw the round, bright, silvery moon, and thought that he should desire nothing better than to soar up thither, and spend his life there. Then he looked downward again, and saw the earth, with its seas, and lakes, and the silver courses of its rivers, and its snowy mountain-peaks, and the breadth of its fields, and the dark cluster of its woods, and its cities of white marble; and, with the moonshine sleeping over the whole scene, it was as beautiful as the moon or any star could be. And, among other objects, he saw the island of Seriphus, where his dear mother was. Sometimes, he and Quicksilver approached a cloud, that, at a distance, looked as if it were made of fleecy silver; although, when they plunged into it, they found themselves chilled and moistened with gray mist. So swift was their flight, however, that, in an instant, they emerged from the cloud into the moonlight again. Once, a high-soaring eagle flew right against the invisible Perseus. The bravest sights were the meteors, that gleamed suddenly out, as if a bonfire had been kindled in the sky, and made the moonshine pale for as much as a hundred miles around them.

As the two companions flew onward, Perseus fancied that he could hear the rustle of a garment close by his side; and it was on the side opposite to the one where he beheld Quicksilver. Yet only Quicksilver was visible.

"Whose garment is this," inquired Perseus, "that keeps rustling close beside me, in the breeze?"

"Oh, it is my sister's!" answered Quicksilver. "She is coming along with us, as I told you she would. We could do nothing without the help of my sister. You have no idea how wise she is. She has such eyes, too! Why, she can see you at this moment, just as distinctly as if you were not invisible; and I'll venture to say, she will be the first to discover the Gorgons."

By this time, in their swift voyage through the air, they had come within sight of the great ocean, and were soon flying over it. Far beneath them, the waves tossed themselves tumultuously, in mid-sea, or rolled a white surf-line upon the long beaches, or foamed against the rocky cliffs, with a roar that was thunderous, in the lower world; although it became a gentle murmur, like the voice of a baby half-asleep, before it reached the ears of Perseus. Just then, a voice spoke in the air, close by him. It seemed to be a woman's voice, and was melodious, though not exactly what might be called sweet, but grave and mild.

"Perseus," said the voice, "there are the Gorgons."

"Where?" exclaimed Perseus. "I cannot see them!"

"On the shore of that island, beneath you," replied the voice. "A pebble, dropt from your hand, would strike in the midst of them."

"I told you she would be the first to discover them," said Quicksilver to Perseus. "And there they are!"

Straight downward, two or three thousand feet below him, Perseus perceived a small island, with the sea breaking into white foam all round its rocky shore, except on one side, where there was a beach of snowy sand. He descended towards it, and looking earnestly at a cluster or heap of brightness, at the foot of a precipice of black rocks, behold! there were the terrible Gorgons. They lay fast asleep, soothed by the thunder of the sea; for it required a tumult that would have deafened everybody else, to lull such fierce creatures into slumber. The moonlight glistened on their steely scales, and on their golden wings, which drooped idly over the sand. Their brazen claws, horrible to look at, were thrust out, and clutched the wave-beaten fragments of rock, while the sleeping Gorgons dreamed of tearing some poor mortal all to pieces. The snakes, that served them instead of hair, seemed likewise to be asleep; although, now and then, one would writhe, and lift its head, and thrust out its forked tongue, emitting a drowsy hiss, and then let itself subside among its sister snakes.

The Gorgons were more like an awful, gigantic kind of insect—immense, golden-winged beetles, or dragon-flies, or things of that sort—at once ugly and beautiful—than like anything else; only that they were a thousand and a million times as big. And with all this, there was something partly human about them, too. Luckily for Perseus, their faces were completely hidden from him by the posture in which they lay; for, had he but looked one instant at them, he would have fallen heavily out of the air, an image of senseless stone.

"Now," whispered Quicksilver, as he hovered by the side of Perseus, "now is your time to do the deed! Be quick; for if one of the Gorgons should awake, you are too late!"

"Which shall I strike at?" asked Perseus, drawing his sword and descending a little lower. "They all three look alike! All three have snaky locks! Which of the three is Medusa?"

It must be understood, that Medusa was the only one of these dragon-monsters, whose head Perseus could possibly cut off. As for the other two, let him have the sharpest sword that ever was forged, and he might have hacked away by the hour together, without doing them the least harm.

"Be cautious!" said the calm voice which had before spoken to him. "One of the Gorgons is stirring in her sleep, and is just about to turn over. That is Medusa. Do not look at her! The sight would turn you to stone! Look at the reflection of her face and figure, in the bright mirror of your shield."

Perseus now understood Quicksilver's motive for so earnestly exhorting him to polish his shield. In its surface, he could safely look at the reflection of the Gorgon's face. And there it was—that terrible countenance—mirrored in the brightness of the shield, with the moonlight falling over it, and displaying all its horror. The snakes, whose venomous natures could not altogether sleep, kept twisting themselves over the forehead. It was the fiercest and most horrible face that ever was seen or imagined, and yet with a strange, fearful, and savage kind of beauty in it. The eyes were closed, and the Gorgon was still in a deep slumber; but there was an unquiet expression disturbing her features, as if the monster were troubled with an ugly dream. She gnashed her white tusks, and dug into the sand with her brazen claws.

The snakes, too, seemed to feel Medusa's dream, and to be made more restless by it. They twined themselves into tumultuous knots, writhed fiercely, and uplifted a hundred hissing heads, without opening their eyes.

"Now, now!" whispered Quicksilver, who was growing impatient. "Make a dash at the monster!"

"But be calm!" said the grave, melodious voice, at the young man's side. "Look in your shield, as you fly downward, and take care that you do not miss your first stroke!"

Perseus flew cautiously downward, still keeping his eyes on Medusa's face, as reflected in his shield. The nearer he came, the more terrible did the snaky visage and metallic body of the monster grow. At last, when he found himself hovering over her within arm's length, Perseus uplifted his sword; while, at the same instant, each separate snake upon the Gorgon's head stretched threateningly upward, and Medusa unclosed her eyes. But she awoke too late. The sword was sharp; the stroke fell like a lightning-flash; and the head of the wicked Medusa tumbled from her body!

"Admirably done!" cried Quicksilver. "Make haste, and clap the head into your magic wallet!"

To the astonishment of Perseus, the small, embroidered wallet, which he had hung about his neck, and which had hitherto been no bigger than a purse, grew all at once large enough to contain Medusa's head. As quick as thought, he snatched it up, with the snakes still writhing upon it, and thrust it in.

"Your task is done," said the calm voice. "Now, fly; for the other Gorgons will do their utmost to take vengeance for Medusa's death."

It was indeed necessary to take flight; for Perseus had not done the deed so quietly, but that the clash of his sword, and the hissing of the snakes, and the thump of Medusa's head as it tumbled upon the sea-beaten sand, awoke the other two monsters. There they sat, for an instant, sleepily rubbing their eyes with their brazen-fingers, while all the snakes on their heads reared themselves on end with surprise, and with venomous malice against they knew not what. But when the Gorgons saw the scaly carcass of Medusa, headless, and her golden wings all ruffled, and half spread out on the sand, it was really awful to hear what yells and screeches they set up. And then the snakes! They sent forth a hundred-fold hiss, with one consent, and Medusa's snakes answered them, out of the magic wallet.

No sooner were the Gorgons broad awake, than they hurtled upward into the air, brandishing their brass talons, gnashing their horrible tusks, and flapping their huge wings so wildly that some of the golden feathers were shaken out, and floated down upon the shore. And there, perhaps, those very feathers lie scattered, till this day. Uprose the Gorgons, as I tell you, staring horribly about, in hopes of turning somebody to stone. Had Perseus looked them in the face, or had he fallen into their clutches, his poor mother would never have kissed her boy again! But he took good care to turn his eyes another way; and, as he wore the helmet of invisibility, the Gorgons knew not in what direction to follow him; nor did he fail to make the best use of the winged slippers, by soaring upward a perpendicular mile or so. At that height, when the screams of those abominable creatures sounded faintly beneath him, he made a straight course for the island of Seriphus, in order to carry Medusa's head to King Polydectes.

I have no time to tell you of several marvellous things that befel Perseus, on his way homeward; such as his killing a hideous sea-monster, just as it was on the point of devouring a beautiful maiden; nor how he changed an enormous giant into a mountain of stone, merely by showing him the head of the Gorgon. If you doubt this latter story, you may make a voyage to Africa, some day or other, and see the very mountain, which is still known by the ancient giant's name.

Finally, our brave Perseus arrived at the island, where he expected to see his dear mother. But, during his absence, the wicked king had treated Danaë so very ill, that she was compelled to make her escape, and had taken refuge in a temple, where some good old priests were extremely kind to her. These praiseworthy priests—and the kind-hearted fisherman, who had first shown hospitality to Danaë and little Perseus, when he found them afloat in the chest—seem to have been the only persons in the island who cared about doing right. All the rest of the people, as well as King Polydectes himself, were remarkably ill-behaved, and deserved no better destiny than that which was now to happen.

Not finding his mother at home, Perseus went straight to the palace, and was immediately ushered into the presence of the king. Polydectes was by no means rejoiced to see him; for he had felt almost certain, in his own evil mind, that the Gorgons would have torn the poor young man to pieces, and have eaten him up, out of the way. However, seeing him safely returned, he put the best face he could upon the matter, and asked Perseus how he had succeeded.

"Have you performed your promise?" inquired he. "Have you brought me the head of Medusa with the snaky locks? If not, young man, it will cost you dear; for I must have a bridal present for the beautiful Princess Hippodamia, and there is nothing else that she would admire so much!"

"Yes; please your majesty," answered Perseus, in a quiet way, as if it were no very wonderful deed for such a young man as he to perform. "I have brought you the Gorgon's head, snaky locks and all!"

"Indeed! Pray let me see it!" quoth King Polydectes. "It must be a very curious spectacle, if all that travellers tell about it be true!"

"Your majesty is in the right," replied Perseus. "It is really an object that will be pretty certain to fix the regards of all who look at it. And, if your majesty think fit, I would suggest that a holiday be proclaimed, and that all your majesty's subjects be summoned to behold this wonderful curiosity. Few of them, I imagine, have seen a Gorgon's head before, and perhaps never may again!"

The king well knew that his subjects were an idle set of reprobates, and very fond of sight-seeing, as idle persons usually are. So he took the young man's advice, and sent out heralds and messengers, in all directions, to blow the trumpet at the street-corners, and in the market-places, and wherever two roads met, and summon everybody to court. Thither, accordingly, came a great multitude of good-for-nothing vagabonds, all of whom, out of pure love of mischief, would have been glad if Perseus had met with some ill-hap, in his encounter with the Gorgons. If there were any better people in the island, (as I really hope there may have been, although the story tells nothing about any such,) they staid quietly at home, minding their own business, and taking care of their little children. Most of the inhabitants, at all events, ran as fast as they could to the palace, and shoved, and pushed, and elbowed one another, in their eagerness to get near a balcony, on which Perseus showed himself, holding the embroidered wallet in his hand.

On a platform, within full view of the balcony, sat the mighty King Polydectes, amid his evil-counsellors, and with his flattering courtiers in a semi-circle round about him. Monarch, counsellors, courtiers, and subjects, all gazed eagerly towards Perseus.

"Show us the head! Show us the head!" shouted the people; and there was a fierceness in their cry, as if they would tear Perseus to pieces, unless he should satisfy them with what he had to show. "Show us the head of Medusa with the snaky locks!"

A feeling of sorrow and pity came over the youthful Perseus.

"Oh, King Polydectes," cried he, "and ye many people, I am very loth to show you the Gorgon's head!"

"Ah, the villain and coward!" yelled the people, more fiercely than before. "He is making game of us! He has no Gorgon's head! Show us the head, if you have it, or we will take your own head for a foot-ball!"

The evil-counsellors whispered bad advice in the king's ear; the courtiers murmured, with one consent, that Perseus had shown disrespect to their royal lord and master; and the great King Polydectes himself waved his hand, and ordered him, with the stern, deep voice of authority, on his peril to produce the head.

"Show me the Gorgon's head; or I will cut off your own!"

And Perseus sighed.

"This instant," repeated Polydectes; "or you die!"

"Behold it, then!" cried Perseus, in a voice like the blast of a trumpet.

And suddenly holding up the head, not an eyelid had time to wink before the wicked King Polydectes, his evil-counsellors, and all his fierce subjects, were no longer anything but the mere images of a monarch and his people. They were all fixed, forever, in the look and attitude of that moment. At the first glimpse of the terrible head of Medusa, they whitened into marble! And Perseus thrust the head back into his wallet, and went to tell his dear mother that she need no longer be afraid of the wicked King Polydectes.

TANGLEWOOD PORCH

AFTER THE STORY

"WAS NOT that a very fine story?" asked Eustace. "Oh, yes, yes!" cried Cowslip, clapping her hands. "And those funny old women with only one eye amongst them! I never heard of anything so strange."

"As to their one tooth, which they shifted about," observed Primrose, "there was nothing so very wonderful in that. I suppose it was a false tooth! But think of your turning Mercury into Quicksilver, and talking about his sister! You are too ridiculous!"

"And was she not his sister?" asked Eustace Bright. "If I had thought of it sooner, I would have described her as a maiden lady, who kept a pet-owl!"

"Well, at any rate," said Primrose, "your story seems to have driven away the mist."

And, indeed, while the tale was going forward, the vapors had been quite exhaled from the landscape. A scene was now disclosed, which the spectators might almost fancy as having been created, since they had last looked in the direction where it lay. About half a mile distant, in the lap of the valley, now appeared a beautiful lake, which reflected a perfect image of its own wooded banks, and of the summits

· 35 ·

of the more distant hills. It gleamed in perfect tranquillity, without the trace of a winged breeze on any part of its bosom. Beyond its farther shore was Monument Mountain, in a recumbent position, stretching almost across the valley. Eustace Bright compared it to a huge, headless Sphinx, wrapped in a Persian shawl; and, indeed, so rich and diversified was the autumnal foliage of its woods, that the simile of the shawl was by no means too high-colored for the reality. In the lower ground between Tanglewood and the lake, the clumps of trees and borders of woodland were chiefly golden-leaved, or dusky brown, as having suffered more from frost than the foliage on the hill-sides.

Over all this scene there was a genial sunshine, intermingled with a slight haze, which made it unspeakably soft and tender. Oh, what a day of Indian Summer was it going to be! The children snatched their baskets and set forth, with hop, skip, and jump, and all sorts of frisks and gambols; while Cousin Eustace proved his fitness to preside over the party by outdoing all their antics, and performing several new capers, which none of them could ever hope to imitate. Behind went a good old dog, whose name was Ben. He was one of the most respectable and kind-hearted of quadrupeds, and probably felt it to be his duty not to trust the children away from their parents, without some better guardian than this feather-brained Eustace Bright.

SHADOW BROOK

A T NOON, our juvenile party assembled in a dell, through the depths of which ran a little brook. The dell was narrow, and its steep sides, from the margin of the stream, upward, were thickly set with trees, chiefly walnuts and chestnuts, among which grew a few oaks and maples. In the summer-time, the shade of so many clustering branches, meeting and intermingling across the rivulet, was deep enough to produce a noontide twilight. Hence came the name of Shadow Brook. But now, ever since Autumn had crept into this secluded place, all the dark verdure was changed to gold; so that it really kindled up the dell, instead of shading it. The bright yellow leaves, even had it been a cloudy day, would have seemed to keep the sunlight among them; and enough of them had fallen, to strew all the bed and margin of the brook with sunlight, too. Thus the shady nook, where Summer had cooled herself, was now the sunniest spot anywhere to be found.

The little brook ran along over its pathway of gold, here pausing to form a pool, in which minnows were darting to-and-fro; and then it hurried onward at a swifter pace, as if in haste to reach the lake; and forgetting to look whither it went, it tumbled over the root of a tree, which stretched quite across its current. You would have laughed to hear how noisily it babbled about this accident. And even after it had run onward, the brook still kept talking to itself, as if it were in a maze. It was wonder-smitten, I suppose, at finding its dark dell so illuminated, and at hearing the prattle and merriment of so many children. So it stole away as quickly as it could, and hid itself in the lake.

In the dell of Shadow Brook, Eustace Bright and his little friends had eaten their dinner. They had brought plenty of good things from Tanglewood, in their baskets, and had spread them out on the stumps of trees, and on mossy trunks, and had feasted merrily, and made a very nice dinner indeed. After it was over, nobody felt like stirring.

"We will rest ourselves here," said several of the children, "while Cousin Eustace tells us another of his pretty stories."

Cousin Eustace had a good right to be tired, as well as the children; for he had performed great feats, on that memorable forenoon. Dandelion, Clover, Cowslip, and Butter-cup, were almost persuaded that he had winged slippers, like those which the Nymphs gave Perseus; so often had the student shown himself at the tip-top of a nut-tree, when only a moment before, he had been standing on the ground. And then what showers of walnuts had he sent rattling down upon their heads, for their busy little hands to gather into the baskets! In short, he had been as active as a squirrel or a monkey, and now, flinging himself down on the yellow leaves, seemed inclined to take a little rest.

But children have no mercy nor consideration for any-body's weariness; and if you had but a single breath left, they would ask you to spend it in telling them a story.

"Cousin Eustace," said Cowslip, "that was a very nice story of the Gorgon's Head. Do you think you could tell us another as good?"

"Yes, child," said Eustace, pulling the brim of his cap over his eyes, as if preparing for a nap. "I can tell you a dozen, as good or better, if I choose."

"Oh, Primrose and Periwinkle, do you hear what he says?" cried Cowslip, dancing with delight. "Cousin Eustace is going to tell us a dozen better stories than that about the Gorgon's Head!"

"I did not promise you even one, you foolish little Cowslip!" said Eustace, half-pettishly. "However, I suppose you must have it. This is the consequence of having earned a reputation! I wish I were a great deal duller than I am, or that I had never shown half the bright qualities with which Nature has endowed me; and then I might have had my nap out, in peace and comfort!"

But Cousin Eustace, as I think I have hinted before, was as fond of telling his stories, as the children of hearing them. His mind was in a free and happy state, and took delight in its own activity, and scarcely required any external impulse to set it at work. How different is this spontaneous play of the intellect, from the trained diligence of maturer years, when toil has perhaps grown easy by long habit, and the day's work may have become essential to the day's comfort, although the zest of the matter has bubbled away! This remark, however, is not meant for the children to hear.

Without further solicitation, Eustace Bright proceeded to tell the following really splendid story. It had come into his mind, as he lay looking upward into the depths of a tree, and observing how the touch of Autumn had transmuted every one of its green leaves into what resembled the purest gold. And this change, which we have all of us witnessed, is as wonderful as anything that Eustace told about, in the story of Midas.

THE GOLDEN TOUCH

ONCE upon a time, there lived a very rich man, and
a king besides, whose name was Midas; and he
had a little daughter, whom nobody but myself ever
heard of, and whose name I either never knew, or have
entirely forgotten. So, because I love odd names for little
girls, I choose to call her Marygold.

This King Midas was fonder of gold than of any thing else
in the world. He valued his royal crown chiefly because it
was composed of that precious metal. If he loved anything
better, or half so well, it was the one little maiden who
played so merrily around her father's footstool. But, the more
Midas loved his daughter, the more did he desire and seek
for wealth. He thought, foolish man! that the best thing he
could possibly do for this dear child, would be, to bequeath
her the immensest pile of yellow, glistening coin, that had
ever been heaped together since the world was made. Thus,
he gave all his thoughts and all his time to this one purpose.
If ever he happened to gaze, for an instant, at the gold-tinted
clouds of sunset, he wished that they were real gold, and
that they could be squeezed safely into his strong-box. When
little Marygold ran to meet him, with a bunch of butter-cups
and dandelions, he used to say—"Poh, poh, child! If these

flowers were as golden as they look, they would be worth the plucking!"

And yet, in his earlier days, before he was so entirely possessed with this insane desire for riches, King Midas had shown a great taste for flowers. He had planted a garden, in which grew the biggest, and beautifullest, and sweetest roses, that any mortal ever saw or smelt. These roses were still growing in the garden, as large, as lovely, and as fragrant, as when Midas used to pass whole hours in gazing at them, and inhaling their perfume. But now, if he looked at them at all, it was only to calculate how much the garden would be worth, if each of the innumerable rose-petals were a thin plate of gold! And though he once was fond of music, (in spite of an idle story about his ears, which were said to resemble those of an ass,) the only music for poor Midas, now, was the chink of one coin against another.

At length, (as people always grow more and more foolish, unless they take care to grow wiser and wiser,) Midas had got to be so exceedingly unreasonable, that he could scarcely bear to see or touch any object that was not gold. He made it his custom, therefore, to pass a large portion of every day in a dark and dreary apartment, under ground, at the basement of his palace. It was here that he kept his wealth. To this dismal hole—for it was little better than a dungeon—Midas betook himself, whenever he wanted to be particularly happy. Here, after carefully locking the door, he would take a bag of gold coin, or a gold cup, as big as a wash-bowl, or a heavy golden bar, or a peck-measure of gold dust, and bring them from the obscurer corners of the room into the one bright and narrow sunbeam, that fell from the dungeon-like window. He valued the sunbeam, for no other reason but that his treasure would not shine without its help. And then would he reckon over the coins in the bag—toss up the bar, and catch it as it came down—sift the gold dust through his fingers—look at the funny image of his own face, as reflected in the burnished circumference of the cup—and whisper to himself, "Oh Midas, rich King Midas, what a happy man art thou!" But it was laughable to see how the image of his face kept grinning at him, out of the polished surface of the cup. It seemed to be aware of his foolish behavior, and to have a naughty inclination to make fun of him.

Midas called himself a happy man, but felt that he was not yet quite so happy as he might be. The very tip-top of enjoyment would never be reached, unless the whole world were to become his treasure-room, and be filled with yellow metal which should be all his own.

Now, I need hardly remind such wise little people as you are, that in the old, old times, when King Midas was alive, a great many things came to pass, which we should consider wonderful, if they were to happen in our own day and country. And, on the other hand, a great many things take place now-a-days, which seem not very wonderful to us, but at which the people of old times would have stared their eyes out. On the whole, I regard our own times as the strangest of the two; but, however that may be, I must go on with my story.

Midas was enjoying himself in his treasure-room, one day, as usual, when he perceived a shadow fall over the heaps of gold; and looking suddenly up, what should he behold but the figure of a stranger, standing in the bright and narrow sunbeam! It was a young man, with a cheerful and ruddy face. Whether it was that the imagination of King Midas threw a yellow tinge over everything, or whatever the cause might be, he could not help fancying that the smile, with which the stranger regarded him, had a kind of golden radiance in it. Certainly, although his figure intercepted the sunshine, there was now a brighter gleam upon all the piled-up treasures, than before. Even the remotest corners had their share of it, and were lighted up, when the stranger smiled, as with tips of flame and sparkles of fire.

As Midas knew that he had carefully turned the key in the lock, and that no mortal strength could possibly break into his treasure-room, he of course concluded that his visiter must be something more than mortal. It is no matter about telling you who he was. In those days, when the earth was comparatively a new affair, it was supposed to be often the resort of beings, endowed with supernatural powers, and who used to interest themselves in the joys and sorrows of men, women, and children, half playfully, and half seriously. Midas had met such beings, before now, and was not sorry to meet one of them again. The stranger's aspect, indeed, was so good-humored and kindly, if not beneficent, that it would have been unreasonable to suspect him of intending any mischief. It was far more probable that he came to do Midas a favor. And what could that favor be, unless to multiply his heaps of treasure?

The stranger gazed about the room; and when his lustrous smile had glistened upon all the golden objects that were there, he turned again to Midas.

"You are a wealthy man, friend Midas!" he observed. "I doubt whether any other four walls, on earth, contain so much gold as you have contrived to pile up in this room."

"I have done pretty well—pretty well," answered Midas, in a discontented tone. "But, after all, it is but a trifle, when you consider that it has taken me my whole life to get it together. If one could live a thousand years, he might have time to grow rich!"

"What!" exclaimed the stranger. "Then you are not satisfied?"

Midas shook his head.

"And pray what would satisfy you?" asked the stranger. "Merely for the curiosity of the thing, I should be glad to know."

Midas paused and meditated. He felt a presentiment that this stranger, with such a golden lustre in his good-humored smile, had come thither with both the power and the purpose of gratifying his utmost wishes. Now, therefore, was the fortunate moment, when he had but to speak, and obtain whatever possible, or seemingly impossible thing it might come into his head to ask. So he thought, and thought, and thought, and heaped up one golden mountain upon another, in his imagination, without being able to imagine them big enough. At last, a bright idea occurred to King Midas. It seemed really as bright as the glistening metal which he loved so much.

Raising his head, he looked the lustrous stranger in the face.

"Well, Midas," observed his visiter, "I see that you have at length hit upon something that will satisfy you. Tell me your wish!"

"It is only this!" replied Midas. "I am weary of collecting my treasures with so much trouble, and beholding the heap so diminutive, after I have done my best. I wish everything that I touch to be changed to gold!"

The stranger's smile grew so very broad, that it seemed to fill the room like an outburst of the sun, gleaming into a shadowy dell, where the yellow autumnal leaves—for so looked the lumps and particles of gold—lie strewn in the glow of light.

"The Golden Touch!" exclaimed he. "You certainly deserve credit, friend Midas, for striking out so brilliant a conception. But are you quite sure that this will satisfy you?"

"How could it fail?" said Midas.

"And will you never regret the possession of it?"

"What could induce me?" asked Midas. "I ask nothing else, to render me perfectly happy!"

"Be it as you wish, then," replied the stranger, waving his hand in token of farewell. "Tomorrow, at sunrise, you will find yourself gifted with the Golden Touch!"

The figure of the stranger then became exceedingly bright, and Midas involuntarily closed his eyes. On opening them again, he beheld only one yellow sunbeam in the room, and, all around him, the glistening of the precious metal which he had spent his life in hoarding up.

Whether Midas slept as usual, that night, the story does not say. Asleep or awake, however, his mind was probably in the state of a child's, to whom a beautiful new plaything has been promised, in the morning. At any rate, day had hardly peeped over the hills, when King Midas was broad awake, and stretching his arms out of bed, began to touch the objects that were within reach. He was anxious to prove whether the Golden Touch had really come, according to the stranger's promise. So he laid his finger on a chair by the bedside, and on various other things, but was grievously disappointed to perceive that they remained of exactly the same substance as before. Indeed, he felt very much afraid that he had only dreamed about the lustrous stranger, or else that the latter had been making game of him. And what a miserable affair would it be, if, after all his hopes, Midas must content himself with what little gold he could scrape together by ordinary means, instead of creating it by a touch!

All this while, it was only the gray of the morning, with but a streak of brightness along the edge of the sky, where Midas could not see it. He lay in a very disconsolate mood, regretting the downfal of his hopes, and kept growing sadder and sadder, until the earliest sunbeam shone through the window, and gilded the ceiling over his head. It seemed to Midas, that this bright yellow sunbeam was reflected, in rather a singular way, on the white covering of the bed. Looking more closely, what was his astonishment and delight, when he found that this linen fabric had been transmuted to what seemed a woven texture of the purest and brightest gold! The Golden Touch had come to him, with the first sunbeam!

Midas started up, in a kind of joyful frenzy, and ran about the room, grasping at everything that happened to be in his way. He seized one of the bed-posts, and it became immediately a fluted golden pillar. He pulled aside a window-curtain, in order to admit a clear spectacle of the wonders which he was performing; and the tassel grew heavy in his hand, a mass of gold. He took up a book from the table. At his first touch, it assumed the appearance of such a splendidly bound and gilt-edged volume, as one often meets with, now-a-days; but, on running his fingers through the leaves, behold! it was a bundle of thin golden plates, in which all the wisdom of the book had grown illegible. He hurriedly put on his clothes, and was enraptured to see himself in a magnificent suit of gold cloth, which retained its flexibility and softness, although it burthened him a little with its weight. He drew out his handkerchief, which little Marygold had hemmed for him. That was likewise gold, with the dear child's neat and pretty stitches running all along the border, in gold thread!

Somehow or other, this last transformation did not quite please King Midas. He would rather that his little daughter's handiwork should have remained just the same as when she climbed his knee, and put it into his hand.

But it was not worth while to vex himself about a trifle. Midas now took his spectacles from his pocket, and put them on his nose, in order that he might see more distinctly what he was about. In those days, spectacles for common people had not been invented, but were already worn by kings; else how could Midas have had any? To his great perplexity, however, excellent as the glasses were, he discovered that he could not possibly see through them. But this was the most natural thing in the world; for, on taking them off, the transparent crystals turned out to be plates of yellow metal, and, of course, were worthless, as spectacles, though valuable as gold. It struck Midas as rather inconvenient, that, with all his wealth, he could never again be rich enough to own a pair of serviceable spectacles!

"It is no great matter, nevertheless," said he to himself, very philosophically. "We cannot expect any great good, without its being accompanied with some small inconvenience. The Golden Touch is worth the sacrifice of a pair of spectacles, at least, if not of one's very eyesight. My own eyes will serve for ordinary purposes; and little Marygold will soon be old enough to read to me."

Wise King Midas was so exalted by his good fortune, that the palace seemed not sufficiently spacious to contain him. He therefore went down stairs, and smiled, on observing that the balustrade of the staircase became a bar of burnished gold, as his hand passed over it, in his descent. He lifted the door-latch, (it was brass, only a moment ago, but golden, when his fingers quitted it,) and emerged into the garden. Here, as it happened, he found a great number of beautiful roses in full bloom, and others in all the stages of lovely bud and blossom. Very delicious was their fragrance in the morning breeze! Their delicate blush was one of the fairest sights in the world; so gentle, so modest, and so full of sweet tranquillity, did these roses seem to be.

But Midas knew a way to make them far more precious, according to his way of thinking, than roses had ever been before. So he took great pains in going from bush to bush, and exercised his magic touch most indefatigably; until every individual flower and bud, and even the worms at the heart of some of them, were changed to gold. By the time this good work was completed, King Midas was summoned to breakfast;

and, as the morning air had given him an excellent appetite, he made haste back to the palace.

What was usually a king's breakfast, in the days of Midas, I really do not know, and cannot stop now to investigate. To the best of my belief, however, on this particular morning, the breakfast consisted of hot cakes, some nice little brook-trout, roasted potatoes, fresh boiled eggs, and coffee, for King Midas himself, and a bowl of bread and milk for his daughter Marygold. At all events, this is a breakfast fit to set before a king; and, whether he had it or no, King Midas could not have had a better.

Little Marygold had not yet made her appearance. Her father ordered her to be called, and, seating himself at table, awaited the child's coming, in order to begin his own break-fast. To do Midas justice, he really loved his daughter, and loved her so much the more, this morning, on account of the good fortune which had befallen him. It was not a great while before he heard her coming along the passage-way, crying bitterly. This circumstance surprised him, because Marygold was one of the cheerfullest little people whom you would see in a summer's day, and hardly shed a thimble-full of tears in a twelvemonth. When Midas heard her sobs, he determined to put little Marygold into better spirits by an agreeable surprise; so, leaning across the table, he touched his daughter's bowl, (which was a china one, with pretty figures all around it,) and transmuted it to gleaming gold.

Meanwhile, Marygold slowly and disconsolately opened the door, and showed herself with her apron at her eyes, still sobbing as if her heart would break.

"How now, my little lady!" cried Midas. "Pray what is the matter with you, this bright morning?"

Marygold, without taking the apron from her eyes, held out her hand, in which was one of the roses which Midas had so recently transmuted.

"Beautiful!" exclaimed her father. "And what is there in this magnificent golden rose, to make you cry?"

"Ah, dear father," answered the child, as well as her sobs would let her, "it is not beautiful, but the ugliest flower that ever grew! As soon as I was dressed, I ran into the garden to gather some roses for you; because I know you like them, and like them the better when gathered by your little daughter. But, Oh, dear, dear me! What do you think has happened? Such a misfortune! All the beautiful roses, that smelled so sweetly, and had so many lovely blushes, are blighted and spoilt! They are grown quite yellow, as you see this one, and have no longer any fragrance! What can have been the matter with them?"

"Poh, my dear little girl, pray don't cry about it!" said Midas, who was ashamed to confess that he himself had wrought the change, which so greatly afflicted her. "Sit down and eat your bread and milk! You will find it easy enough to exchange a golden rose like that (which will last hundreds of years) for an ordinary one, which would wither in a day."

"I don't care for such roses as this," cried Marygold, tossing it contemptuously away. "It has no smell, and the hard petals prick my nose!"

The child now sat down to table, but was so occupied with her grief for the blighted roses, that she did not even notice the wonderful transmutation of her china bowl. Perhaps this was all the better; for Marygold was accustomed to take pleasure in looking at the queer figures, and strange trees and houses, that were painted on the circumference of the bowl; and these ornaments were now entirely lost in the yellow hue of the metal.

Midas, meanwhile, had poured out a cup of coffee; and, as a matter of course, the coffee-pot, whatever metal it may have been when he took it up, was gold when he set it down. He thought to himself, that it was rather an extravagant style of splendor, in a king of his simple habits, to breakfast off a service of gold, and began to be puzzled with the difficulty of keeping his treasures safe. The cupboard and the kitchen would no longer be a secure place of deposit for articles so valuable as golden bowls and coffee-pots.

Amid these thoughts, he lifted a spoonfull of coffee to his lips, and sipping it, was astonished to perceive that, the instant his lips touched the liquid, it became molten gold, and, the next moment, hardened into a lump!

"Ha!" exclaimed Midas, rather aghast.

"What is the matter, father?" asked little Marygold, gazing at him with the tears still standing in her eyes.

"Nothing, child, nothing!" said Midas. "Eat your milk, before it gets quite cold."

He took one of the nice little trouts on his plate, and, by way of experiment, touched its tail with his finger. To his horror, it was immediately transmuted from an admirably fried brook-trout into a gold fish, though not one of those gold-fishes which people often keep in glass globes, as ornaments for the parlor. No; but it was really a metallic fish, and looked as if it had been very cunningly made by the nicest goldsmith in the world. Its little bones were now golden wires; its fins and tail were thin plates of gold; and there were the marks of the fork in it, and all the delicate, frothy appearance of a nicely fried fish, exactly imitated in metal. A very pretty piece of work, as you may suppose; only King Midas, just at that moment, would much rather have had a real trout in his dish, than this elaborate and valuable imitation of one!

"I don't quite see," thought he to himself, "how I am to get any breakfast!"

He took one of the smoking hot cakes, and had scarcely broken it, when, to his cruel mortification—though, a moment before, it had been of the whitest wheat—it assumed the yellow hue of Indian meal. To say the truth, if it had really been a hot Indian cake, Midas would have prized it a good deal more than he now did, when its solidity and increased weight made him too bitterly sensible that it was gold. Almost in despair, he helped himself to a boiled egg, which immediately underwent a change similar to those of the trout and the cake. The egg, indeed, might have been mistaken for one of those which the famous goose, in the story-book, was in the habit of laying; but King Midas was the only goose that had had any thing to do with the matter!

"Well; this is a quandary!" thought he, leaning back in his chair, and looking quite enviously at little Marygold, who was now eating her bread and milk, with great satisfaction. "Such a costly breakfast before me, and nothing that can be eaten!"

Hoping that, by dint of great dispatch, he might avoid what he now felt to be a considerable inconvenience, King Midas next snatched a hot potatoe, and attempted to cram it into his mouth and swallow it in a hurry. But the Golden Touch was too nimble for him. He found his mouth full, not of mealy potatoe, but of solid metal, which so burnt his tongue that he roared aloud, and jumping up from the table began to dance and stamp about the room, both with pain and affright.

"Father, dear father," cried little Marygold, who was a very affectionate child, "pray what is the matter? Have you burnt your mouth?"

"Ah, dear child," groaned Midas, dolefully, "I don't know what is to become of your poor father!"

And, truly, my dear little folks, did you ever hear of such a pitiable case in all your lives? Here was literally the richest breakfast that could be set before a king; and its very richness made it absolutely good for nothing. The poorest laborer, sitting down to his crust of bread and cup of water, was far better off than King Midas, whose delicate food was really worth its weight in gold. And what was to be done? Already, at breakfast, Midas was excessively hungry. Would he be less so, by dinner-time? And how ravenous would be his appetite for supper, which must undoubtedly consist of the same sort of indigestible dishes as those now before him? How many days, think you, could he survive a continuance of this rich fare?

These reflections so troubled wise King Midas, that he began to doubt whether, after all, riches are the one desirable thing in the world, or even the most desirable. But this was only a passing thought. So fascinated was Midas with the glitter of the yellow metal, that he would still have refused to give up the Golden Touch for so paltry a consideration as a breakfast. Just imagine what a price for one meal's victuals! It would have been the same as paying millions and millions of money, (and as many millions more as would take forever to reckon up,) for some fried trout, an egg, a potatoe, a hot cake, and a cup of coffee!

"It would be quite too dear!" thought Midas.

Nevertheless, so great was his hunger and the perplexity of his situation, that he again groaned aloud, and very grievously too. Our pretty Marygold could endure it no longer. She sat, a moment, gazing at her father, and trying with all the might of her little wits to find out what was the matter with him. Then, with a sweet and sorrowful impulse to comfort him, she started from her chair, and running to Midas, threw her arms affectionately about his knees. He bent down and kissed her. He felt that his little daughter's love was worth a thousand times more than he had gained by the Golden Touch.

"My precious, precious Marygold," cried he.

But Marygold made no answer.

Alas, what had he done! How fatal was the gift which the stranger had bestowed! The moment the lips of Midas touched Marygold's forehead, a change had taken place. Her sweet, rosy face, so full of affection as it had been, assumed a glittering yellow color, with yellow tear-drops congealing on her cheeks. Her beautiful brown ringlets took the same tint. Her soft and tender little form grew hard and inflexible within her father's encircling arms. Oh, terrible misfortune! The victim of his insatiable desire for wealth, little Marygold was a human child no longer, but a golden statue!

Yes; there she was, with the questioning look of love, grief, and pity, hardened into her face. It was the prettiest and most woeful sight that ever mortal saw. All the features and tokens of Marygold were there; even the beloved little dimple remained in her golden chin. But, the more perfect was the resemblance, the greater was the father's agony at beholding this golden image, which was all that was left him of a daughter. It had been a favorite phrase of Midas, whenever he felt particularly fond of the child, to say that she was worth her weight in gold. And now the phrase had become literally true. And now, at last, when it was too late, he felt how infinitely a warm and tender heart, that loved him, exceeded in value all the wealth that could be piled up betwixt the earth and sky!

It would be too sad a story, if I were to tell you how Midas, in the fullness of all his gratified desires, began to wring his hands and bemoan himself; and how he could neither bear to look at Marygold, nor yet to look away from her. Except when his eyes were fixed on the image, he could not possibly believe that she was changed to gold. But, stealing another glance, there was the precious little figure, with a yellow tear-drop on its yellow cheek, and a look so piteous and tender, that it seemed as if that very expression must needs soften the gold, and make it flesh again. This, however, could not be. So Midas had only to wring his hands, and to wish that he were the poorest man in the wide world, if the loss of all his wealth might bring back the faintest rose-color to his dear child's face.

While he was in this tumult of despair, he suddenly beheld a stranger, standing near the door. Midas bent down his head, without speaking; for he recognized the same figure which had appeared to him, the day before, in the treasure-room, and had bestowed on him this disastrous faculty of the Golden Touch. The stranger's countenance still wore a smile, which seemed to shed a yellow lustre all about the room, and gleamed on little Marygold's image, and on the other objects that had been transmuted by the touch of Midas.

"Well, friend Midas," said the stranger, "pray how do you succeed with the Golden Touch?"

Midas shook his head.

"I am very miserable!" said he.

"Very miserable, indeed?" exclaimed the stranger. "And how happens that? Have I not faithfully kept my promise with you? Have you not everything that your heart desired?"

"Gold is not everything," answered Midas. "And I have lost all that my heart really cared for!"

"Ah! So you have made a discovery, since yesterday!" observed the stranger. "Let us see, then! Which of these two things do you think is really worth the most—the gift of the Golden Touch, or one cup of clear, cold water?"

"Oh, blessed water!" exclaimed Midas. "It will never moisten my parched throat again!"

"The Golden Touch," continued the stranger, "or a crust of bread?"

"A piece of bread," answered Midas, "is worth all the gold on earth!"

"The Golden Touch," asked the stranger, "or your own little Marygold, warm, soft, and loving, as she was an hour ago?"

"Oh, my child, my dear child!" cried poor Midas, wringing his hands. "I would not have given that one small dimple in her chin, for the power of changing this whole big earth into a solid lump of gold!"

"You are wiser than you were, King Midas!" said the stranger, looking seriously at him. "Your own heart, I perceive, has not been entirely changed from flesh to gold. Were it so, your case would indeed be desperate. But you appear to be still capable of understanding that the commonest things, such as lie within everybody's grasp, are more valuable than the riches which so many mortals sigh and struggle after. Tell me, now! Do you sincerely desire to rid yourself of this Golden Touch?"

"It is hateful to me!" replied Midas.

A fly settled on his nose, but immediately fell to the floor; for it, too, had become gold. Midas shuddered.

"Go, then," said the stranger, "and plunge into the river that glides past the bottom of your garden. Take likewise a vase of the same water, and sprinkle it over any object, that you may desire to change back again from gold into its former substance. If you do this in earnestness and sincerity, it may possibly repair the mischief which your avarice has occasioned!"

King Midas bowed low; and when he lifted his head, the lustrous stranger had vanished.

You will easily believe, that Midas lost no time in snatching up a great earthen pitcher (but, alas me! it was no longer earthen after he touched it) and hastening to the river-side. As he scampered along, and forced his way through the shrubbery, it was positively marvellous to see how the foliage turned yellow behind him, as if the Autumn had been there, and nowhere else. On reaching the river's brink, he plunged headlong in, without waiting so much as to pull off his shoes.

"Poof! poof! poof!" snorted King Midas, as his head emerged out of the water. "Well; this is really a refreshing bath, and I think it must have quite washed away the Golden Touch. And now for filling my pitcher!"

As he dipt the pitcher into the water, it gladdened his very heart to see it change from gold into the same good, honest earthen vessel which it had been, before he touched it. He was conscious, also, of a change within himself. A cold, hard, and heavy weight seemed to have gone out of his bosom. No doubt, his heart had been gradually losing its human substance, and transmuting itself into insensible metal, but had now softened back again into flesh. Perceiving a violet, that grew on the bank of the river, Midas touched it with his finger, and was overjoyed to find that the delicate flower retained its purple hue, instead of undergoing a yellow blight. The curse of the Golden Touch had therefore really been removed from him.

King Midas hastened back to the palace; and, I suppose, the servants knew not what to make of it, when they saw their royal master so carefully bringing home an earthen pitcher of water. But that water, which was to undo all the mischief that his folly had wrought, was more precious to Midas than an ocean of molten gold would have been. The first thing he did, as you need hardly be told, was to sprinkle it by handfulls over the golden figure of little Marygold.

No sooner did it fall on her, than you would have laughed to see how the rosy color came back to the dear child's cheek!—and how she began to sneeze and sputter!—and how astonished she was to find herself dripping wet, and her father still throwing more water over her!

"Pray do not, dear father!" cried she. "See how you have wet my nice frock, which I put on only this morning!"

For Marygold did not know that she had been a little golden statue; nor could she remember anything that had happened, since the moment when she ran, with outstretched arms, to comfort poor King Midas.

Her father did not think it necessary to tell his beloved child how very foolish he had been, but contented himself with showing how much wiser he had now grown. For this purpose, he led little Marygold into the garden, where he sprinkled all the remainder of the water over the rose-bushes, and with such good effect that above five thousand roses recovered their beautiful bloom. There were two circumstances, however, which, as long as he lived, used to put King Midas in mind of the Golden Touch. One was, that the sands of the river sparkled like gold; the other, that little Marygold's hair had now a golden tinge, which he had never observed in it, before she had been transmuted by the effect of his kiss. This change of hue was really an improvement, and made Marygold's hair richer than in her babyhood.

When King Midas had grown quite an old man, and used to trot Marygold's children on his knee, he was fond of telling them this marvellous story, pretty much as I have now told it to you. And then would he stroke their glossy ringlets, and tell them that their hair, likewise, had a rich shade of gold, which they had inherited from their mother.

"And, to tell you the truth, my precious little folks," quoth King Midas, diligently trotting the children all the while, "ever since that morning, I have hated the very sight of all other gold, save this!"

SHADOW BROOK

AFTER THE STORY

WELL, children," inquired Eustace, who was very fond of eliciting a definite opinion from his auditors, "did you ever, in all your lives, listen to a better story than this of 'The Golden Touch'?"

"Why, as to the story of King Midas," said saucy Primrose, "it was a famous one, thousands of years before Mr. Eustace Bright came into the world, and will continue to be so, as long after he quits it. But some people have what we may call 'The Leaden Touch,' and make everything dull and heavy that they lay their fingers upon!"

"You are a smart child, Primrose, to be not yet in your teens," said Eustace, taken rather aback by the piquancy of her criticism. "But you well know, in your naughty little heart, that I have burnished the old gold of Midas all over anew, and have made it shine as it never shone before. And then that figure of Marygold! Do you perceive no nice workmanship in that? And how finely I have brought out and deepened the moral! What say you, Sweet Fern, Dandelion, Clover, Periwinkle? Would any of you, after hearing this story, be so foolish as to desire the faculty of changing things to gold?"

"I should like," said Periwinkle, a girl of ten, "to have the power of turning everything to gold with my right forefinger; but, with my left forefinger, I should want the power of changing it back again, if the first change did not please me. And I know what I would do, this very afternoon!"

"Pray tell me," said Eustace.

"Why," answered Periwinkle, "I would touch every one of these golden leaves on the trees, with my left forefinger, and make them all green again; so that we might have the summer back at once, with no ugly winter in the mean time."

"Oh, Periwinkle," cried Eustace Bright, "there you are wrong, and would do a great deal of mischief. Were I Midas, I would make nothing else but just such golden days as these, over and over again, all the year throughout. My best thoughts always come a little too late. Why did not I tell you how old King Midas came to America, and changed the dusky autumn, such as it is in other countries, into the burnished beauty which it here puts on? He gilded the leaves of the great volume of Nature."

"Cousin Eustace," said Sweet Fern, a good little boy, who was always making particular inquiries about the precise height of giants and the littleness of fairies, "how big was Marygold, and how much did she weigh, after she was turned to gold?"

"She was about as tall as you are," replied Eustace, "and, as gold is very heavy, she weighed at least two thousand pounds, and might have been coined into thirty or forty thousand gold dollars. I wish Primrose were worth half as much. Come, little people, let us clamber out of the dell, and look about us."

They did so. The sun was now an hour or two beyond its noontide mark, and filled the great hollow of the valley with its western radiance; so that it seemed to be brimming with mellow light, and to spill it over the surrounding hill-sides, like golden wine out of a bowl. It was such a day, that you could not help saying of it—"There never was such a day before!"—although yesterday was just such a day, and tomorrow will be just such another. Ah, but there are very few of them in a twelvemonth's circle! It is a remarkable peculiarity of these October days, that each of them seems to occupy a great deal of space; although the sun rises rather tardily, at that season of the year, and goes to bed, as little children ought, at sober six o'clock, or even earlier. We cannot, therefore, call the days long; but they appear, somehow or other, to make up for their shortness by their breadth; and when the cool night comes, we are conscious of having enjoyed a big armfull of life, since morning.

"Come, children, come!" cried Eustace Bright. "More nuts, more nuts, more nuts! Fill all your baskets; and, at Christmastime, I will crack them for you, and tell you beautiful stories!"

So away they went; all of them in excellent spirits, except little Dandelion, who, I am sorry to tell you, had been sitting on a chestnut-burr, and was stuck as full as a pincushion of its prickles. Dear me, how uncomfortably he must have felt!

TANGLEWOOD PLAY-ROOM

INTRODUCTORY TO "THE PARADISE OF CHILDREN"

THE GOLDEN DAYS of October passed away, as so many other Octobers have, and brown November likewise, and the greater part of chill December, too. At last came merry Christmas, and Eustace Bright along with it, making it all the merrier by his presence. And, the day after his arrival from college, there came a mighty snow-storm. Up to this time, the winter had held back, and had given us a good many mild days, which were like smiles upon its wrinkled visage. The grass had kept itself green, in sheltered places, such as the nooks of southern hill-slopes, and along the lee of the stone-fences. It was but a week or two ago, and since the beginning of the month, that the children had found a dandelion in bloom, on the margin of Shadow Brook, where it glides out of the dell.

But no more green grass and dandelions, now! This was such a snow-storm! Twenty miles of it might have been visible at once, between the windows of Tanglewood and the Dome of Taconic, had it been possible to see so far, among the eddying drifts that whitened all the atmosphere. It seemed as if the hills were giants, and were flinging monstrous handfulls of snow at one another, in their enormous sport. So thick were the fluttering snow-flakes, that even the trees, mid-way down the valley, were hidden by them, the greater part of the time. Sometimes, it is true, the little prisoners of Tanglewood could discern a dim outline of Monument Mountain, and the smooth whiteness of the frozen lake at its base, and the black or gray tracts of woodland, in the nearer landscape. But these were merely peeps through the tempest.

Nevertheless, the children rejoiced greatly in the snowstorm. They had already made acquaintance with it, by tumbling heels over head into its highest drifts, and flinging snow at one another, as we have just fancied the Berkshire mountains to be doing. And now they had come back to their spacious play-room, which was as big as the great drawing-room, and was lumbered with all sorts of playthings, large and small. The biggest was a rocking-horse, that looked like a real pony; and there was a whole family of wooden, waxen, plaster and china-dolls, besides rag-babies; and blocks enough to build Bunker-hill monument, and nine-pins, and balls, and humming-tops, and battledoors, and grace-sticks, and skipping-ropes, and more of such valuable property than I could tell of, in a printed page. But the children liked the snow-storm better than them all. It suggested so many brisk enjoyments for tomorrow, and all the remainder of the winter! The sleigh-ride; the slides down-hill into the valley; the snow-images that were to be shaped out; the snow-fortresses that were to be built, and the snow-balling to be carried on!

So the little folks blessed the snow-storm, and were glad to see it come thicker and thicker, and watched hopefully the long drift that was piling itself up in the avenue, and was already higher than any of their heads.

"Why, we shall be blocked up till spring!" cried they, with the hugest delight. "What a pity, that the house is too high to be quite covered up! The little red house, down yonder, will be buried up to its eaves."

"You silly children, what do you want of more snow?" asked Eustace, who, tired of some novel that he was skimming through, had strolled into the play-room. "It has done mischief enough already, by spoiling the only skating that I could hope for, through the winter. We shall see nothing more of the lake, till April; and this was to have been my first day upon it! Don't you pity me, Primrose?"

"Oh, to be sure!" answered Primrose, laughing. "But, for your comfort, we will listen to another of your old stories, such as you told us under the porch, and down in the hollow, by Shadow Brook. Perhaps I shall like them better now, when there is nothing to do, than while there were nuts to be gathered, and beautiful weather to enjoy."

Hereupon, Periwinkle, Clover, Sweet Fern, and as many others of the little fraternity and cousinhood as were still at Tanglewood, gathered about Eustace, and earnestly besought him for a story. The student yawned, stretched himself, and then, to the vast admiration of the small people, skipped three times back and forth over the top of a chair, in order, as he explained to them, to set his wits in motion.

"Well, well, children," said he, after these preliminaries, "since you insist, and Primrose has set her heart upon it, I will see what can be done for you. And, that you may know what happy days there were, before snow-storms came into fashion, I will tell you a story of the oldest of all old times, when the world was as new as Sweet Fern's bran-new humming-top. There was then but one season in the year, and that was the delightful summer; and but one age for mortals—and that was childhood."

"I never heard of that before," said Primrose.

"Of course, you never did," answered Eustace. "It shall be a story of what nobody but myself ever dreamed of—a Paradise of Children—and how, by the naughtiness of just such a little imp as Primrose here, it all came to nothing."

So Eustace Bright sat down in the chair which he had just been skipping over, took Cowslip upon his knee, ordered silence throughout the auditory, and began a story about a sad naughty child, whose name was Pandora, and about her playfellow Epimetheus. You may read it, word for word, in the pages that come next.

THE PARADISE OF CHILDREN

LONG, long ago, when this old world was in its tender infancy, there was a child, named Epimetheus, who never had either father or mother; and that he might not be lonely, another child, fatherless and motherless like himself, was sent from a far country, to live with him, and be his playfellow and helpmate. Her name was Pandora.

The first thing that Pandora saw, when she entered the cottage where Epimetheus dwelt, was a great box. And almost the first question which she put to him, after crossing the threshold, was this:—

"Epimetheus, what have you in that box?"

"My dear little Pandora," answered Epimetheus, "that is a secret; and you must be kind enough not to ask any questions about it. The box was left here to be kept safely, and I do not myself know what it contains."

"But who gave it to you?" asked Pandora. "And where did it come from?"

"That is a secret too," replied Epimetheus.

"How provoking!" exclaimed Pandora, pouting her lip. "I wish the great ugly box were out of the way!"

"Oh, come, don't think of it any more!" cried Epimetheus. "Let us run out of doors, and have some nice play with the other children!"

It is thousands of years since Epimetheus and Pandora were alive; and the world, now-a-days, is a very different sort of thing from what it was in their time. Then, everybody was a child. There needed no fathers and mothers, to take care of the children; because there was no danger, nor trouble of any kind, and no clothes to be mended, and there was always plenty to eat and drink. Whenever a child wanted his dinner, he found it growing on a tree; and, if he looked at the tree in the morning, he could see the expanding blossom of that night's supper; or, at eventide, he saw the tender bud of tomorrow's breakfast. It was a very pleasant life indeed. No labor to be done, no tasks to be studied; nothing but sports and dances, and sweet voices of children talking, or carolling like birds, or gushing out in merry laughter, throughout the live-long day.

What was most wonderful of all, the children never quarrelled among themselves; neither had they any crying-fits; nor, since time first began, had a single one of these little mortals ever gone apart into a corner, and sulked! Oh, what a good time was that, to be alive in! The truth is, those ugly little winged monsters, called Troubles, which are now almost as numerous as musquitoes, had never yet been seen on the earth. It is probable that the very greatest disquietude, which a child had ever experienced, was Pandora's vexation at not being able to discover the secret of the mysterious box.

This was at first only the faint shadow of a Trouble; but, every day, it grew more and more substantial; until, before a great while, the cottage of Epimetheus and Pandora was less sunshiny than those of the other children.

"Whence can the box have come!" Pandora continually kept saying to herself and to Epimetheus. "And what in the world can be inside of it!"

"Always talking about this box!" said Epimetheus, at last; for he had grown extremely tired of the subject. "I wish, dear Pandora, you would try to talk of something else. Come; let us go and gather some ripe figs, and eat them under the trees, for our supper! And I know a vine that has the sweetest and juiciest grapes you ever tasted!"

"Always talking about grapes and figs!" cried Pandora, pettishly.

"Well then," said Epimetheus, who was a very good-tempered child, like a multitude of children, in those days, "let us run out and have a merry time with our playmates!"

"I am tired of merry times, and don't care if I never have any more," answered our pettish little Pandora. "And, besides, I never do have any! This ugly box! I am so taken up with thinking about it, all the time! I insist upon your telling me what is inside of it."

"As I have already said, fifty times over, I do not know!" replied Epimetheus, getting a little vexed. "How, then, can I tell you what is inside?"

"You might open it," said Pandora, looking sideways at Epimetheus, "and then we could see for ourselves."

"Pandora, what are you thinking of!" exclaimed Epimetheus.

And his face expressed so much horror at the idea of looking into a box, which had been confided to him on the condition of his never opening it, that Pandora thought it best not to suggest it any more. Still, however, she could not help thinking and talking about the box.

"At least," said she, "you can tell me how it came here."

"It was left at the door," replied Epimetheus, "just before you came, by a person who looked very smiling and intelligent, and who could hardly forbear laughing, as he put it down. He was dressed in an odd kind of a cloak, and had on a cap that seemed to be made partly of feathers, so that it looked almost as if it had wings."

"What sort of a staff had he?" asked Pandora.

"Oh, the most curious staff you ever saw!" cried Epimetheus. "It was like two serpents twisting around a stick, and was carved so naturally, that I at first thought the serpents were alive."

"I know him," said Pandora, thoughtfully. "Nobody else has such a staff. It was Quicksilver; and he brought me hither, as well as the box. No doubt, he intended it for me; and, most probably, it contains pretty dresses for me to wear, or toys for you and me to play with, or something very nice for us both to eat!"

"Perhaps so," answered Epimetheus, turning away. "But, until Quicksilver comes back and tells us so, we have neither of us any right to lift the lid of the box!"

"What a dull boy he is!" muttered Pandora, as Epimetheus left the cottage. "I do wish he had a little more enterprise!"

For the first time since her arrival, Epimetheus had gone out, without asking Pandora to accompany him. He went to gather figs and grapes by himself, or to seek whatever amusement he could find, in other society than his little playfellow's. He was tired to death of hearing about the box, and heartily wished that Quicksilver, or whatever was the messenger's name, had left it at some other child's door, where Pandora would never have set eyes on it. So perseveringly as she did babble about this one thing! The box; the box; and nothing but the box! It seemed as if the box were bewitched, and as if the cottage were not big enough to hold it, without Pandora's continually stumbling over it, and making Epimetheus stumble over it likewise, and bruising all four of their shins.

Well; it was really hard that poor Epimetheus should have a box in his ears, from morning till night; especially as the little people of the earth were so unaccustomed to vexations, in those happy days, that they knew not how to deal with them. Thus, a small vexation made as much disturbance, then, as a far bigger one would, in our own times.

After Epimetheus was gone, Pandora stood gazing at the box. She had called it ugly, above a hundred times; but, in spite of all that she had said against it, it was positively a very handsome article of furniture, and would have been quite an ornament to any room in which it should be placed. It was made of a beautiful kind of wood, with dark and rich veins spreading over its surface, which was so highly polished that little Pandora could see her face in it. As the child had no other looking-glass, it is odd that she did not value the box, merely on this account.

The edges and corners of the box were carved with most wonderful skill. Around the margin there were figures of graceful men and women, and the prettiest children ever seen, reclining or sporting amid a profusion of flowers and foliage; and these various objects were so exquisitely represented, and were wrought together in such harmony, that flowers, foliage and human beings, seemed to combine into a wreath of mingled beauty. But, here and there, peeping forth from behind the carved foliage, Pandora once or twice fancied that she saw a face not so lovely, or something or other that was disagreeable, and which stole the beauty out of all the rest. Nevertheless, on looking more closely, and touching the spot with her finger, she could discover nothing of the kind. Some face, that was really beautiful, had been made to look ugly by her catching a sideway glimpse at it.

The most beautiful face of all was done, in what is called high relief, in the centre of the lid. There was nothing else, save the dark, smooth richness of the polished wood, and this one face, in the centre, with a garland of flowers about its brow. Pandora had looked at this face, a great many times, and imagined that the mouth could smile if it liked, or be graver, when it chose, the same as any living mouth. The features, indeed, all wore a very lively and rather mischievous expression, which looked almost as if it needs must burst out of the carved lips, and utter itself in words.

Had the mouth spoken, it would probably have been something like this:—

"Do not be afraid, Pandora! What harm can there be in opening the box? Never mind that poor, simple Epimetheus! You are wiser than he, and have ten times as much spirit. Open the box, and see if you do not find something very pretty!"

The box, I had almost forgotten to say, was fastened; not by a lock, nor by any other such contrivance, but by a very intricate knot of gold cord. There appeared to be no end to this knot, and no beginning. Never was a knot so cunningly twisted, nor with so many ins and outs, which roguishly defied the skilfullest fingers to disentangle them. And yet, by the very difficulty that there was in it, Pandora was the more tempted to examine the knot, and just see how it was made. Two or three times, already, she had stooped over the box, and taken the knot between her thumb and forefinger, but without positively trying to undo it.

"I really believe," said she to herself, "that I begin to see how it was done. Nay, perhaps I could tie it up again, after undoing it. There would be no harm in that, surely! Even Epimetheus would not blame me for that. I need not open the box, and should not, of course, without the foolish boy's consent, even if the knot were untied!"

It might have been better for Pandora if she had had a little work to do, or anything to employ her mind upon, so as not to be so constantly thinking of this one subject. But children led so easy a life, before any Troubles came into the world, that they had really a great deal too much leisure. They could not be forever playing at hide-and-seek among the flower-shrubs, or at blindman's buff with garlands over their eyes, or at whatever other games had been found out, while Mother Earth was in her babyhood. When life is all sport, toil is the real play. There was absolutely nothing to do.

A little sweeping and dusting about the cottage, I suppose, and the gathering of fresh flowers, (which were only too abundant, everywhere,) and arranging them in vases;—and poor little Pandora's day's work was over! And then, for the rest of the day, there was the box!

After all, I am not quite so sure that the box was not a blessing to her, in its way. It supplied her with such a variety of ideas to think of, and to talk about, whenever she had anybody to listen! When she was in good humor, she could admire the bright polish of its sides, and the rich border of beautiful faces and foliage that ran all around it. Or, if she chanced to be ill-tempered, she could give it a push, or kick it with her naughty little foot. And many a kick did the box—(but it was a mischievous box, as we shall see, and deserved all it got)—many a kick did it receive! But, certain it is, if it had not been for the box, our active-minded little Pandora would not have known half so well how to spend her time, as she now did.

For it was really an endless employment to guess what was inside. What could it be, indeed? Just imagine, my little hearers, how busy your wits would be, if there were a great box in the house, which, as you might have reason to suppose, contained something new and pretty for your Christmas or New Year's gifts! Do you think that you should be less curious than Pandora? If you were left alone with the box, might you not feel a little tempted to lift the lid? But you would not do it! Oh, fie! No, no! Only, if you thought there were toys in it, it would be so very hard to let slip an opportunity of taking just one peep! I know not whether Pandora expected any toys; for none had yet begun to be made, probably, in those days, when the world itself was one great plaything for the children that dwelt upon it. But Pandora was convinced that there was something very beautiful and valuable in the box; and therefore she felt just as anxious to take a peep, as any of these little girls, here around me, would have felt. And, possibly, a little more so;—but of that, I am not quite so certain.

On this particular day, however, which we have so long been talking about, her curiosity grew so much greater than it usually was, that, at last, she approached the box. She was more than half determined to open it, if she could. Ah, naughty Pandora!

First, however, she tried to lift it. It was heavy; quite too heavy for the slender strength of a child, like Pandora. She raised one end of the box a few inches from the floor, and let it fall again, with a pretty loud thump. A moment afterwards, she almost fancied that she heard something stir, inside of the box. She applied her ear as closely as possible, and listened. Positively, there did seem to be a kind of stifled murmur, within! Or was it merely the singing in Pandora's ears? Or could it be the beating of her heart? The child could not quite satisfy herself whether she had heard anything or no. But, at all events, her curiosity was stronger than ever.

As she drew back her head, her eyes fell upon the knot of gold cord.

"It must have been a very ingenious person who tied this knot," said Pandora to herself. "But I think I could untie it, nevertheless! I am resolved, at least, to find the two ends of the cord."

So she took the golden knot in her fingers, and pryed into its intricacies as sharply as she could. Almost without intending it, or quite knowing what she was about, she was soon busily engaged in attempting to undo it. Meanwhile, the bright sunshine came through the open window; as did likewise the merry voices of the children, playing at a distance, and perhaps the voice of Epimetheus among them. Pandora stopt to listen. What a beautiful day it was! Would it not be wiser, if she were to let the troublesome knot alone, and think no more about the box, but run and join her little playfellows, and be happy?

All this time, however, her fingers were half unconsciously busy with the knot; and happening to glance at the flower-wreathed face, on the lid of the enchanted box, she seemed to perceive it slily grinning at her.

"That face looks very mischievous," thought Pandora. "I wonder whether it smiles because I am doing wrong! I have the greatest mind in the world to run away!"

But, just then, by the merest accident, she gave the knot a kind of a twist, which produced a wonderful result. The gold cord untwined itself, as if by magic, and left the box without a fastening.

"This is the strangest thing I ever knew!" said Pandora. "What will Epimetheus say? And how can I possibly tie it up again?"

She made one or two attempts to restore the knot, but soon found it quite beyond her skill. It had disentangled itself so suddenly, that she could not in the least remember how the strings had been doubled into one another; and when she tried to recollect the shape and appearance of the knot, it seemed to have gone entirely out of her mind. Nothing was to be done, therefore, but to let the box remain as it was, until Epimetheus should come in.

"But," said Pandora, "when he finds the knot untied, he will know that I have done it. How shall I make him believe that I have not looked into the box?"

And then the thought came into her naughty little heart, that, since she would be suspected of having looked into the box, she might just as well do so, at once. Oh, very naughty, and very foolish Pandora! You should have thought only of doing what was right, and of leaving undone what was wrong, and not of what your playfellow Epimetheus would have said or believed. And so perhaps she might, if the enchanted face, on the lid of the box, had not looked so be-witchingly persuasive at her, and if she had not seemed to hear, more distinctly than before, the murmur of small voices within. She could not tell whether it was fancy or no; but there was quite a little tumult of whispers in her ear—or else it was her curiosity that whispered,

"Let us out, dear Pandora, pray let us out! We will be such nice pretty playfellows for you! Only let us out!"

"What can it be?" thought Pandora. "Is there something alive in the box? Well!—yes!—I am resolved to take just one peep! Only one peep; and then the lid shall be shut down as safely as ever! There cannot possibly be any harm in just one little peep!"

But it is now time for us to see what Epimetheus was doing.

This was the first time, since his little playmate had come to dwell with him, that he had attempted to enjoy any pleasure in which she did not partake. But nothing went right; nor was he nearly so happy as on other days. He could not find a sweet grape or a ripe fig, (if Epimetheus had a fault, it was a little too much fondness for figs,) or, if ripe at all, they were over-ripe, and so sweet as to be cloying. There was no mirth in his heart, such as usually made his voice gush out, of its own accord, and swell the merriment of his companions. In short, he grew so uneasy and discon-tented, that the other children could not imagine what was the matter with Epimetheus. Neither did he himself know what ailed him, any better than they did. For you must recollect, that, at the time we are speaking of, it was everybody's nature, and constant habit, to be happy. The world had not yet learned to be otherwise. Not a single soul or body, since these children were first sent to enjoy themselves on the beautiful earth, had ever been sick or out of sorts.

At length, discovering that, somehow or other, he put a stop to all the play, Epimetheus judged it best to go back to

Pandora, who was in a humor better suited to his own. But, with a hope of giving her pleasure, he gathered some flowers and made them into a wreath, which he meant to put upon her head. The flowers were very lovely—roses, and lilies, and orange-blossoms, and a great many more, which left a trail of fragrance behind, as Epimetheus carried them along;—and the wreath was put together with as much skill as could reasonably be expected of a boy. The fingers of little girls, it has always appeared to me, are the fittest to twine flower-wreaths; but boys could do it, in those days, rather better than they can now.

And here I must mention, that a great black cloud had been gathering in the sky, for some time past, although it had not yet overspread the sun. But, just as Epimetheus reached the cottage-door, this cloud began to intercept the sunshine, and thus to make a sudden and sad obscurity.

He entered softly; for he meant, if possible, to steal behind Pandora, and fling the wreath of flowers over her head, before she should be aware of his approach. But, as it happened, there was no need of his treading so very lightly. He might have trod as heavily as he pleased—as heavily as a grown man—as heavily, I was going to say, as an elephant—without much probability of Pandora's hearing his footsteps. She was too intent upon her purpose. At the moment of his entering the cottage, the naughty child had put her hand to the lid, and was on the point of opening the mysterious box. Epimetheus beheld her. If he had cried out, Pandora would probably have withdrawn her hand, and the fatal mystery of the box might never have been known.

But Epimetheus himself, although he said very little about it, had his own share of curiosity to know what was inside. Perceiving that Pandora was resolved to find out the secret, he determined that his playfellow should not be the only wise person in the cottage. And if there were anything pretty or valuable in the box, he meant to take half of it to himself. Thus, after all his sage speeches to Pandora about restraining her curiosity, Epimetheus turned out to be quite as foolish, and nearly as much in fault, as she. So, whenever we blame Pandora for what happened, we must not forget to shake our heads at Epimetheus likewise.

As Pandora raised the lid, the cottage grew very dark and dismal; for the black cloud had now swept quite over the sun, and seemed to have buried it alive. There had, for a little while past, been a low growling and muttering, which all at once broke into a heavy peal of thunder. But Pandora, heeding nothing of all this, lifted the lid nearly upright, and looked inside. It seemed as if a sudden swarm of winged creatures brushed past her, taking flight out of the box; while, at the same instant, she heard the voice of Epimetheus, with a lamentable tone, as if he were in pain.

"Oh, I am stung!" cried he. "I am stung! Naughty Pandora! Why have you opened this wicked box?"

Pandora let fall the lid, and starting up, looked about her, to see what had befallen Epimetheus. The thunder-cloud had so darkened the room, that she could not very clearly discern what was in it. But she heard a disagreeable buzzing, as if a great many huge flies, or gigantic musquitoes, or those insects which we call dor-bugs and pinching-dogs, were darting about. And, as her eyes grew more accustomed to the imperfect light, she saw a crowd of ugly little shapes, with bats' wings, looking abominably spiteful, and armed with terribly long stings in their tails. It was one of these that had stung Epimetheus. Nor was it a great while, before Pandora herself began to scream, in no less pain and affright than her playfellow, and making a vast deal more hubbub about it. An odious little monster had settled on her forehead, and would have stung her I know not how deeply, if Epimetheus had not run and brushed it away.

Now, if you wish to know what these ugly things might be, which had made their escape out of the box, I must tell you that they were the whole family of earthly Troubles. There were evil Passions; there were a great many species of Cares; there were more than a hundred and fifty Sorrows; there were Diseases, in a vast number of miserable and painful shapes; there were more kinds of Naughtiness, than it would be of any use to talk about. In short, everything, that has since afflicted the souls and bodies of mankind, had been shut up in the mysterious box, and given to Epimetheus and Pandora to be kept safely, in order that the happy children of the world might never be molested by them. Had they been faithful to their trust, all would have gone well. No grown person would ever have been sad, nor any child have had cause to shed a single tear, from that hour until this moment.

But—and you may see by this how a wrong act of any one mortal is a calamity to the whole world—by Pandora's lifting the lid of that miserable box, and by the fault of Epimetheus, too, in not preventing her, these Troubles have obtained a foothold among us, and do not seem very likely to be driven away in a hurry. For it was impossible, as you will easily guess, that the two children should keep the ugly swarm in their own little cottage. On the contrary, the first thing that they did was to fling open the doors and windows, in hopes of getting rid of them; and sure enough, away flew the winged Troubles all abroad, and so pestered and tormented the small people, everywhere about, that none of them so much as smiled for many days afterwards. And what was very singular, all the flowers and dewy blossoms on earth, not one of which had hitherto faded, now began to droop and shed their leaves, after a day or two. The children, moreover, who before seemed immortal in their childhood, now grew older, day by day, and came soon to be youths and maidens, and men and women by-and-by, and aged people, before they dreamed of such a thing.

Meanwhile, the naughty Pandora, and hardly less naughty Epimetheus, remained in their cottage. Both of them had been grievously stung, and were in a good deal of pain, which seemed the more intolerable to them, because it was the very first pain that had ever been felt since the world began. Of course, they were entirely unaccustomed to it, and could have no idea what it meant. Besides all this, they were in exceedingly bad humor, both with themselves and with one another. In order to indulge it to the utmost, Epimetheus sat down sullenly in a corner, with his back towards Pandora; while Pandora flung herself upon the floor, and rested her head on the fatal and abominable box. She was crying bitterly, and sobbing as if her heart would break.

Suddenly, there was a gentle little tap, on the inside of the lid.

"What can that be?" cried Pandora, lifting her head.

But either Epimetheus had not heard the tap, or was too much out of humor to notice it. At any rate, he made no answer.

"You are very unkind," said Pandora, sobbing anew, "not to speak to me!"

Again, the tap! It sounded like the tiny knuckles of a fairy's hand, knocking lightly and playfully on the inside of the box.

"Who are you?" asked Pandora, with a little of her former curiosity. "Who are you, inside of this naughty box?"

A sweet little voice spoke from within,

"Only lift the lid, and you shall see!"

"No, no," answered Pandora, again beginning to sob, "I have had enough of lifting the lid! You are inside of the box, naughty creature, and there you shall stay! There are plenty of your ugly brothers and sisters, already flying about the world. You need never think that I shall be so foolish as to let you out!"

She looked towards Epimetheus, as she spoke, perhaps expecting that he would commend her for her wisdom. But the sullen boy only muttered, that she was wise a little too late.

"Ah," said the sweet little voice again, "you had much better let me out! I am not like those naughty creatures that have stings in their tails. They are no brothers and sisters of mine, as you would see at once, if you were only to get a glimpse of me. Come, come, my pretty Pandora! I am sure you will let me out!"

And, indeed, there was a kind of cheerful witchery in the tone, that made it almost impossible to refuse anything which this little voice asked. Pandora's heart had insensibly grown lighter, at every word that came from within the box. Epimetheus, too, though still in the corner, had turned half round, and seemed to be in rather better spirits than before.

"My dear Epimetheus," cried Pandora, "have you heard this little voice?"

"Yes; to be sure I have!" answered he, but in no very good humor, as yet. "And what of it?"

"Shall I lift the lid again?" asked Pandora.

"Just as you please!" said Epimetheus. "You have done so much mischief already, that perhaps you may as well do a little more. One other Trouble, in such a swarm as you have set adrift about the world, can make no very great difference!"

"You might speak a little more kindly!" murmured Pandora, wiping her eyes.

"Ah, naughty boy!" cried the little voice within the box, in an arch and laughing tone. "He knows he is longing to see me! Come, my dear Pandora, lift up the lid! I am in a great hurry to comfort you. Only let me have some fresh air, and you shall soon see that matters are not quite so dismal as you think them!"

"Epimetheus," exclaimed Pandora, "come what may, I am resolved to open the box!"

"And, as the lid seems very heavy," cried Epimetheus, running across the room, "I will help you!"

So, with one consent, the two children again lifted the lid. Out flew a sunny and smiling little personage, and hovered about the room, throwing a light wherever she went. Have you never made the sunshine dance into dark corners, by reflecting it from a bit of looking-glass? Well; so looked the winged cheerfulness of this fairylike stranger, amid the gloom of the cottage. She flew to Epimetheus, and laid the least touch of her finger on the inflamed spot where the Trouble had stung him; and immediately the anguish of it was gone. Then, she kissed Pandora on the forehead; and her hurt was cured likewise.

After performing these good offices, the bright stranger fluttered sportively over the children's heads, and looked so sweetly at them, that they both began to think it not so very much amiss to have opened the box; since, otherwise, their cheery guest must have been kept a prisoner, among those naughty imps with stings in their tails.

"Pray, who are you, beautiful creature?" inquired Pandora.

"I am to be called Hope!" answered the sunshiny figure. "And because I am such a cheery little body, I was packed into the box, to make amends to the human race for that swarm of ugly Troubles, which was destined to be let loose among them. Never fear! we shall do pretty well, in spite of them all."

"Your wings are colored like the rainbow!" exclaimed Pandora. "How very beautiful!"

"Yes; they are like the rainbow," said Hope, "because, glad as my nature is, I am partly made of tears as well as smiles!"

"And will you stay with us," asked Epimetheus, "forever and ever?"

"As long as you need me," said Hope, with her pleasant smile—"and that will be as long as you live in the world—I promise never to desert you! There may come times and seasons, now and then, when you will think that I have utterly vanished. But again, and again, and again, when perhaps you least dream of it, you shall see the glimmer of my wings on the ceiling of your cottage. Yes, my dear children; and I know something very good and beautiful that is to be given you, hereafter!"

"Oh, tell us," they exclaimed, "tell us what it is!"

"Do not ask me," replied Hope, putting her finger on her rosy mouth. "But do not despair, even if it should never happen while you live on this earth. Trust in my promise; for it is true!"

"We do trust you!" cried Epimetheus and Pandora, both in one breath.

And so they did; and not only they, but so has everybody trusted Hope, that has since been alive. And, to tell you the truth, I cannot help being glad—(though, to be sure, it was an uncommonly naughty thing for her to do)—but I cannot help being glad that our foolish Pandora peeped into the box. No doubt—no doubt—the Troubles are still flying about the world, and have increased in multitude, rather than lessened, and are a very ugly set of imps, and carry most venomous stings in their tails. I have felt them already, and expect to feel them more, as I grow older. But then that lovely and lightsome little figure of Hope! What in the world could we do without her? Hope spiritualizes the earth; Hope makes it always new; and, even in the earth's best and brightest aspect, Hope shows it to be only the shadow of an infinite bliss, hereafter!

TANGLEWOOD PLAY-ROOM

AFTER THE STORY

P RIMROSE," asked Eustace, pinching her ear, "how do you like my little Pandora? Don't you think her the exact picture of yourself? But you would not have hesitated half so long about opening the box."

"Then I should have been well punished for my naughtiness," retorted Primrose smartly; "for the first thing to pop out, after the lid was lifted, would have been Mr. Eustace Bright, in the shape of a Trouble!"

"Cousin Eustace," said Sweet Fern, "did the box hold all the trouble that has ever come into the world?"

"Every mite of it!" answered Eustace. "This very snow-storm, which has spoilt my skating, was packed up there."

"And how big was the box?" asked Sweet Fern.

"Why, perhaps three feet long," said Eustace, "two feet wide, and two feet and a half high."

"Ah," said the child, "you are making fun of me, Cousin Eustace! I know there is not trouble enough in the world to fill such a great box as that. As for the snow-storm, it is no trouble at all, but a pleasure; so it could not have been in the box."

"Hear the child!" cried Primrose, with an air of superiority. "How little he knows about the troubles of this world! Poor fellow! He will be wiser when he has seen as much of life as I have."

So saying, she began to skip the rope.

Meantime, the day was drawing towards its close. Out of doors the scene certainly looked dreary. There was a gray drift, far and wide, through the gathering twilight;—the earth was as pathless as the air;—and the bank of snow, over the steps of the porch, proved that nobody had entered or gone out, for a good many hours past. Had there been only one child at the window of Tanglewood, gazing at this wintry prospect, it would perhaps have made him sad. But half-a-dozen children together, though they cannot quite turn the world into a paradise, may defy old Winter and all his storms to put them out of spirits. Eustace Bright, moreover, on the spur of the moment, invented several new kinds of play, which kept them all in a roar of merriment till bedtime, and served for the next stormy day besides.

TANGLEWOOD FIRESIDE

T HE SNOW-STORM lasted another day; but what became of it afterwards, I cannot possibly imagine. At any rate, it entirely cleared away, during the night; and when the sun arose, the next morning, it shone brightly down on as bleak a tract of hill-country, here in Berkshire, as could be seen anywhere in the world. The frost-work had so covered the window-panes, that it was hardly possible to get a glimpse at the scenery outside. But, while waiting for breakfast, the small populace of Tanglewood had scratched peep-holes with their finger-nails, and saw with vast delight, that—unless it were one or two bare patches on a precipitous hill-side, or the gray effect of the snow, inter-mingled with the black pine-forest—all nature was as white as a sheet. How exceedingly pleasant! And, to make it all the better, it was cold enough to nip one's nose short off! If people have but life enough in them to bear it, there is noth-ing that so raises the spirits, and makes the blood ripple and dance so nimbly, like a brook down the slope of a hill, as a bright, hard frost.

No sooner was breakfast over, than the whole party, well muffled in furs and woollens, floundered forth into the midst of the snow. Well, what a day of frosty sport was this! They slid down-hill into the valley, a hundred times, nobody knows how far, and, to make it all the merrier, upsetting their sledges and tumbling head over heels, quite as often as they came safely to the bottom. And, once, Eustace Bright took Periwinkle, Sweet Fern, and Squash Blossom on the sledge with him, by way of ensuring a safe passage; and down they went, full speed. But, behold! half way down, the sledge hit against a hidden stump, and flung all four of its passengers into a heap, and, on gathering themselves up, there was no little Squash Blossom to be found. Why, what could have become of the child? And while they were wondering and staring about, up-started Squash Blossom out of a snow-bank, with the reddest face you ever saw, and looking as if a large scarlet flower had suddenly sprouted up in mid-winter. Then there was a great laugh.

When they had grown tired of sliding down-hill, Eustace set the children to digging a cave in the biggest snow-drift that they could find. Unluckily, just as it was completed, and the party had squeezed themselves into the hollow, down came the roof upon their heads, and buried every soul of them alive! The next moment, up popped all their little heads out of the ruins, and the tall student's head in the midst of them, looking hoary and venerable with the snow-dust that had got amongst his brown curls. And then, to punish Cousin Eustace for advising them to dig such a tumble-down cavern, the children attacked him in a body, and so be-pelted him with snow-balls that he was fain to take to his heels.

So he ran away, and went into the woods, and thence to the margin of Shadow Brook, where he could hear the streamlet grumbling along, under great, overhanging banks of snow and ice, which would scarcely let it see the light of day. There were adamantine icicles, glittering around all its little cascades. Thence he strolled to the shore of the lake, and beheld a white, untrodden plain before him, stretching from his own feet to the foot of Monument Mountain. And, it being now almost sunset, Eustace thought that he had never beheld anything so fresh and beautiful as the scene. He was glad that the children were not with him; for their lively spirits and tumble-about activity would quite have chased away his higher and graver mood; so that he would merely have been merry, (as he had already been, the whole day long,) and would not have known the loveliness of the winter-sunset among the hills.

When the sun was fairly down, our friend Eustace went home to eat his supper. After the meal was over, he betook himself to the study, with a purpose, I rather imagine, to write an ode, or two or three sonnets, or verses of some kind or other, in praise of the purple and golden clouds, which he had seen around the setting sun. But, before he had hammered out the very first rhyme, the door opened, and Primrose and Periwinkle made their appearance.

"Go away, children! I can't be troubled with you now!" cried the student, looking over his shoulder, with the pen between his fingers. "What in the world do you want here? I thought you were all in bed!"

"Hear him, Periwinkle, trying to talk like a grown man!" said Primrose. "And he seems to forget that I am now thirteen years old, and may sit up almost as late as I please. But, Cousin Eustace, you must put off your airs, and come with us to the drawing-room. The children have talked so much about your stories, that my father wishes to hear one of them, in order to judge whether they are likely to do any mischief."

"Poh, poh, Primrose!" exclaimed the student, rather vexed. "I don't believe I can tell one of my stories in the presence of grown people. Besides, your father is a classical scholar; not that I am much afraid of his scholarship, neither, for I doubt not it is as rusty as an old case-knife, by this time. But then he will be sure to quarrel with the admirable nonsense that I put into these stories, out of my own head, and which makes the great charm of the matter for children, like yourself. No man of fifty, who has read the classical myths in his youth, can possibly understand my merit as a re-inventor and improver of them."

"All this may be very true," said Primrose; "but come you must! My father will not open his book, nor will mamma open the piano, till you have given us some of your nonsense, as you very correctly call it. So be a good boy, and come along."

Whatever he might pretend, the student was rather glad than otherwise, on second thoughts, to catch at the opportunity of proving to Mr. Pringle what an excellent faculty he had in modernizing the myths of ancient times. Until twenty years of age, a young man may indeed be rather bashful about showing his poetry and his prose; but, for all that, he is pretty apt to think that these very productions would place him at the tip-top of literature, if once they could be known. Accordingly, without much more resistance, Eustace suffered Primrose and Periwinkle to drag him into the drawing-room.

It was a large and handsome apartment, with a semi-circular window at one end, in the recess of which stood a marble copy of Greenough's Angel and Child. On one side of the fireplace, there were many shelves of books, gravely, but richly bound. The white light of the astral-lamp, and the red glow of the bright coal-fire, made the room brilliant and cheerful; and before the fire, in a deep arm-chair, sat Mr. Pringle, looking just fit to be seated in such a chair, and in such a room. He was a tall and quite a handsome gentleman, with a bald brow, and was always so nicely dressed, that even Eustace Bright never liked to enter his presence, without at least pausing at the threshold to settle his shirt-collar. But now, as Primrose had hold of one of his hands, and Periwinkle of the other, he was forced to make his appearance with a rough-

and-tumble sort of look, as if he had been rolling all day in a snow-bank. And so he had.

Mr. Pringle turned towards the student, benignly enough, but in a way that made him feel how uncombed and unbrushed he was, and how uncombed and unbrushed, likewise, were his mind and thoughts.

"Eustace," said Mr. Pringle, with a smile, "I find that you are producing a great sensation among the little public of Tanglewood, by the exercise of your gifts of narrative. Primrose here, as the little folks choose to call her, and the rest of the children, have been so loud in praise of your stories, that Mrs. Pringle and myself are really curious to hear a specimen. It would be so much the more gratifying to myself, as the stories appear to be an attempt to render the fables of classical antiquity into the idiom of modern fancy and feeling. At least, so I judge from a few of the incidents, which have come to me at second hand."

"You are not exactly the auditor that I should have chosen, Sir," observed the student, "for fantasies of this nature."

"Possibly not," replied Mr. Pringle. "I suspect, however, that a young author's most useful critic is precisely the one whom he would be least apt to choose. Pray oblige me, therefore."

"Sympathy, methinks, should have some little share in the critic's qualifications," murmured Eustace Bright. "However, Sir, if you will find patience, I will find stories. But be kind enough to remember, that I am addressing myself to the imagination and sympathies of the children, not to your own."

Accordingly, the student snatched hold of the first theme which presented itself. It was suggested by a plate of apples that he happened to espy on the mantel-piece.

THE THREE GOLDEN APPLES

D ID YOU ever hear of the golden apples, that grew in the garden of the Hesperides? Ah, those were such apples as would bring a great price, by the bushel, if any of them could be found growing in the orchards of now-a-days. But there is not, I suppose, a graft of that wonderful fruit, on a single tree in the wide world. Not so much as a seed of those apples exists any longer.

And even in the old, old, half-forgotten times, before the garden of the Hesperides was over-run with weeds, a great many people doubted whether there could be real trees, that bore apples of solid gold upon their branches. All had heard of them, but nobody remembered to have seen any. Children, nevertheless, used to listen, open-mouthed, to stories of the golden apple-tree, and resolved to discover it, when they should be big enough. Adventurous young men, who desired to do a braver thing than any of their fellows, set out in quest of this fruit. Many of them returned no more; none of them brought back the apples. No wonder that they found it impossible to gather them! It is said that there was a dragon beneath the tree, with a hundred terrible heads, fifty of which were always on the watch, while the other fifty slept.

In my opinion, it was hardly worth running so much risk for the sake of a solid golden apple. Had the apples been sweet, mellow, and juicy, indeed, that would be another matter. There might then have been some sense in trying to get at them, in spite of the hundred-headed dragon!

But, as I have already told you, it was quite a common thing with young persons, when tired of too much peace and rest, to go in search of the garden of the Hesperides. And, once, the adventure was undertaken by a hero, who had enjoyed very little peace or rest, since he came into the world. At the time of which I am going to speak, he was wandering through the pleasant land of Italy, with a mighty club in his hand, and a bow and quiver slung across his shoulders. He was wrapt in the skin of the biggest and fiercest lion that ever had been seen, and which he himself had killed; and though, on the whole, he was kind, and generous, and noble, there was a good deal of the lion's fierceness in his heart. As he went on his way, he continually inquired whether that were the right road to the famous garden. But none of the country people knew anything about the matter, and many looked as if they would have laughed at the question, if the stranger had not carried so very big a club.

So he journeyed on and on, still making the same inquiry; until, at last, he came to the brink of a river, where some beautiful young women sat twining wreaths of flowers.

"Can you tell me, pretty maidens," asked the stranger, "whether this is the right way to the garden of the Hesperides?"

The young women had been having a fine time together, weaving the flowers into wreaths, and crowning one another's heads. And there seemed to be a kind of magic in the touch of their fingers, that made the flowers more fresh and dewy, and of brighter hues, and sweeter fragrance, while they played with them, than even when they had been growing on their native stems. But, on hearing the stranger's question, they dropt all their flowers on the grass, and gazed at him with astonishment.

"The garden of the Hesperides!" cried one. "We thought mortals had been weary of seeking it, after so many disappointments. And, pray, adventurous traveller, what do you want there?"

"A certain king, who is my cousin," replied he, "has ordered me to get him three of the golden apples."

"Most of the young men, who go in quest of these apples," observed another of the damsels, "desire to obtain them for themselves, or to present them to some fair maiden whom they love. Do you then love this king, your cousin, so very much?"

"Perhaps not," replied the stranger, sighing. "He has often been severe and cruel to me. But it is my destiny to obey him!"

"And do you know," asked the damsel who had first spoken, "that a terrible dragon, with a hundred heads, keeps watch under the golden apple-tree?"

"I know it well," answered the stranger, calmly. "But from my cradle upwards, it has been my business, and almost my pastime, to deal with serpents and dragons."

The young women looked at his massive club, and at the shaggy lion's skin which he wore, and likewise at his heroic limbs and figure; and they whispered to each other, that the stranger appeared to be one, who might reasonably expect to perform deeds far beyond the might of other men. But, then, the dragon with a hundred heads! What mortal, even if he possessed a hundred lives, could hope to escape the fangs of such a monster? So kind-hearted were the maidens, that they could not bear to see this brave and handsome traveller attempt what was so very dangerous, and devote himself, most probably, to become a meal for the dragon's hundred ravenous mouths.

"Go back," cried they all, "go back to your own home! Your mother, beholding you safe and sound, will shed tears of joy; and what can she do more, should you win ever so great a victory? No matter for the golden apples! No matter for the king, your cruel cousin! We do not wish the dragon with the hundred heads to eat you up!"

The stranger seemed to grow impatient at these remonstrances. He carelessly lifted his mighty club, and let it fall upon a rock that lay half-buried in the earth, near by. With the force of that idle blow, the great rock was shattered all to pieces. It cost the stranger no more effort to achieve this feat of a giant's strength, than for one of the young maidens to touch her sister's rosy cheek with a flower.

"Do you not believe," said he, looking at the damsels with a smile, "that such a blow would have crushed one of the dragon's hundred heads?"

Then he sat down on the grass, and told them the story of his life, or as much of it as he could remember, from the day when he was first cradled in a warrior's brazen shield. While he lay there, two immense serpents came gliding over the floor, and opened their hideous jaws to devour him; and he, a baby of a few months old, had griped one of the fierce snakes in each of his little fists, and strangled them to death. When he was but a stripling he had killed a huge lion, almost as big as the one whose vast and shaggy hide he now wore upon his shoulders. The next thing that he had done, was to fight a battle with an ugly sort of monster, called a hydra, which had no less than nine heads, and exceedingly sharp teeth in every one of them.

"But the dragon of the Hesperides, you know," observed one of the damsels, "has a hundred heads!"

"Nevertheless," replied the stranger, "I would rather fight two such dragons than a single hydra. For, as fast as I cut off a head, two others grew in its place; and, besides, there was one of the heads that could not possibly be killed, but kept biting as fiercely as ever, long after it was cut off. So I was forced to bury it under a stone, where it is doubtless alive, to this very day. But the hydra's body, and its eight other heads, will never do any further mischief."

The damsels, judging that the story was likely to last a good while, had been preparing a repast of bread and grapes, that the stranger might refresh himself in the intervals of his talk. They took pleasure in helping him to this simple food; and, now and then, one of them would put a sweet grape between her rosy lips, lest it should make him bashful, to eat alone.

The traveller proceeded to tell how he had chased a very swift stag, for a twelvemonth together, without ever stopping to take breath, and had at last caught it by the antlers, and carried it home alive. And he had fought with a very odd race of people, half horses and half men, and had put them all to death, from a sense of duty, in order that their ugly figures might never be seen any more. Besides all this, he took to himself great credit for having cleaned out a stable.

"Do you call that a wonderful exploit?" asked one of the young maidens, with a smile. "Any clown in the country has done as much!"

"Had it been an ordinary stable," replied the stranger, "I should not have mentioned it. But this was so gigantic a task that it would have taken me all my life to perform it, if I had not luckily thought of turning the channel of a river through the stable-door. That did the business, in a very short time!"

Seeing how earnestly his fair auditors listened, he next told them how he had shot some monstrous birds, and had caught a wild bull alive, and let him go again, and had tamed a number of very wild horses, and had conquered Hippolyta, the warlike queen of the Amazons. He mentioned, likewise, that he had taken off Hippolyta's enchanted girdle, and had given it to the daughter of his cousin, the king.

"Was it the girdle of Venus," inquired the prettiest of the damsels, "which makes women beautiful?"

"No," answered the stranger. "It had formerly been the sword-belt of Mars; and it can only make the wearer valiant and courageous."

"An old sword-belt!" cried the damsel, tossing her head. "Then I should not care about having it!"

"You are right," said the stranger.

Going on with his wonderful narrative, he informed the maidens that as strange an adventure, as ever happened, was when he fought with Geryon, the six-legged man. This was a very odd and frightful sort of figure, as you may well believe. Any person, looking at his tracks in the sand or snow, would suppose that three sociable companions had been walking along together. Or, hearing his footsteps at a little distance, it was no more than reasonable to judge that several people must be coming. But it was only the strange man, Geryon, clattering onward, with his six legs!

Six legs and one gigantic body! Certainly, he must have been a very queer monster to look at; and, my stars, what a waste of shoe-leather!

When the stranger had finished the story of his adventures, he looked around at the attentive faces of the maidens.

"Perhaps you may have heard of me before," said he, modestly. "My name is Hercules!"

"We had already guessed it," replied the maidens; "for your wonderful deeds are known all over the world. We do not think it strange, any longer, that you should set out in quest of the golden apples of the Hesperides. Come, sisters, let us crown the hero with flowers!"

Then they flung beautiful wreaths over his stately head and mighty shoulders, so that the lion's skin was almost entirely covered with roses. They took possession of his ponderous club, and so entwined it about with the brightest, softest, and most fragrant blossoms, that not a finger's breadth of its oaken substance could be seen. It looked all like a huge bunch of flowers. Lastly, they joined hands, and danced around him, chanting words which became poetry of their own accord, and grew into a choral song, in honor of the illustrious Hercules.

And Hercules was rejoiced, as any other hero would have been, to know that these fair young girls had heard of the valiant deeds, which it had cost him so much toil and danger to achieve. But, still, he was not satisfied. He could not think that what he had already done was worthy of so much honor, while there remained any bold or difficult adventure to be undertaken.

"Dear maidens," said he, when they paused to take breath, "now that you know my name, will you not tell me how I am to reach the garden of the Hesperides?"

"Ah, must you go so soon?" they exclaimed. "You—that have performed so many wonders, and spent such a toilsome life—cannot you content yourself to repose, a little while, on the margin of this peaceful river?"

Hercules shook his head.

"I must depart now!" said he.

"We will then give you the best directions we can," replied the damsels. "You must go to the sea-shore, and find out the Old One, and compel him to inform you where the golden apples are to be found."

"The Old One!" repeated Hercules, laughing at this odd name. "And, pray, who may the Old One be?"

"Why, the Old Man of the Sea, to be sure!" answered one of the damsels. "He has fifty daughters, whom some people call very beautiful; but we do not think it proper to be acquainted with them, because they have sea-green hair, and taper away like fishes. You must talk with this Old Man of the Sea. He is a sea-faring person, and knows all about the garden of the Hesperides; for it is situated in an island, which he is often in the habit of visiting."

Hercules then asked whereabouts the Old One was most likely to be met with. When the damsels had informed him, he thanked them for all their kindness—for the bread and grapes, with which they had fed him, the lovely flowers with which they had crowned him, and the songs and dances wherewith they had done him honor—and he thanked them, most of all, for telling him the right way, and immediately set forth upon his journey.

But, before he was out of hearing, one of the maidens called after him.

"Keep fast hold of the Old One, when you catch him!" cried she, smiling, and lifting her finger to make the caution more impressive. "Do not be astonished at anything that may happen. Only hold him fast, and he will tell you what you wish to know."

Hercules again thanked her, and pursued his way, while the maidens resumed their pleasant labor of making flower-wreaths. They talked about the hero, long after he was gone.

"We will crown him with the loveliest of our garlands," said they, "when he returns hither with the three golden apples, after slaying the dragon with a hundred heads!"

Meanwhile, Hercules travelled constantly onward, over hill and dale, and through the solitary woods. Sometimes he swung his club aloft, and splintered a mighty oak with a downright blow. His mind was so full of the giants and monsters, with whom it was the business of his life to fight, that perhaps he mistook the great tree for a giant or a monster. And so eager was Hercules to achieve what he had undertaken, that he almost regretted to have spent so much time with the damsels, wasting idle breath upon the story of his adventures. But thus it always is with persons who are destined to perform great things. What they have already done, seems less than nothing. What they have taken in hand to do, seems worth toil, danger, and life itself.

Persons, who happened to be passing through the forest, must have been affrighted to see him smite the trees with his great club. With but a single blow, the trunk was riven as by the stroke of lightning, and the broad boughs came rustling and crashing down.

Hastening forward, without ever pausing or looking behind, he by-and-by heard the sea roaring at a distance. At this sound, he increased his speed, and soon came to a beach, where the great surf-waves tumbled themselves upon the hard sand, in a long line of snowy foam. At one end of the beach, however, there was a pleasant spot, where some green shrubbery clambered up a cliff, making its rocky face look soft and beautiful. A carpet of verdant grass, largely inter-mixed with sweet-smelling clover, covered the narrow space between the bottom of the cliff and the sea. And what should Hercules espy there, but an old man, fast asleep!

But was it really and truly an old man? Certainly, at first sight, it looked very like one; but, on closer inspection, it rather seemed to be some kind of a creature that lived in the sea. For, on his legs and arms, there were scales, such as fishes have; he was web-footed and web-fingered, after the fashion of a duck; and his long beard, being of a greenish tinge, had more the appearance of a tuft of sea-weed than of an ordinary beard. Have you never seen a stick of timber, that has been long tossed about by the waves, and has got all overgrown with barnacles, and, at last drifting ashore, seems to have been thrown up from the very deepest bottom of the sea? Well; the old man would have put you in mind of just such a wave-tost spar! But, Hercules, the instant he set eyes on this strange figure, was convinced that it could be no other than the Old One, who was to direct him on his way.

Yes; it was the self-same Old Man of the Sea, whom the hospitable maidens had talked to him about. Thanking his stars for the lucky accident of finding the old fellow asleep, Hercules stole on tiptoe towards him, and caught him by the arm and leg.

"Tell me," cried he, before the Old One was well awake, "which is the way to the garden of the Hesperides?"

As you may easily imagine, the Old Man of the Sea awoke in a fright. But his astonishment could hardly have been greater than was that of Hercules, the next moment. For, all of a sudden, the Old One seemed to disappear out of his grasp, and he found himself holding a stag by the fore and hind-leg! But still he kept fast hold. Then the stag disappeared, and in its stead there was a sea-bird, fluttering and screaming, while Hercules clutched it by the wing and claw. But the bird could not get away. Immediately afterwards, there was an ugly three-headed dog, which growled and barked at Hercules, and snapt fiercely at the hands by which he held him. But Hercules would not let him go. In another minute, instead of the three-headed dog, what should appear but Geryon, the six-legged man-monster, kicking at Hercules with five of his legs, in order to get the remaining one at liberty! But Hercules held on. By-and-by, no Geryon was there, but a huge snake, like one of those which Hercules had strangled in his babyhood, only a hundred times as big; and it twisted and twined about the hero's neck and body, and threw its tail high into the air, and opened its deadly jaws as if to devour him outright; so that it was really a very terrible spectacle. But Hercules was no whit disheartened, and squeezed the great snake so tightly that he soon began to hiss with pain.

You must understand that the Old Man of the Sea, though he generally looked so much like the wave-beaten figure-head of a vessel, had the power of assuming any shape he pleased.

When he found himself so roughly seized by Hercules, he had been in hopes of putting him into such surprise and terror, by these magical transformations, that the hero would be glad to let him go. If Hercules had relaxed his grasp, the Old One would certainly have plunged down to the very bottom of the sea, whence he would not soon have given himself the trouble of coming up, in order to answer any impertinent questions. Ninety-nine people out of a hundred, I suppose, would have been frightened out of their wits by the very first of his ugly shapes, and would have taken to their heels at once. For, one of the hardest things in this world is, to see the difference between real dangers and imaginary ones.

But, as Hercules held on so stubbornly, and only squeezed the Old One so much the tighter at every change of shape, and really put him to no small torture, he finally thought it best to re-appear in his own figure. So there he was again, a fishy, scaly, web-footed sort of personage, with something like a tuft of sea-weed at his chin.

"Pray what do you want with me?" cried the Old One, as soon as he could take breath; for it is quite a tiresome affair to go through so many false shapes. "Why do you squeeze me so hard? Let me go, this moment; or I shall begin to consider you an extremely uncivil person!"

"My name is Hercules!" roared the mighty stranger. "And you will never get out of my clutch, until you tell me the nearest way to the garden of the Hesperides!"

When the old fellow heard who it was that had caught him, he saw, with half an eye, that it would be necessary to tell him everything that he wanted to know. The Old One was an inhabitant of the sea, you must recollect, and roamed about everywhere, like other sea-faring people. Of course, he had often heard of the fame of Hercules, and of the wonderful things that he was constantly performing, in various parts of the earth, and how determined he always was to accomplish whatever he undertook. He therefore made no more attempts to escape, but told the hero how to find the garden of the Hesperides, and likewise warned him of many difficulties which must be overcome, before he could arrive thither.

"You must go on, thus and thus," said the Old Man of the Sea, after taking the points of the compass, "till you come in sight of a very tall giant, who holds the sky on his shoulders. And the giant, if he happens to be in the humor, will tell you exactly where the garden of the Hesperides lies."

"And if the giant happens not to be in the humor," remarked Hercules, balancing his club on the tip of his finger, "perhaps I shall find means to persuade him!"

Thanking the Old Man of the Sea, and begging his pardon for having squeezed him so roughly, the hero resumed his journey. He met with a great many strange adventures, which would be well worth your hearing, if I had leisure to narrate them as minutely as they deserve.

It was in this journey, if I mistake not, that he encountered a prodigious giant, who was so wonderfully contrived by nature, that, every time he touched the earth, he became ten times as strong as ever he had been before. His name was Antæus. You may see, plainly enough, that it was a very difficult business to fight with such a fellow; for, as often as he got a knock-down blow, up he started again, stronger, fiercer, and abler to use his weapons, than if his enemy had let him alone. Thus, the harder Hercules pounded the giant with his club, the farther he seemed from winning the victory. I have sometimes argued with such people, but never fought with one. The only way in which Hercules found it possible to finish the battle, was by lifting Antæus off his feet into the air, and squeezing, and squeezing, and squeezing him, until, finally, the strength was quite squeezed out of his enormous body.

When this affair was finished, Hercules continued his travels, and went to the land of Egypt, where he was taken prisoner and would have been put to death, if he had not slain the king of the country, and made his escape. Passing through the deserts of Africa, and going as fast as he could, he arrived at last on the shore of the great ocean. And here, unless he could walk on the crests of the billows, it seemed as if his journey must needs be at an end.

Nothing was before him, save the foaming, dashing, measureless ocean. But, suddenly, as he looked towards the horizon, he saw something, a great way off, which he had not seen, the moment before. It gleamed very brightly, almost as you may have beheld the round, golden disk of the sun, when it rises or sets over the edge of the world. It evidently drew nearer; for, at every instant, this wonderful object became larger and more lustrous. At length, it had come so nigh, that Hercules discovered it to be an immense cup or bowl, made either of gold or burnished brass. How it had got afloat upon the sea, is more than I can tell you. There it was, at all events, rolling on the tumultuous billows, which tossed it up and down, and heaved their foamy tops against its sides, but without ever throwing their spray over the brim.

"I have seen many giants, in my time," thought Hercules; "but never one that would need to drink his wine out of a cup like this!"

And, true enough, what a cup it must have been! It was as large—as large—but, in short, I am afraid to say how immeasurably large it was. To speak within bounds, it was ten times larger than a great mill-wheel; and, all of metal as it was, it floated over the heaving surges more lightly than an acorn-cup a-down the brook. The waves tumbled it onward, until it grazed against the shore, within a short distance of the spot where Hercules was standing.

As soon as this happened, he knew what was to be done; for he had not gone through so many remarkable adventures without learning pretty well how to conduct himself, whenever anything came to pass, a little out of the common rule.

It was just as clear as daylight, that this marvellous cup had been set adrift by some unseen power, and guided hitherward, in order to carry Hercules across the sea on his way to the garden of the Hesperides. Accordingly, without a moment's delay, he clambered over the brim, and slid down on the inside, where, spreading out his lion's skin, he proceeded to take a little repose. He had scarcely rested, until now, since he bade farewell to the damsels on the margin of the river. The waves dashed, with a pleasant and ringing sound, against the circumference of the hollow cup; it rocked lightly to-and-fro; and the motion was so soothing, that it speedily rocked Hercules into an agreeable slumber.

His nap had probably lasted a good while, when the cup chanced to graze against a rock, and, in consequence, immediately resounded and reverberated through its golden or brazen substance, a hundred times as loudly as ever you heard a church-bell. The noise awoke Hercules, who instantly started up and gazed around him, wondering whereabouts he was. He was not long in discovering that the cup had floated across a great part of the sea, and was approaching the shore of what seemed to be an island. And, on that island, what do you think he saw?

No;—you will never guess it; not if you were to try fifty-thousand times! It positively appears to me, that this was the most marvellous spectacle that had ever been seen by Hercules, in the whole course of his wonderful travels and adventures. It was a greater marvel than the hydra with nine heads, which kept growing twice as fast as they were cut off; greater than the six-legged man-monster; greater than Antæus; greater than anything that was ever beheld by anybody, before or since the days of Hercules, or than anything that remains to be beheld, by travellers in all time to come. It was a giant!

But, such an intolerably big giant! A giant, as tall as a mountain; so vast a giant, that the clouds rested about his midst, like a girdle, and hung like a hoary beard from his chin, and flitted before his huge eyes, so that he could neither see Hercules nor the golden cup in which he was voyaging. And, most wonderful of all, the giant held up his great hands and appeared to support the sky, which, so far as Hercules could discern through the clouds, was resting upon his head! This does really seem almost too much to believe.

Meanwhile, the bright cup continued to float onward, and finally touched the strand. Just then, a breeze wafted away the clouds from before the giant's visage, and Hercules beheld it, with all its enormous features;—eyes, each of them as big as yonder lake, a nose a mile long, and a mouth of the same width. It was a countenance terrible from its enormity of size, but disconsolate and weary, even as you may see the faces of many people, now-a-days, who are compelled to sustain burthens above their strength. What the sky was to the giant, such are the cares of earth to those who let themselves be weighed down by them. And whenever men undertake what is beyond the just measure of their abilities, they encounter precisely such a doom as had befallen this poor giant.

Poor fellow! He had evidently stood there a long while. An ancient forest had been growing and decaying around his feet; and oak-trees, of six or seven centuries old, had sprung from the acorn and forced themselves between his toes.

The giant now looked down from the far height of his great eyes, and perceiving Hercules, roared out in a voice that resembled thunder, proceeding out of the cloud that had just flitted away from his face.

"Who are you, down at my feet there? And whence do you come, in that little cup?"

"I am Hercules!" thundered back the hero, in a voice pretty nearly or quite as loud as the giant's own. "And I am seeking for the garden of the Hesperides!"

"Ho! Ho! Ho!" roared the giant, in a fit of immense laughter. "That is a wise adventure, truly!"

"And why not?" cried Hercules, getting a little angry at the giant's mirth. "Do you think I am afraid of the dragon with a hundred heads?"

Just at this time, while they were talking together, some black clouds gathered about the giant's middle, and burst into a tremendous storm of thunder and lightning, causing such a pother that Hercules found it impossible to distinguish a word. Only the giant's immeasurable legs were to be seen, standing up into the obscurity of the tempest and, now-and-then, a momentary glimpse of his whole figure, mantled in a volume of mist. He seemed to be speaking, most of the time; but his big, deep, rough voice chimed in with the reverberations of the thunder-claps, and rolled away over the hills, like them. Thus, by talking out of season, the foolish giant expended an incalculable quantity of breath, to no purpose; for the thunder spoke quite as intelligibly as he.

At last, the storm swept over, as suddenly as it had come. And there again was the clear sky, and the weary giant holding it up, and the pleasant sunshine beaming over his vast height, and illuminating it against the back-ground of the sullen thunder-clouds. So far above the shower had been his head, that not a hair of it was moistened by the rain-drops.

When the giant could see Hercules, still standing on the sea-shore, he roared out to him anew.

"I am Atlas, the mightiest giant in the world! And I hold the sky upon my head!"

"So I see!" answered Hercules. "But, can you show me the way to the garden of the Hesperides?"

"What do you want there?" asked the giant.

"I want three of the Golden Apples," shouted Hercules, "for my cousin, the king!"

"There is nobody but myself," quoth the giant, "that can go to the garden of the Hesperides, and gather the golden apples. If it were not for this little business of holding up the sky, I would make half-a-dozen steps across the sea, and get them for you."

"You are very kind," replied Hercules. "And cannot you rest the sky upon a mountain?"

"None of them are quite high enough," said Atlas, shaking his head. "But, if you were to take your stand on the summit of that nearest one, your head would be pretty nearly on a level with mine. You seem to be a fellow of some strength. What if you should take my burthen on your shoulders, while I do your errand for you?"

Hercules, as you must be careful to remember, was a remarkably strong man; and though it certainly requires a great deal of muscular power to uphold the sky, yet, if any mortal could be supposed capable of such an exploit, he was the one. Nevertheless, it seemed so difficult an undertaking, that, for the first time in his life, he hesitated.

"Is the sky very heavy?" he inquired.

"Why, not particularly so, at first," answered the giant, shrugging his shoulders. "But it gets to be a little burthensome, after a thousand years!"

"And how long a time," asked the hero, "will it take you to get the golden apples?"

"Oh, that will be done in a few moments," cried Atlas. "I shall take ten or fifteen miles at a stride, and be at the garden and back again, before your shoulders begin to ache."

"Well then," answered Hercules, "I will climb the mountain, behind you there, and relieve you of your burthen!"

The truth is, Hercules had a kind heart of his own, and considered that he should be doing the giant a favor, by allowing him this opportunity for a ramble. And, besides, he thought that it would be still more for his own glory, if he could boast of upholding the sky, than merely to do so ordinary a thing as to conquer a dragon with a hundred heads. Accordingly, without more words, the sky was shifted from the shoulders of Atlas, and placed upon those of Hercules.

When this was safely accomplished, the first thing that the giant did was to stretch himself; and you may imagine what a prodigious spectacle he was then! Next, he slowly lifted one of his feet out of the forest that had grown up around it; then, the other. Then, all at once, he began to caper, and leap, and dance, for joy at his freedom; flinging himself nobody knows how high into the air, and floundering down again with a shock that made the earth tremble. Then he laughed—Ho! Ho! Ho!—with a thunderous roar that was echoed from the mountains, far and near, as if they and the giant had been so many rejoicing brothers. When his joy had a little subsided, he stept into the sea; ten miles at the first stride, which brought him mid-leg deep; and ten miles at the second, when the water came just above his knees; and ten miles more at the third, by which he was immersed nearly to his waist. This was the greatest depth of the sea.

Hercules watched the giant, as he still went onward; for it was really a wonderful sight—this immense human form, more than thirty miles off, half-hidden in the ocean, but with his upper half as tall, and misty, and blue, as a distant mountain! At last, the gigantic shape faded entirely out of view. And now Hercules began to consider what he should do, in case Atlas should be drowned in the sea, or if he were to be stung to death by the dragon with the hundred heads, which guarded the golden apples of the Hesperides. If any such misfortune were to happen, how could he ever get rid of the sky? And, by-the-by, its weight began already to be a little irksome to his head and shoulders.

"I really pity the poor giant," thought Hercules. "If it wearies me so much, in ten minutes, how must it have wearied him, in a thousand years!"

Oh, my sweet little people, you have no idea what a weight there was in that same blue sky, which looks so soft and aerial above our heads! And there, too, was the bluster of the wind, and the chill and watery clouds, and the blazing sun, all taking their turns to make Hercules uncomfortable! He began to be afraid that the giant would never come back. He gazed wistfully at the world beneath him, and acknowledged to himself, that it was a far happier kind of life to be a shepherd at the foot of a mountain, than to stand on its dizzy summit, and bear up the firmament with his might and main! For, of course, as you will easily understand, Hercules had an immense responsibility on his mind, as well as a weight on his head and shoulders. Why, if he did not stand perfectly still, and keep the sky immoveable, the sun would perhaps be put ajar! Or, after nightfall, a great many of the stars might be loosened from their places, and shower down like fiery rain upon the people's heads! And how ashamed would the hero be, if, owing to his unsteadiness beneath its weight, the sky should crack, and show a great fissure quite across it!

I know not how long it was, before, to his unspeakable joy, he beheld the huge shape of the giant, like a cloud on the far-off edge of the sea. At his nearer approach, Atlas held up his hand, in which Hercules could perceive three magnificent golden apples, as big as pumpkins, all hanging from one branch.

"I am glad to see you again!" shouted Hercules, when the giant was within hearing. "So, you have got the golden apples!"

"Certainly, certainly," answered Atlas; "and very fair apples they are. I took the finest that grew on the tree, I assure you. Ah, it is a beautiful spot, that garden of the Hesperides! Yes; and the dragon with a hundred heads is a sight worth any man's seeing. After all, you had better have gone for the apples yourself!"

"No matter!" replied Hercules. "You have had a pleasant ramble, and have done the business as well as I could. I heartily thank you for your trouble. And now, as I have a long way to go, and am rather in haste—and as the king, my cousin, is anxious to receive the golden apples—will you be kind enough to take the sky off my shoulders again?"

"Why, as to that," said the giant, chucking the golden apples into the air, twenty miles high, or thereabouts, and catching them as they came down—"as to that, my good friend, I consider you a little unreasonable! Cannot I carry the golden apples to the king, your cousin, much quicker than you could? As his majesty is in such a hurry to get them, I promise you to take my longest strides. And, besides, I have no fancy for burthening myself with the sky, just now!"

Here Hercules grew impatient, and gave a great shrug of his shoulders. It being now twilight, you might have seen two or three stars tumble out of their places. Everybody on earth looked upward in affright, thinking that the sky might be going to fall next.

"Oh, that will never do!" cried Giant Atlas, with a great roar of laughter. "I have not let fall so many stars, within the last five centuries. By the time you have stood there as long as I did, you will begin to learn patience!"

"What!" shouted Hercules, very wrathfully. "Do you intend to make me bear this burthen forever?"

"We will see about that, one of these days," answered the giant. "At all events, you ought not to complain, if you have to bear it the next hundred years, or perhaps the next thousand. I bore it a good while longer, in spite of the back-ache. Well, then, after a thousand years, if I happen to feel in the mood, we may possibly shift about again. You are certainly a very strong man, and can never have a better opportunity to prove it. Posterity will talk of you, I warrant it!"

"Pish! A fig for its talk!" cried Hercules, with another hitch of his shoulders. "Just take the sky upon your head, one instant, will you? I want to make a cushion of my lion's skin, for the weight to rest upon. It really chafes me, and will cause unnecessary inconvenience in so many centuries as I am to stand here!"

"That's no more than fair, and I'll do it!" quoth the giant; for he had no unkind feeling towards Hercules, and was merely acting with a too selfish consideration of his own ease. "For just five minutes, then, I'll take back the sky. Only for five minutes, recollect! I have no idea of spending another thousand years, as I spent the last. Variety is the spice of life, say I!"

Ah, the thick-witted old rogue of a giant! He threw down the golden apples, and received back the sky, from the head and shoulders of Hercules, upon his own, where it rightly belonged. And Hercules picked up the three golden apples, that were as big or bigger than pumpkins, and straightway set out on his journey homeward, without paying the slightest heed to the thundering tones of the giant, who bellowed after him to come back. Another forest sprang up around his feet, and grew ancient there; and again might be seen oak-trees, of six or seven centuries old, that had waxed thus aged betwixt his enormous toes.

And there stands the giant, to this day; or, at any rate, there stands a mountain as tall as he, and which bears his name; and when the thunder rumbles about its summit, we may imagine it to be the voice of Giant Atlas, bellowing after Hercules!

TANGLEWOOD FIRESIDE

AFTER THE STORY

COUSIN EUSTACE," demanded Sweet Fern, who had been sitting at the story-teller's feet, with his mouth wide open, "exactly how tall was this giant?"

"Oh, Sweet Fern, Sweet Fern," cried the student, "do you think I was there, to measure him with a yard-stick? Well, if you must know to a hair's breadth, I suppose he might be from three to fifteen miles straight upward, and that he might have seated himself on Taconic, and had Monument Mountain for a footstool!"

"Dear me," ejaculated the good little boy, with a contented sort of a grunt, "that was a giant, sure enough! And how long was his little finger?"

"As long as from Tanglewood to the lake," said Eustace.

"Sure enough, that was a giant!" repeated Sweet Fern, in an ecstasy at the precision of these measurements. "And how broad, I wonder, were the shoulders of Hercules?"

"That is what I have never been able to find out," answered the student. "But I think they must have been a great deal broader than mine, or than your father's, or than almost any shoulders which one sees, now-a-days."

"I wish," whispered Sweet Fern, with his mouth close to the student's ear, "that you would tell me how big were some of the oak-trees, that grew between the giant's toes!"

"They were bigger," said Eustace, "than the great chestnut-tree, which stands beyond Captain Smith's house."

"Eustace," remarked Mr. Pringle, after some deliberation, "I find it impossible to express such an opinion of this story as will be likely to gratify, in the smallest degree, your pride of authorship. Pray let me advise you never more to meddle with a classical myth. Your imagination is altogether Gothic, and will inevitably gothicise everything that you touch. The effect is like bedaubing a marble statue with paint. This giant, now! How can you have ventured to thrust his huge, disproportioned mass among the seemly outlines of Grecian fable, the tendency of which is to reduce even the extravagant within limits, by its pervading elegance?"

"I described the giant as he appeared to me," replied the student, rather piqued. "And, Sir, if you would only bring your mind into such a relation with these fables, as is necessary, in order to re-model them, you would see at once that an old Greek had no more exclusive right to them, than a modern Yankee has. They are the common property of the world, and of all time. The ancient poets re-modelled them at pleasure, and held them plastic in their hands; and why should they not be plastic in my hands as well?"

Mr. Pringle could not forbear a smile.

"And besides," continued Eustace, "the moment you put any warmth of heart, any passion or affection, any human or divine morality, into a classic mould, you make it quite another thing from what it was before. My own opinion is, that the Greeks, by taking possession of these legends, (which were the immemorial birthright of mankind,) and putting them into shapes of indestructible beauty, indeed, but cold and heartless, have done all subsequent ages an incalculable injury."

"Which you, doubtless, were born to remedy," said Mr. Pringle, laughing outright. "Well, well, go on; but take my advice, and never put any of your travesties on paper. And, as your next effort, what if you should try your hand on some one of the legends of Apollo?"

"Ah, Sir, you propose it as an impossibility," observed the student, after a moment's meditation; "and, to be sure, at first thought, the idea of a Gothic Apollo strikes one rather ludicrously. But I will turn over your suggestion in my mind, and do not quite despair of success."

During the above discussion, the children (who understood not a word of it) had grown very sleepy, and were now sent off to bed. Their drowsy babble was heard, ascending the staircase, while a north-west wind roared loudly among the tree-tops of Tanglewood, and played an anthem around the house. Eustace Bright went back to the study, and again endeavored to hammer out some verses, but fell asleep between two of the rhymes.

THE HILL-SIDE

INTRODUCTORY TO "THE MIRACULOUS PITCHER"

A ND WHEN, and where, do you think we find the children, next? No longer in the winter-time, but in the merry month of May. No longer in Tanglewood play-room, or at Tanglewood fireside, but more than half-way up a monstrous hill, or a mountain, as perhaps it would be better pleased to have us call it. They had set out from home with the mighty purpose of climbing this high hill, even to the very tip-top of its bald head. To be sure it was not quite so high as Chimborazo, or Mount Blanc, and was even a good deal lower than old Graylock. But, at any rate, it was higher than a thousand ant-hillocks, or a million of mole-hills, and, when measured by the short strides of little children, might be reckoned a very respectable mountain.

And was Cousin Eustace with the party? Of that you may be certain; else how could the book go on a step farther? He was now in the middle of the Spring vacation, and looked pretty much as we saw him, four or five months ago, except that, if you gazed quite closely at his upper lip, you could discern the funniest little bit of a moustache upon it. Setting aside this mark of mature manhood, you might have considered Cousin Eustace just as much a boy, as when you first became acquainted with him. He was as merry, as playful, as good-humored, as light of foot and of spirits, and equally a favorite with the little folks, as he had always been. This expedition up the mountain was entirely of his contrivance. All the way up the steep ascent, he had encouraged the elder children with his cheerful voice, and when Dandelion, Cowslip, and Squash Blossom grew weary, he had lugged them along, alternately, on his back. In this manner, they had passed through the orchards and pastures, on the lower part of the hill, and had reached the wood, which extends thence towards its bare summit.

The month of May, thus far, had been more amiable than it often is; and this was as sweet and genial a day, as the heart of man or child could wish. In their progress up the hill, the small people had found enough of violets, blue and white, and some that were as golden as if they had the touch of Midas on them. That sociablest of flowers, the little Houstonia, was very abundant. It is a flower that never lives alone, but which loves its own kind and is always fond of dwelling with a great many friends and relatives around it. Sometimes you see a family of them, covering a space no bigger than the palm of your hand, and sometimes a large community, whitening a whole tract of pasture, and all keeping one another in cheerful heart and life.

Within the verge of the wood, there were columbines, looking more pale than red, because they were so modest, and had thought proper to seclude themselves too anxiously from the sun. There were wild geraniums, too, and a thousand white blossoms of the strawberry. The trailing arbutus was not yet quite out of bloom; but it hid its precious flowers under the last year's withered forest-leaves, as carefully as a mother-bird hides its little young ones. It knew, I suppose, how beautiful and sweet-scented they were. So cunning was their concealment, that the children sometimes smelt the delicate richness of their perfume, before they knew whence it proceeded.

Amid so much new life, it was strange and truly pitiful to behold, here and there, in the fields and pastures, the hoary periwigs of dandelions that had already gone to seed. They had done with summer, before the summer came. Within those small globes of winged seeds, it was autumn now!

Well; but we must not waste our valuable pages with any more talk about the spring-time and wild flowers. There is something, we hope, more interesting to be talked about. If you look at the group of children, you may see them all gathered around Eustace Bright, who, sitting on the stump of a tree, seems to be just beginning a story. The fact is, the younger part of the troop have found out that it takes rather too many of their short strides, to measure the long ascent of the hill. Cousin Eustace, therefore, has decided to leave Sweet Fern, Cowslip, Squash Blossom, and Dandelion, at this point, mid-way up, until the return of the rest of the party from the summit. And because they complain a little, and do not quite like to stay behind, he gives them some apples out of his pocket, and proposes to tell them a very pretty story. Hereupon, they brighten up, and change their grieved looks into the broadest kind of smiles.

As for the story, I was there to hear it, hidden behind a bush, and shall tell it over to you in the pages that come next.

THE MIRACULOUS PITCHER

ONE EVENING, in times long ago, old Philemon and his old wife Baucis sat at their cottage-door, enjoying the calm and beautiful sunset. They had already eaten their frugal supper, and intended now to spend a quiet hour or two, before bedtime. So they talked together about their garden, and their cow, and their bees, and their grape-vine, which clambered over the cottage-wall, and on which the grapes were beginning to turn purple. But the rude shouts of children and the fierce barking of dogs, in the village near at hand, grew louder and louder; until, at last, it was hardly possible for Baucis and Philemon to hear each other speak.

"Ah, wife," cried Philemon, "I fear some poor traveller is seeking hospitality among our neighbors yonder; and instead of giving him food and lodging they have set their dogs at him, as their custom is!"

"Well-a-day!" answered old Baucis, "I do wish our neighbors felt a little more kindness for their fellow-creatures! And only think of bringing up their children in this naughty way, and patting them on the head when they fling stones at strangers!"

"Those children will never come to any good," said Philemon, shaking his white head. "To tell you the truth, wife, I

should not wonder if some terrible thing were to happen to
all the people in the village, unless they mend their manners.
But as for you and me, so long as Providence affords us a
crust of bread, let us be ready to give half to any poor, homeless stranger, that may come along and need it!"

"That's right, husband!" said Baucis. "So we will!"

These old folks, you must know, were quite poor, and
had to work pretty hard for a living. Old Philemon toiled
diligently in his garden, while Baucis was always busy with
her distaff, or making a little butter and cheese with their
cow's milk, or doing one thing and another about the cottage.
Their food was seldom anything but bread, milk, and vegetables, with sometimes a portion of honey from their bee-hive,
and now and then a bunch of grapes, that had ripened
against the cottage-wall. But they were two of the kindest
old people in the world, and would cheerfully have gone
without their dinners, any day, rather than refuse a slice of
their brown loaf, a cup of new milk, and a spoonfull of
honey, to the weary traveller who might pause before their
door. They felt as if such guests had a sort of holiness, and
that they ought therefore to treat them better and more
bountifully than their own selves.

Their cottage stood on a rising ground, at some short distance from a village, which lay in a hollow valley that was
about half a mile in breadth. This valley, in past ages, when
the world was new, had probably been the bed of a lake.
There, fishes had glided to-and-fro, in the depths, and water-
weeds had grown along the margin, and trees and hills had
seen their reflected images in the broad and peaceful mirror.
But, as the waters subsided, men had cultivated the soil and
built houses on it; so that it was now a fertile spot, and bore
no traces of the ancient lake, except a very small brook, which
meandered through the midst of the village, and supplied the
inhabitants with water. The valley had been dry land so

long, that oaks had sprung up, and grown great and high, and perished with old age, and been succeeded by others, as tall and stately as the first. Never was there a prettier or more fruitful valley. The very sight of the plenty around them should have made the inhabitants kind and gentle, and ready to show their gratitude to Providence by doing good to their fellow-creatures.

But, we are sorry to say, the people of this lovely village were not worthy to dwell in a spot on which heaven had smiled so beneficently. They were a very selfish and hard-hearted people, and had no pity for the poor, nor sympathy with the homeless. They would only have laughed, had anybody told them that human beings owe a debt of love to one another, because there is no other method of paying the debt of love and care, which all of us owe to Providence. You will hardly believe what I am going to tell you. These naughty people taught their children to be no better than themselves, and used to clap their hands, by way of encouragement, when they saw the little boys and girls run after some poor stranger, shouting at his heels, and pelting him with stones. They kept large and fierce dogs; and whenever a traveller ventured to show himself in the village-street, this pack of disagreeable curs scampered to meet him, barking, snarling, and showing their teeth. Then they would seize him by his leg, or by his clothes, just as it happened; and if he were ragged when he came, he was generally a pitiable object before he had time to run away. This was a very terrible thing to poor travellers, as you may suppose, especially when they chanced to be sick, or feeble, or lame, or old. Such persons (if they once knew how badly these unkind people, and their unkind children and curs, were in the habit of behaving) would go miles and miles out of their way, rather than try to pass through the village again.

What made the matter seem worse, if possible, was, that when rich persons came in their chariots, or riding on beautiful horses, with their servants in rich liveries attending on them, nobody could be more civil and obsequious than the inhabitants of the village. They would take off their hats, and make the humblest bows you ever saw. If the children were rude, they were pretty certain to get their ears boxed; and as for the dogs, if a single cur in the pack presumed to yelp, his master instantly beat him with a club, and tied him up without any supper. This would have been all very well; only it proved that the villagers cared much about the money that a stranger had in his pocket, and nothing whatever for the human soul, which lives equally in the beggar and the prince.

So now you can understand why old Philemon spoke so sorrowfully, when he heard the shouts of the children and the barking of the dogs, at the farther extremity of the village-street. There was a confused din, which lasted a good while, and seemed to pass quite through the breadth of the valley.

"I never heard the dogs so loud!" observed the good old man.

"Nor the children so rude!" answered his good old wife.

They sat shaking their heads, one to another, while the noise came nearer and nearer; until, at the foot of the little eminence on which their cottage stood, they saw two travellers approaching on foot. Close behind them came the fierce dogs, snarling at their very heels. A little farther off, ran a crowd of children, who sent up shrill cries, and flung stones at the two strangers, with all their might. Once or twice, the younger of the two men (he was a slender and very active figure) turned about, and drove back the dogs with a staff which he carried in his hand. His companion, who was a very tall person, walked calmly along, as if disdaining to notice either the naughty children, or the pack of curs, whose manners the children seemed to imitate.

Both of the travellers were very humbly clad, and looked as if they might not have money enough in their pockets to pay for a night's lodging. And this, I am afraid, was the reason why the villagers had allowed their children and dogs to treat them so rudely.

"Come, wife," said Philemon to Baucis, "let us go and meet these poor people! No doubt, they feel almost too heavy-hearted to climb the hill."

"Go you and meet them," answered Baucis, "while I make haste within doors, and see whether we can get them any-thing for supper. A comfortable bowl of bread and milk would do wonders towards raising their spirits."

Accordingly, she hastened into the cottage. Philemon, on his part, went forward, and extended his hand with so hos-pitable an aspect that there was no need of saying, what nevertheless he did say, in the heartiest tone imaginable:—

"Welcome, strangers, welcome!"

"Thank you!" replied the younger of the two, in a lively kind of way, notwithstanding his weariness and trouble. "This is quite another greeting than we have met with yon-der, in the village. Pray, why do you live in such a bad neighborhood?"

"Ah," observed old Philemon, with a quiet and benign smile, "Providence put me here, I hope, among other reasons, in order that I may make you what amends I can for the inhospitality of my neighbors!"

"Well said, old father!" cried the traveller, laughing; "and, if the truth must be told, my companion and myself need some amends. Those children (the little rascals!) have bespat-tered us finely with their mud-balls; and one of the curs has torn my cloak, which was ragged enough already. But I took him across the muzzle with my staff; and I think you may have heard him yelp, even thus far off!"

Philemon was glad to see him in such good spirits; nor, indeed, would you have fancied, by the traveller's look and manner, that he was weary with a long day's journey, besides being disheartened by rough treatment at the end of it. He was dressed in rather an odd way, with a sort of cap on his head, the brim of which stuck out over both ears. Though it was a summer evening, he wore a cloak, which he kept wrapt closely about him, perhaps because his under garments were shabby. Philemon perceived, too, that he had on a singular pair of shoes; but, as it was now growing dusk, and as the old man's eyesight was none of the sharpest, he could not precisely tell in what the strangeness consisted. One thing, certainly, seemed queer. The traveller was so wonderfully light and active, that it appeared as if his feet sometimes rose from the ground of their own accord, or could only be kept down by an effort.

"I used to be light-footed in my youth," said Philemon to the traveller. "But I always found my feet grow heavier, towards nightfall."

"There is nothing like a good staff to help one along," answered the stranger; "and I happen to have an excellent one, as you see!"

This staff, in fact, was the oddest-looking staff, that Philemon had ever beheld. It was made of olive-wood, and had something like a little pair of wings near the top. Two snakes, carved in the wood, were represented as twining themselves about the staff, and were so very skilfully executed, that old Philemon (whose eyes, you know, were getting rather dim) almost thought them alive, and that he could see them wriggling and twisting.

"A curious piece of work, sure enough!" said he. "A staff with wings! It would be an excellent kind of stick for a little boy to ride astride of!"

By this time, Philemon and his two guests had reached the cottage-door.

"Friends," said the old man, "sit down and rest yourselves here on this bench. My good wife Baucis has gone to see what you can have for supper. We are poor folks; but you shall be welcome to whatever we have in the cupboard."

The younger stranger threw himself carelessly on the bench, letting his staff fall as he did so. And here happened something rather marvellous, though trifling enough, too. The staff seemed to get up from the ground of its own accord, and, spreading its little pair of wings, it half hopt, half flew, and leaned itself against the wall of the cottage. There it stood quite still, except that the snakes continued to wriggle. But, in my private opinion, old Philemon's eyesight had been playing him tricks again.

Before he could ask any questions, the elder stranger drew his attention from the wonderful staff, by speaking to him.

"Was there not," asked the stranger, in a remarkably deep tone of voice, "a lake, in very ancient times, covering the spot where now stands yonder village?"

"Not in my day, friend," answered Philemon; "and yet I am an old man, as you see. There were always the fields and meadows, just as they are now, and the old trees, and the little stream murmuring through the midst of the valley. My father, nor his father before him, ever saw it otherwise, so far as I know; and doubtless it will still be the same, when old Philemon shall be gone and forgotten!"

"That is more than can be safely foretold," observed the stranger; and there was something very stern in his deep voice. He shook his head, too, so that his dark and heavy curls were shaken with the movement. "Since the inhabitants of yonder village have forgotten the affections and sympathies of their nature, it were better that the lake should be rippling over their dwellings again!"

The traveller looked so stern, that Philemon was really almost frightened; the more so, that, at his frown, the twilight seemed suddenly to grow darker, and that, when he shook his head, there was a roll as of thunder in the air.

But, in a moment afterwards, the stranger's face became so kindly and mild, that the old man quite forgot his terror. Nevertheless, he could not help feeling that this elder traveller must be no ordinary personage, although he happened now to be attired so humbly, and to be journeying on foot. Not that Philemon fancied him a prince in disguise, or any character of that sort, but rather some exceedingly wise man, who went about the world in this poor garb, despising wealth and all worldly objects, and seeking everywhere to add a mite to his wisdom. This idea appeared the more probable, because, when Philemon raised his eyes to the stranger's face, he seemed to see more thought there, in one look, than he could have studied out, in a lifetime.

While Baucis was getting the supper, the travellers both began to talk very sociably with Philemon. The younger, indeed, was extremely loquacious, and made such shrewd and witty remarks, that the good old man continually burst out a-laughing, and pronounced him the merriest fellow whom he had seen for many a day.

"Pray, my young friend," said he, as they grew familiar together, "what may I call your name?"

"Why, I am very nimble, as you see," answered the traveller. "So, if you call me Quicksilver, the name will fit tolerably well!"

"Quicksilver? Quicksilver!" repeated Philemon, looking in the traveller's face to see if he were making fun of him. "It is a very odd name! And your companion there? Has he as strange a one?"

"You must ask the thunder to tell it you!" replied Quicksilver, putting on a mysterious look. "No other voice is loud enough!"

This remark, whether it were serious, or in jest, might have caused Philemon to conceive a very great awe of the elder stranger, if, on venturing to gaze at him, he had not beheld so much beneficence in his visage. But, undoubtedly, here was the grandest figure that ever sate so humbly beside a cottage-door. When the stranger conversed, it was with gravity, and in such a way that Philemon felt irresistibly moved to tell him everything which he had most at heart. This is always the feeling that people have, when they meet with any one wise enough to comprehend all their good and evil, and to despise not a tittle of it.

But Philemon, simple and kind-hearted old man that he was! had not many secrets to disclose. He talked, however, quite garrulously, about the events of his past life, in the whole course of which, he had never been a score of miles from this very spot. His wife Baucis and himself had dwelt in the cottage, from their youth upward, earning their bread by honest labor, always poor, but still contented. He told what excellent butter and cheese Baucis made, and how nice were the vegetables which he raised in his garden. He said, too, that, because they loved one another so very much, it was the wish of both that Death might not separate them, but that they should die, as they had lived, together.

As the stranger listened, a smile beamed over his countenance, and made its expression as sweet as it was grand.

"You are a good old man," said he to Philemon, "and you have a good old wife to be your help-meet. It is fit that your wish be granted!"

And it seemed to Philemon, just then, as if the sunset clouds threw up a bright flush from the west, and kindled a sudden light in the sky.

Baucis had now got supper ready, and coming to the door, began to make apologies for the poor fare which she was forced to set before her guests.

"Had we known you were coming," said she, "my good man and myself would have gone without a morsel, rather than you should lack a better supper. But I took the most part of to-day's milk to make cheese; and our last loaf is already half-eaten. Ah, me! I never feel the sorrow of being poor, save when a poor traveller knocks at our door!"

"All will be very well!—do not trouble yourself, my good dame," replied the elder stranger, kindly. "An honest, hearty welcome to a guest works miracles with the fare, and is capable of turning the coarsest food to nectar and ambrosia."

"A welcome you shall have," cried Baucis; "and likewise a little honey that we happen to have left, and a bunch of purple grapes besides!"

"Why, Mother Baucis, it is a feast," exclaimed Quicksilver laughing, "an absolute feast; and you shall see how bravely I will play my part at it! I think I never felt hungrier in my life."

"Mercy on us!" whispered Baucis to her husband. "If the young man has such a terrible appetite, I am afraid there will not be half enough supper!"

They all went into the cottage.

And now, my little auditors, shall I tell you something that will make you open your eyes very wide? It is really one of the oddest circumstances in the whole story. Quicksilver's staff, you recollect, had set itself up against the wall of the cottage. Well; when its master entered the door, leaving this wonderful staff behind, what should it do, but immediately spread its little wings, and go hopping and fluttering up the door-steps! Tap, tap, went the staff, on the kitchen-floor; nor did it rest, until it had stood itself on end, with the greatest gravity and decorum, beside Quicksilver's chair. Old Philemon, however, as well as his wife, was so taken up in attending to their guests, that no notice was given to what the staff had been about.

As Baucis had said, there was but a scanty supper for two hungry travellers. In the middle of the table was the remnant of a brown loaf, with a piece of cheese on one side of it, and a dish of honeycomb on the other. There was a pretty good bunch of grapes for each of the guests. A moderately sized earthen pitcher, nearly full of milk, stood at a corner of the board; and when Baucis had filled two bowls, and set them before the strangers, only a little milk remained in the bottom of the pitcher. Alas! it is a very sad business, when a bountiful heart finds itself pinched and squeezed among narrow circumstances. Poor Baucis kept wishing that she might starve, for a week to come, if it were possible, by so doing, to provide these hungry folks a more plentiful supper.

And since the supper was so exceedingly small, she could not help wishing that their appetites had not been quite so large. Why, at their very first sitting down, the travellers both drank off all the milk in their two bowls, at a draught!

"A little more milk, kind Mother Baucis, if you please!" said Quicksilver. "The day has been hot, and I am very much athirst."

"Now, my dear people," answered Baucis, in great confusion, "I am so sorry and ashamed! But the truth is, there is hardly a drop more milk in the pitcher. Oh, husband, husband, why didn't we go without our supper!"

"Why, it appears to me," cried Quicksilver, starting up from table and taking the pitcher by the handle, "it really appears to me that matters are not quite so bad as you represent them. Here is certainly more milk in the pitcher!"

So saying, and to the vast astonishment of Baucis, he proceeded to fill not only his own bowl, but his companion's likewise, from the pitcher that was supposed to be almost empty. The good woman could scarcely believe her eyes. She had certainly poured out nearly all the milk, and had peeped in, afterwards, and seen the bottom of the pitcher, as she set it down upon the table.

"But I am old," thought Baucis to herself, "and apt to be forgetful. I suppose I must have made a mistake. At all events, the pitcher cannot help being empty, now, after filling the bowls twice over!"

"What excellent milk!" observed Quicksilver, after quaffing the contents of the second bowl. "Excuse me, my kind hostess, but I must really ask you for a little more!"

Now Baucis had seen, as plainly as she could see anything, that Quicksilver had turned the pitcher upside down, and consequently had poured out every drop of milk, in filling the last bowl. Of course, there could not possibly be any left. However, in order to let him know precisely how the case was, she lifted the pitcher, and made a gesture as if pouring milk into Quicksilver's bowl, but without the remotest idea that any milk would stream forth. What was her surprise, therefore, when such an abundant cascade fell bubbling into the bowl, that it was immediately filled to the brim, and overflowed upon the table! The two snakes that were twisted about Quicksilver's staff (but neither Baucis nor Philemon happened to observe this circumstance) stretched out their heads and began to lap up the spilt milk.

And then what a delicious fragrance the milk had! It seemed as if Philemon's only cow must have pastured, that day, on the richest herbage that could be found anywhere in the world. I only wish that each of you, my beloved little souls, could have a bowl of such nice milk, at supper-time!

"And now a slice of your brown loaf, Mother Baucis," said Quicksilver; "and a little of that honey!"

Baucis cut him a slice, accordingly; and though the loaf, when she and her husband ate of it, had been rather too dry and crusty to be palatable, it was now as light and moist as if but a few hours out of the oven. Tasting a crumb, which had fallen on the table, she found it more delicious than bread ever was before, and could hardly believe that it was a loaf of her own kneading and baking. Yet, what other loaf could it possibly be?

But, oh, the honey! I may just as well let it alone, without trying to describe how exquisitely it smelt and looked. Its color was that of the purest and most transparent gold; and it had the odor of a thousand flowers, but of such flowers as never grew in an earthly garden, and, to seek which, the bees must have flown high above the clouds. The wonder is, that, after alighting on a flower-bed of so delicious fragrance and immortal bloom, they should have been content to fly down again to their hive in Philemon's garden. Never was such honey tasted, seen, or smelt. The perfume floated around the kitchen, and made it so delightful, that, had you closed your eyes, you would instantly have forgotten the low ceiling and smoky walls, and have fancied yourself in an arbor, with celestial honeysuckles creeping over it.

Although good Mother Baucis was a simple old dame, she could not but think that there was something rather out of the common way, in all that had been going on. So, after helping the guests to bread and honey, and laying a bunch of grapes by each of their plates, she sat down by Philemon, and told him what she had seen, in a whisper.

"Did you ever hear the like?" asked she.

"No; I never did," answered Philemon with a smile. "And I rather think, my dear old wife, you have been walking about in a sort of a dream! If I had poured out the milk, I should have seen through the business, at once. There happened to be a little more in the pitcher than you thought—that is all!"

"Ah, husband," said Baucis, "say what you will, these are very uncommon people!"

"Well, well," replied Philemon, still smiling, "perhaps they are. They certainly do look as if they had seen better days; and I am heartily glad to see them making so comfortable a supper."

Each of the guests had now taken his bunch of grapes upon his plate. Baucis (who rubbed her eyes, in order to see the more clearly) was of opinion that the clusters had grown larger and richer, and that each separate grape seemed to be on the point of bursting with ripe juice. It was entirely a mystery to her, how such grapes could ever have been produced from the old, stunted vine that clambered against the cottage-wall.

"Very admirable grapes these!" observed Quicksilver, as he swallowed one after another, without apparently diminishing his cluster. "Pray, my good host, whence did you gather them?"

"From my own vine," answered Philemon. "You may see one of its branches twisting across the window, yonder. But, wife and I have never thought the grapes very fine ones."

"I never tasted better," said the guest. "Another cup of this delicious milk, if you please; and I shall then have supt better than a prince!"

This time, old Philemon bestirred himself and took up the pitcher; for he was curious to discover whether there was any reality in the marvels which Baucis had whispered to him. He knew that his good old wife was incapable of false-hood, and that she was seldom mistaken in what she supposed to be true; but this was so very singular a case, that he wanted to see into it with his own eyes. On taking up the pitcher, therefore, he slily peeped into it, and was fully satis-fied that it contained not so much as a single drop. All at once, however, he beheld a little white fountain, which gushed up from the bottom of the pitcher, and speedily filled it to the brim with foaming and deliciously fragrant milk. It was lucky that Philemon, in his surprise, did not drop the miraculous pitcher from his hand.

"Who are ye, wonder-working strangers?" cried he, even more bewildered than his wife had been.

"Your guests, my good Philemon, and your friends!" replied the elder traveller, in his mild, deep voice, that had some-thing at once sweet and awe-inspiring in it. "Give me likewise a cup of the milk; and may your pitcher never be empty for kind Baucis and yourself, any more than for the needy wayfarer!"

The supper being now over, the strangers requested to be shown to their place of repose. The old people would gladly have talked with them a little longer, and have expressed the wonder which they felt, and their delight at finding the poor and meagre supper prove so much better and more abundant than they hoped. But the elder traveller had inspired them with such reverence, that they dared not ask him any questions. And when Philemon drew Quicksilver aside, and inquired how, under the sun, a fountain of milk could have got into an old earthen pitcher, this latter personage pointed to his staff.

"There is the whole mystery of the affair," quoth Quicksilver; "and if you can make it out, I'll thank you to let me know! I can't tell what to make of my staff. It is always playing such odd tricks as this;—sometimes getting me a supper, and, quite as often, stealing it away. If I had any faith in such nonsense, I should say the stick was bewitched!"

He said no more, but looked so slily in their faces, that they rather fancied he was laughing at them. The magic staff went hopping at his heels, as Quicksilver quitted the room. When left alone, the good old couple spent some little time in conversation about the events of the evening, and then lay down on the floor, and fell fast asleep. They had given up their sleeping-room to the guests, and had no other bed for themselves, save these planks, which I wish had been as soft as their own hearts.

The old man and his wife were stirring, betimes, in the morning, and the strangers likewise arose with the sun, and made their preparations to depart. Philemon hospitably entreated them to remain a little longer, until Baucis could milk the cow, and bake a cake upon the hearth, and perhaps find them a few fresh eggs, for breakfast. The guests, however, seemed to think it better to accomplish a good part of their journey, before the heat of the day should come on. They therefore persisted in setting out immediately, but asked Philemon and Baucis to walk forth with them, a short distance, and show them the road which they were to take.

So they all four issued from the cottage, chatting together like old friends. It was very remarkable, indeed, how familiar the old couple insensibly grew with the elder traveller, and how their good and simple spirits melted into his, even as two drops of water would melt into the illimitable ocean. And as for Quicksilver, with his keen, quick, laughing wits, he appeared to discover every little thought that but peeped into their minds, before they suspected it themselves. They sometimes wished, it is true, that he had not been quite so quick-witted, and also that he would fling away his staff, which looked so mysteriously mischievous, with the snakes always writhing about it. But then, again, Quicksilver showed himself so very good-humored, that they would have been rejoiced to keep him in their cottage, staff, snakes, and all, every day, and the whole day long.

"Ah me! Well-a-day!" exclaimed Philemon, when they had walked a little way from their door. "If our neighbors only knew what a blessed thing it is to show hospitality to strangers, they would tie up all their dogs, and never allow their children to fling another stone!"

"It is a sin and shame for them to behave so!—that it is!" cried good old Baucis, vehemently. "And I mean to go, this very day, and tell some of them what naughty people they are!"

"I fear," remarked Quicksilver, slily smiling, "that you will find none of them at home!"

The elder traveller's brow, just then, assumed such a grave, stern, and awful grandeur, yet serene withal, that neither Baucis nor Philemon dared to speak a word. They gazed reverently into his face, as if they had been gazing at the sky.

"When men do not feel towards the humblest stranger as if he were a brother," said the traveller, in tones so deep that they sounded like those of an organ, "they are unworthy to exist on earth, which was created as the abode of a great human brotherhood!"

"And, by-the-by, my dear old people," cried Quicksilver, with the liveliest look of fun and mischief in his eyes, "where is this same village that you talk about? On which side of us does it lie? Methinks I do not see it, hereabouts!"

Philemon and his wife turned towards the valley, where, at sunset, only the day before, they had seen the meadows, the houses, the gardens, the clumps of trees, the wide, green-margined street, with children playing in it, and all the tokens of business, enjoyment, and prosperity. But what was their astonishment! There was no longer any appearance of a village! Even the fertile vale, in the hollow of which it lay, had ceased to have existence. In its stead, they beheld the broad, blue surface of a lake, which filled the great basin of the valley, from brim to brim, and reflected the surrounding hills in its bosom; with as tranquil an image as if it had been there ever since the creation of the world. For an instant, the lake remained perfectly smooth. Then, a little breeze sprang up, and caused the water to dance, glitter, and sparkle in the early sunbeams, and to dash, with a pleasant rippling murmur, against the hither shore.

The lake seemed so strangely familiar, that the old couple were greatly perplexed, and felt as if they could only have been dreaming about a village having lain there. But, the next moment, they remembered the vanished dwellings, and the faces and characters of the inhabitants, far too distinctly for a dream. The village had been there, yesterday, and now was gone!

"Alas," cried these kind-hearted old people, "what has become of our poor neighbors!"

"They exist no longer as men and women," said the elder traveller, in his grand and deep voice, while a roll of thunder seemed to echo it, at a distance. "There was neither use nor beauty in such a life as theirs; for they never softened or sweetened the hard lot of mortality by the exercise of kindly affections, between man and man. They retained no image of the better life, in their bosoms. Therefore, the lake, that was of old, has spread itself forth again, to reflect the sky!"

"And as for those foolish people," said Quicksilver, with his mischievous smile, "they are all transformed to fishes. There needed but little change; for they were already a scaly set of rascals, and the coldest-blooded beings in existence. So, kind Mother Baucis, whenever you or your husband have an appetite for a dish of broiled trout, he can throw in a line, and pull out half-a-dozen of your old neighbors!"

"Ah," cried Baucis, shuddering, "I would not, for the world, put one of them on the gridiron!"

"No," added Philemon, making a wry face, "we could never relish them!"

"As for you, good Philemon," continued the elder traveller,—"and you, kind Baucis—you, with your scanty means, have mingled so much heart-felt hospitality with your entertainment of the homeless stranger, that the milk became an inexhaustible fount of nectar, and the brown loaf and the honey were ambrosia. Thus, the divinities have feasted at your board, off the same viands that supply their banquets, on Olympus. You have done well, my dear old friends! Wherefore, request whatever favor you have most at heart, and it is granted!"

Philemon and Baucis looked at one another; and then—I know not which of the two it was, who spoke—but that one uttered the desire of both their hearts.

"Let us live together, while we live, and leave the world

at the same instant, when we die! For we have always loved one another!"

"Be it so!" replied the stranger, with majestic kindness. "Now, look towards your cottage!"

They did so. But what was their surprise, on beholding a tall edifice of white marble, with a wide-open portal, occupying the spot where their humble residence had so lately stood!

"There is your home!" said the stranger, beneficently smiling on them both. "Exercise your hospitality in yonder palace, as freely as in the poor hovel to which you welcomed us, last evening!"

The old folks fell on their knees, to thank him: but, behold! neither he nor Quicksilver was there.

So Philemon and Baucis took up their residence in the marble palace, and spent their time, with vast satisfaction to themselves, in making everybody jolly and comfortable, who happened to pass that way. The milk-pitcher, I must not forget to say, retained its marvellous quality of being never empty, when it was desirable to have it full. Whenever an honest, good-humored, and free-hearted guest took a draught from this pitcher, he invariably found it the sweetest and most invigorating fluid, that ever ran down his throat. But if a cross and disagreeable curmudgeon happened to sip, he was pretty certain to twist his visage into a hard knot, and pronounce it a pitcher of sour milk!

Thus, the old couple lived in their palace, a great, great while, and grew older, and older, and very old indeed. At length, however, there came a summer-morning, when Philemon and Baucis failed to make their appearance, as on other mornings, with one hospitable smile over-spreading both their pleasant faces, to invite the guests of over-night to breakfast. The guests searched everywhere, from top to bottom of the spacious palace, and all to no purpose. But, after a great deal of perplexity, they espied, in front of the portal, two venerable trees, which nobody could remember to have seen there, the day before. Yet there they stood, with their roots fastened deep into the soil, and a huge breadth of foliage over-shadowing the whole front of the edifice. One was an oak, and the other a linden-tree. Their boughs—it was strange and beautiful to see—were intertwined together, and embraced one another, so that each tree seemed to live in the other tree's bosom, much more than in its own.

While the guests were marvelling how these trees, that must have required at least a century to grow, could have come to be so tall and venerable in a single night, a breeze sprang up and set their intermingled boughs a-stir. And then there was a deep, broad murmur in the air, as if the two mysterious trees were speaking.

"I am old Philemon!" murmured the oak.

"I am old Baucis!" murmured the linden-tree.

But, as the breeze grew stronger, the trees both spoke at once—"Philemon! Baucis! Baucis! Philemon!"—as if one were both, and both were one, and talking together in the depths of their mutual heart. It was plain enough to perceive, that the good old couple had renewed their age; and were now to spend a quiet and delightful hundred years or so, Philemon as an oak, and Baucis as a linden-tree. And, Oh, what a hospitable shade did they fling around them! Whenever a wayfarer paused beneath it, he heard a pleasant whisper of the leaves above his head, and wondered how the sound should so much resemble words like these:—

"Welcome, welcome, dear traveller, welcome!"

And some kind soul, that knew what would have pleased old Baucis and old Philemon best, built a circular seat around both their trunks, where, for a great while afterwards, the weary, and the hungry, and the thirsty, used to repose themselves, and quaff milk abundantly out of the miraculous pitcher.

And I wish, for all our sakes, that we had the pitcher here, now!

THE HILL-SIDE

AFTER THE STORY

H OW MUCH did the pitcher hold?" asked Sweet Fern.

"It did not hold quite a quart," answered the student; "but you might keep pouring milk out of it, till you should fill a hogshead, if you pleased. The truth is, it would run on forever, and not be dry even at mid-summer—which is more than can be said of yonder rill, that goes babbling down the hill-side."

"And what has become of the pitcher now?" inquired the little boy.

"It was broken, I am sorry to say, about twenty-five thousand years ago," replied Cousin Eustace. "The people mended it, as well as they could; but, though it would hold milk pretty well, it was never afterwards known to fill itself of its own accord. So, you see, it was no better than any other cracked earthen pitcher."

"What a pity!" cried all the children at once.

The respectable dog Ben had accompanied the party, as did likewise a half-grown Newfoundland puppy, who went by the name of Bruin, because he was just as black as a bear. Ben, being elderly, and of very circumspect habits, was respectfully requested by Cousin Eustace to stay behind, with the four little children, in order to keep them out of mischief. As for black Bruin, who was himself nothing but a child, the student thought it best to take him along, lest, in his rude play with the other children, he should trip them up, and send them rolling and tumbling down the hill. Advising Cowslip, Sweet Fern, Dandelion, and Squash Blossom, to sit pretty still, in the spot where he left them, the student, with Primrose and the elder children, began to ascend, and were soon out of sight among the trees.

BALD SUMMIT

U PWARD, along the steep and wooded hill-side, went Eustace Bright and his companions. The trees were not yet in full leaf, but had budded forth sufficiently to throw an airy shadow, while the sunshine filled them with green light. There were moss-grown rocks, half-hidden among the old, brown, fallen leaves; there were rotten tree-trunks, lying at full length where they had long ago fallen; there were decayed boughs, that had been shaken down by the wintry gales, and were scattered everywhere about. But still, though these things looked so aged, the aspect of the wood was that of the newest life; for, whichever way you turned your eyes, something fresh and green was springing forth, so as to be ready for the summer.

At last, the young people reached the upper verge of the wood, and found themselves almost at the summit of the hill. It was not a peak, nor a great round ball, but a pretty wide plain, or table-land, with a house and barn upon it, at some distance. That house was the home of a solitary family; and oftentimes the clouds, whence fell the rain, and whence the snow-storm drifted down into the valley, hung lower than this bleak and lonely dwelling-place.

On the highest point of the hill was a heap of stones, in the centre of which was stuck a long pole, with a little flag fluttering at the end of it. Eustace led the children thither, and bade them look around, and see how large a tract of our beautiful world they could take in at a glance. And their eyes grew wider as they looked.

Monument Mountain, to the southward, was still in the centre of the scene, but seemed to have sunk and subsided; so that it was now but an undistinguished member of a large family of hills. Beyond it, the Taconic range looked higher and bulkier than before. Our pretty lake was seen, with all its little bays and inlets; and not that alone, but two or three new lakes were opening their blue eyes to the sun. Several white villages, each with its steeple, were scattered about in the distance. There were so many farm-houses, with their acres of woodland, pasture, mowing-fields, and tillage, that the children could hardly make room in their minds to receive all these different objects. There, too, was Tanglewood, which they had hitherto thought such an important apex of the world. It now occupied so small a space, that they gazed far beyond it, and on either side, and searched a good while with all their eyes, before discovering whereabout it stood.

White fleecy clouds were hanging in the air, and threw the dark spots of their shadow here and there over the landscape. But, by-and-by, the sunshine was where the shadow had been, and the shadow was somewhere else.

Far to the westward was a range of blue mountains, which Eustace Bright told the children were the Catskills. Among those misty hills, he said, was a spot where some old Dutchmen were playing an everlasting game of nine-pins, and where an idle fellow, whose name was Rip Van Winkle, had fallen asleep, and slept twenty years at a stretch. The children eagerly besought Eustace to tell them all about this wonderful affair. But the student replied, that the story had been told once already, and better than it ever could be told again, and that nobody would have a right to alter a word of it, until it should have grown as old as "The Gorgon's Head," and "The Three Golden Apples," and the rest of those miraculous legends.

"At least," said Periwinkle, "while we rest ourselves here, and are looking about us, you can tell us another of your own stories."

"Yes, Cousin Eustace," cried Primrose, "I advise you to tell us a story here. Take some lofty subject or other, and see if your imagination will not come up to it. Perhaps the mountain air may make you poetical, for once. And no matter how strange and wonderful the story may be. Now that we are up among the clouds, we can believe anything!"

"Can you believe," asked Eustace, "that there was once a winged horse?"

"Yes," said saucy Primrose; "but I am afraid you will never be able to catch him!"

"For that matter, Primrose," rejoined the student, "I might possibly catch Pegasus, and get upon his back, too, as well as a dozen other fellows that I know of. At any rate, here is a story about him; and, of all places in the world, it ought certainly to be told upon a mountain-top!"

So, sitting on the pile of stones, while the children clustered themselves at its base, Eustace fixed his eyes on a white cloud that was sailing by, and began as follows.

THE CHIMÆRA

ONCE, in the old, old times (for all the strange things, which I tell you about, happened long before anybody can remember) a fountain gushed out of a hill-side, in the marvellous land of Greece. And, for aught I know, after so many thousand years, it is still gushing out of the very self-same spot. At any rate, there was the pleasant fountain, welling freshly forth and sparkling adown the hill-side, in the golden sunset, when a handsome young man, named Bellerophon, drew near its margin. In his hand he held a bridle, studded with brilliant gems, and adorned with a golden bit. Seeing an old man, and another of middle age, and a little boy, near the fountain, and likewise a maiden, who was dipping up some of the water in a pitcher, he paused, and begged that he might refresh himself with a draught.

"This is very delicious water," he said to the maiden, as he rinsed and filled her pitcher, after drinking out of it. "Will you be kind enough to tell me whether the fountain has any name?"

"Yes; it is called the Fountain of Pirene," answered the maiden; and then she added, "My grandmother has told me that this clear fountain was once a beautiful woman; and when her son was killed by the arrows of the huntress Diana, she melted all away into tears. And so the water, which you find so cool and sweet, is the sorrow of that poor mother's heart!"

"I should not have dreamed," observed the young stranger, "that so clear a well-spring, with its gush and gurgle, and its cheery dance out of the shade into the sunlight, had so much as one tear-drop in its bosom! And this, then, is Pirene! I thank you, pretty maiden, for telling me its name. I have come from a far-away country to find this very spot."

A middle-aged country fellow (he had driven his cow to drink out of the spring) stared hard at young Bellerophon, and at the handsome bridle which he carried in his hand.

"The water-courses must be getting low, friend, in your part of the world," remarked he, "if you come so far only to find the Fountain of Pirene. But, pray, have you lost a horse? I see you carry the bridle in your hand; and a very pretty one it is, with that double row of bright stones upon it! If the horse was as fine as the bridle, you are much to be pitied for losing him."

"I have lost no horse," said Bellerophon, with a smile. "But I happen to be seeking a very famous one, which, as wise people have informed me, must be found hereabouts, if anywhere. Do you know whether the winged horse Pegasus still haunts the Fountain of Pirene, as he used to do, in your forefathers' days?"

But then the country fellow laughed.

Some of you, my little friends, have probably heard, that this Pegasus was a snow-white steed, with beautiful silvery wings, who spent most of his time on the summit of Mount Helicon. He was as wild, and as swift, and as buoyant, in his flight through the air, as any eagle that ever soared into the clouds. There was nothing else like him in the world. He had no mate; he had never been backed or bridled by a master; and, for many a long year, he led a solitary and a happy life.

Oh, how fine a thing it is to be a winged horse! Sleeping at night, as he did, on a lofty mountain-top, and passing the greater part of the day in the air, Pegasus seemed hardly to be a creature of the earth. Whenever he was seen, up very high above people's heads, with the sunshine on his silvery wings, you would have thought that he belonged to the sky, and that, skimming a little too low, he had got astray among our mists and vapors, and was seeking his way back again. It was very pretty to behold him plunge into the fleecy bosom of a bright cloud, and be lost in it, for a moment or two, and then break forth from the other side. Or, in a sullen rain-storm, when there was a gray pavement of clouds over the whole sky, it would sometimes happen that the winged horse descended right through it, and the glad light of the upper region would gleam after him. In another instant, it is true, both Pegasus and the pleasant light would be gone away together. But any one, that was fortunate enough to see this wondrous spectacle, felt cheerful the whole day afterwards, and as much longer as the storm lasted.

In the summer-time, and in the beautifullest of weather, Pegasus often alighted on the solid earth, and, closing his silvery wings, would gallop over hill and dale for pastime, as fleetly as the wind. Oftener than in any other place, he had been seen near the Fountain of Pirene, drinking the delicious water, or rolling himself upon the soft grass of the margin. Sometimes, too, (but Pegasus was very dainty in his food,) he would crop a few of the clover-blossoms that happened to be sweetest.

To the Fountain of Pirene, therefore, people's great-grand-fathers had been in the habit of going (as long as they were youthful, and retained their faith in winged horses) in hopes of getting a glimpse at the beautiful Pegasus. But, of late years, he had been very seldom seen. Indeed, there were many of the country folks, dwelling within half an hour's walk of the fountain, who had never beheld Pegasus, and did not believe that there was any such creature in existence. The country fellow, to whom Bellerophon was speaking, chanced to be one of those incredulous persons.

And that was the reason why he laughed.

"Pegasus, indeed!" cried he, turning up his nose, as high as such a flat nose could be turned up. "Pegasus, indeed! A winged horse, truly! Why, friend, are you in your senses? Of what use would wings be to a horse? Could he drag the plough so well, think you? To be sure, there might be a little saving in the expense of shoes; but then how would a man like to see his horse flying out of the stable-window?— yes; or whisking him up above the clouds, when he only wanted to ride to mill? No, no! I don't believe in Pegasus. There never was such a ridiculous kind of a horse-fowl made!"

"I have some reason to think otherwise," said Bellerophon, quietly.

And then he turned to an old, gray man, who was leaning on a staff and listening very attentively, with his head stretched forward and one hand at his ear, because, for the last twenty years, he had been getting rather deaf.

"And what say you, venerable Sir?" inquired he. "In your younger days, I should imagine, you must frequently have seen the winged steed!"

"Ah, young stranger, my memory is very poor!" said the aged man. "When I was a lad, if I remember rightly, I used to believe there was such a horse, and so did everybody else. But, now-a-days, I hardly know what to think, and very seldom think about the winged horse at all. If I ever saw the creature, it was a long, long while ago; and, to tell you the truth, I doubt whether I ever did see him. One day, to be sure, when I was quite a youth, I remember seeing some hoof-tramps roundabout the brink of the fountain. Pegasus might have made those hoof-marks; and so might some other horse!"

"And have you never seen him, my fair maiden?" asked

Bellerophon of the girl, who stood with the pitcher on her head, while this talk went on. "You certainly could see Pegasus, if anybody can, for your eyes are very bright!"

"Once I thought I saw him," replied the maiden, with a smile and a blush. "It was either Pegasus, or a large white bird, a very great way up in the air. And one other time, as I was coming to the fountain with my pitcher, I heard a neigh. Oh, such a brisk and melodious neigh as that was! My very heart leaped with delight at the sound! But it startled me, nevertheless; so that I ran home without filling my pitcher."

"That was truly a pity!" said Bellerophon.

And he turned to the child, whom I mentioned at the beginning of the story, and who was gazing at him, as children are apt to gaze at strangers, with his rosy mouth wide open.

"Well, my little fellow," cried Bellerophon, playfully pulling one of his curls, "I suppose you have often seen the winged horse!"

"That I have!" answered the child, very readily. "I saw him yesterday, and many times before!"

"You are a fine little man!" said Bellerophon, drawing the child closer to him. "Come; tell me all about it!"

"Why," replied the child, "I often come here to sail little boats in the fountain, and to gather pretty pebbles out of its basin. And sometimes, when I look down into the water, I see the image of the winged horse, in the picture of the sky that is there. I wish he would come down, and take me on his back, and let me ride him up to the moon! But, if I so much as stir to look at him, he flies far away out of sight!"

And Bellerophon put his faith in the child, who had seen the image of Pegasus in the water, and in the maiden, who had heard him neigh so melodiously, rather than in the middle-aged clown who believed only in cart-horses, or in the old man, who had forgotten the beautiful things of his youth.

Therefore, he haunted about the Fountain of Pirene, for a great many days afterwards. He kept continually on the watch, looking upward at the sky, or else down into the water, hoping forever that he should see either the reflected image of the winged horse, or the marvellous reality. He held the bridle, with its bright gems and golden bit, always ready in his hand. The rustic people, who dwelt in the neighborhood, and drove their cattle to the fountain to drink, would often laugh at poor Bellerophon, and sometimes take him pretty severely to task. They told him that an able-bodied young man, like himself, ought to have better business than to be wasting his time in such an idle pursuit. They offered to sell him a horse, if he wanted one; and when Bellerophon declined the purchase, they tried to drive a bargain with him for his fine bridle.

Even the country boys thought him so very foolish, that they used to have a great deal of sport about him, and were rude enough not to care a fig, although Bellerophon saw and heard it. One little urchin, for example, would play Pegasus, and cut the oddest imaginable capers, by way of flying; while one of his schoolfellows would scamper after him, holding forth a twist of bulrushes, which was intended to represent Bellerophon's ornamented bridle. But the gentle child, who had seen the picture of Pegasus in the water, comforted the young stranger more than all the naughty boys could torment him. The dear little fellow, in his play-hours, often sat down beside him, and, without speaking a word, would look down into the fountain and up towards the sky, with so innocent a faith that Bellerophon could not help feeling encouraged.

Now, you will perhaps wish to be told why it was, that Bellerophon had undertaken to catch the winged horse. And we shall find no better opportunity to speak about this matter, than while he is waiting for Pegasus to appear.

If I were to relate the whole of Bellerophon's previous

adventures, they might easily grow into a very long story. It will be quite enough to say, that, in a certain country of Asia, a terrible monster called a Chimæra had made its appearance, and was doing more mischief than could be talked about between now and sunset. According to the best accounts which I have been able to obtain, this Chimæra was nearly, if not quite, the ugliest and most poisonous creature, and the strangest and unaccountablest, and the hardest to fight with, and the most difficult to run away from, that ever came out of the earth's inside. It had a tail like a boa-constrictor; its body was like I do not care what; and it had three separate heads, one of which was a lion's, the second a goat's, and the third an abominably great snake's. And a hot blast of fire came flaming out of each of its three mouths! Being an earthly monster, I doubt whether it had any wings; but, wings or no, it ran like a goat and a lion, and wriggled along like a serpent, and thus contrived to make about as much speed as all the three together.

Oh, the mischief, and mischief, and mischief, that this naughty creature did! With its flaming breath, it could set a forest on fire, or burn up a field of grain, or, for that matter, a village with all its fences and houses. It laid waste the whole country roundabout, and used to eat up people and animals alive, and cook them afterwards in the burning oven of its stomach. Mercy on us, little children, I hope neither you nor I will ever happen to meet a Chimæra!

While the hateful beast (if a beast we can anywise call it) was doing all these horrible things, it so chanced that Bellerophon came to that part of the world, on a visit to the king. The king's name was Iobates, and Lycia was the country which he ruled over. Bellerophon was one of the bravest youths in the world, and desired nothing so much as to do some valiant and beneficent deed, such as would make all mankind admire and love him. In those days, the only way for a young man to distinguish himself was by fighting battles, either with the enemies of his country, or with wicked giants, or with troublesome dragons, or with wild beasts, when he could find nothing more dangerous to encounter. King Iobates, perceiving the courage of his youthful visiter, proposed to him to go and fight the Chimæra, which everybody else was afraid of, and which, unless it should be soon killed, was likely to convert Lycia into a desert. Bellerophon hesitated not a moment, but assured the king that he would either slay this dreaded Chimæra, or perish in the attempt.

But in the first place, as the monster was so prodigiously swift, he bethought himself that he should never win the victory by fighting on foot. The wisest thing he could do, therefore, was to get the very best and fleetest horse, that could anywhere be found. And what other horse, in all the world, was half so fleet as the marvellous horse Pegasus, who had wings as well as legs, and was even more active in the air than on the earth! To be sure, a great many people denied that there was any such horse with wings, and said that the stories about him were all poetry and nonsense. But, wonderful as it appeared, Bellerophon believed that Pegasus was a real steed, and hoped that he himself might be fortunate enough to find him; and, once fairly mounted on his back, he would be able to fight the Chimæra at better advantage.

And this was the purpose with which he had travelled from Lycia to Greece, and had brought the beautifully ornamented bridle in his hand. It was an enchanted bridle. If he could only succeed in putting the golden bit into the mouth of Pegasus, the winged horse would be submissive, and would own Bellerophon for his master, and fly whithersoever he might choose to turn the rein.

But, indeed, it was a weary and anxious time, while Bellerophon waited and waited for Pegasus, in hopes that he would come and drink at the Fountain of Pirene. He was afraid lest King Iobates should imagine that he had fled from the Chimæra. It pained him, too, to think how much mischief the monster was doing, while he himself, instead of fighting with it, was compelled to sit idly poring over the bright waters of Pirene, as they gushed out of the sparkling sand. And as Pegasus came thither so seldom, in these latter years, and scarcely alighted there more than once in a lifetime, Bellerophon feared that he might grow an old man, and have no strength left in his arms nor courage in his heart, before the winged horse would appear. Oh, how heavily passes the time, while an adventurous youth is yearning to do his part in life, and to gather in the harvest of his renown! How hard a lesson it is, to wait! Our life is brief; and how much of it is spent in teaching us only this!

Well was it for Bellerophon, that the gentle child had grown so fond of him, and was never weary of keeping him company. Every morning, the child gave him a new hope to put in his bosom, instead of yesterday's withered one.

"Dear Bellerophon," he would cry, looking up hopefully into his face, "I think we shall see Pegasus to-day!"

And, at length, if it had not been for the little boy's unwavering faith, Bellerophon would have given up all hope, and would have gone back to Lycia, and have done his best to slay the Chimæra without the help of the winged horse. And in that case, poor Bellerophon would at least have been terribly scorched by the creature's breath, and would most probably have been killed and devoured. Nobody should ever try to fight an earth-born Chimæra, unless he can first get upon the back of an aerial steed!

One morning, the child spoke to Bellerophon even more hopefully than usual.

"Dear, dear Bellerophon," cried he, "I know not why it is; but I feel as if we should certainly see Pegasus to-day!"

And all that day, he would not stir a step from Bellerophon's side; so they ate a crust of bread together, and drank some of the water of the fountain. In the afternoon, there they sat; and Bellerophon had thrown his arm around the child, who likewise had put one of his little hands into Bellerophon's. The latter was lost in his own thoughts, and was fixing his eyes vacantly on the trunks of the trees that overshadowed the fountain, and on the grape-vines that clambered up among their branches. But the gentle child was gazing down into the water; he was grieved, for Bellerophon's sake, that the hope of another day should be deceived, like so many before it; and two or three quiet tear-drops fell from his eyes, and mingled with what were said to be the many tears of Pirene, when she wept for her slain children.

But, when he least thought of it, Bellerophon felt the pressure of the child's little hand, and heard a soft, almost breathless whisper.

"See there, dear Bellerophon! There is an image in the water!"

The young man looked down into the dimpling mirror of the fountain, and saw what he took to be the reflection of a bird, which seemed to be flying at a great height in the air, with a gleam of sunshine on its snowy or silvery wings.

"What a splendid bird it must be!" said he. "And how very large it looks, though it must really be flying higher than the clouds!"

"It makes me tremble!" whispered the child. "I am afraid to look up into the air! It is very beautiful; and yet I dare only look at its image in the water. Dear Bellerophon, do you not see that it is no bird? It is the winged horse Pegasus!"

Bellerophon's heart began to throb! He gazed keenly upward, but could not see the winged creature, whether bird or horse; because, just then, it had plunged into the fleecy depths of a summer-cloud. It was but a moment, however, before the object re-appeared, sinking lightly down out of the cloud, although still at a vast distance from the earth. Bellerophon caught the child in his arms, and shrank back with him, so that they were both hidden among the thick shrubbery which grew all around the fountain. Not that he was afraid of any harm; but he dreaded lest, if Pegasus caught a glimpse of them, he would fly far away, and alight on some inaccessible mountain-top. For it was really the winged horse! After they had expected him so long, he was coming to quench his thirst with the water of Pirene!

Nearer and nearer came the aerial wonder, flying in great circles, as you may have seen a dove when about to alight. Downward came Pegasus, in those wide, sweeping circles, which grew narrower, and narrower still, as he gradually approached the earth. The nigher the view of him, the more beautiful he was, and the more marvellous the sweep of his silvery wings. At last, with so light a pressure as hardly to bend the grass about the fountain, or imprint a hoof-tramp in the sand of its margin, he alighted, and, stooping his wild head, began to drink. He drew in the water, with long and pleasant sighs, and tranquil pauses of enjoyment, and then another draught, and another, and another. For, nowhere in the world, or up among the clouds, did Pegasus love any water as he loved this of Pirene! And when his thirst was slaked, he cropt a few of the honey-blossoms of the clover, delicately tasting them, but not caring to make a hearty meal; because the herbage, just beneath the clouds, on the lofty sides of Mount Helicon, suited his palate better than this ordinary grass.

After thus drinking to his heart's content, and, in his dainty fashion, condescending to take a little food, the winged horse began to caper to-and-fro, and dance, as it were, out of mere idleness and sport. There never was a more playful creature made, than this very Pegasus. So there he frisked, in a way that it delights me to think about, fluttering his great wings as lightly as ever did a linnet, and running little races, half on earth and half in air, and which I know not whether to call a flight or a gallop. When a creature is perfectly able to fly, he sometimes chooses to run, just for the pastime of the thing; and so did Pegasus, although it cost him some little trouble to keep his hoofs so near the ground. Bellerophon, meanwhile, holding the child's hand, peeped forth from the shrubbery, and thought that never was any sight so beautiful as this, nor ever a horse's eyes so wild and spirited as those of Pegasus. It seemed a sin to think of bridling him and riding on his back.

Once or twice, Pegasus stopt, and snuffed the air, pricking up his ears, tossing his head, and turning it on all sides, as if he partly suspected some mischief or other. Seeing nothing, however, and hearing no sound, he soon began his antics again.

At length—not that he was weary, but only idle and luxurious—Pegasus folded his wings, and lay down on the soft green turf. But, being too full of aerial life to remain quiet for many moments together, he soon rolled over on his back, with his four slender legs in the air. It was beautiful to see him, this one solitary creature, whose mate had never been created, but who needed no companion, and, living a great many hundred years, was as happy as the centuries were long! The more he did such things as mortal horses are accustomed to do, the less earthly and the more wonderful he seemed. Bellerophon and the child almost held their breath, partly from a delightful awe, but still more because they dreaded lest the slightest stir or murmur should send him up, with the speed of an arrow-flight, into the farthest blue of the sky.

Finally, when he had had enough of rolling over and over, Pegasus turned himself about, and, indolently, like any other horse, put out his fore-legs, in order to rise from the ground; and Bellerophon, who had guessed that he would do so, darted suddenly from the thicket, and leaped astride of his back.

Yes; there he sat, on the back of the winged horse!

But what a bound did Pegasus make, when, for the first time, he felt the weight of a mortal man upon his loins! A bound, indeed! Before he had time to draw a breath, Bellerophon found himself five hundred feet aloft, and still shooting upward; while the winged horse snorted and trembled with terror and anger. Upward he went, up, up, up, until he plunged into the cold, misty bosom of a cloud, at which, only a little while before, Bellerophon had been gazing, and fancying it a very pleasant spot. Then again, out of the heart of the cloud, Pegasus shot down like a thunderbolt, as if he meant to dash both himself and his rider headlong against a rock. Then he went through about a thousand of the wildest caprioles that had ever been performed either by a bird or a horse.

I cannot tell you half that he did. He skimmed straightforward, and sideways, and backward. He reared himself erect, with his fore-legs on a wreath of mist, and his hind-legs on nothing at all. He flung out his heels behind, and put down his head between his legs, with his wings pointing right upward. At about two miles' height above the earth, he turned a somerset, so that Bellerophon's heels were where his head should have been, and he seemed to look down into the sky, instead of up. He twisted his head about, and looking Bellerophon in the face, with fire flashing from his eyes, made a terrible attempt to bite him. He fluttered his pinions so wildly that one of the silver feathers was shaken out, and floating earthward, was picked up by the child, who kept it as long as he lived, in memory of Pegasus and Bellerophon.

But the latter (who, as you may judge, was as good a horseman as ever galloped) had been watching his opportunity, and at last clapt the golden bit of the enchanted bridle between the winged steed's jaws. No sooner was this done, than Pegasus became as manageable as if he had taken food, all his life, out of Bellerophon's hand. To speak what I really feel, it was almost a sadness, to see so wild a creature grow suddenly so tame. And Pegasus seemed to feel it so, likewise. He looked round to Bellerophon, with the tears in his beautiful eyes, instead of the fire that so recently flashed from them. But when Bellerophon patted his head, and spoke a few authoritative, yet kind and soothing words, another look came into the eyes of Pegasus; for he was glad at heart, after so many lonely centuries, to have found a companion and a master.

Thus it always is with winged horses, and with all such wild and solitary creatures. If you can catch and overcome them, it is the surest way to win their love.

While Pegasus had been doing his utmost to shake Bellerophon off his back, he had flown a very long distance; and they had come within sight of a lofty mountain, by the time the bit was in his mouth. Bellerophon had seen this mountain before, and knew it to be Helicon, on the summit of which was the winged horse's abode. Thither (after looking gently into his rider's face, as if to ask leave) Pegasus now flew, and alighting, waited patiently until Bellerophon should please to dismount. The young man, accordingly, leaped from his steed's back, but still held him fast by the bridle. Meeting his eyes, however, he was so affected by the gentleness of his aspect, and by his beauty, and by the thought of the free life which Pegasus had heretofore lived, that he could not bear to keep him a prisoner, if he really desired his liberty.

Obeying this generous impulse, he slipt the enchanted bridle off the head of Pegasus, and took the bit from his mouth.

"Leave me, Pegasus!" said he. "Either leave me, or love me!" In an instant, the winged horse shot almost out of sight, soaring straight upward from the summit of Mount Helicon. Being long after sunset, it was now twilight on the mountain-top, and dusky evening over all the country roundabout. But Pegasus flew so high, that he overtook the departed day, and was bathed in the upper radiance of the sun. Ascending higher and higher, he looked like a bright speck, and, at last, could no longer be seen in the hollow waste of the sky. And Bellerophon was afraid that he should never behold him more. But, while he was lamenting his own folly, the bright speck re-appeared, and drew nearer and nearer, until it descended lower than the sunshine; and behold, Pegasus had come back! After this trial, there was no more fear of the winged horse's making his escape. He and Bellerophon were friends, and put loving faith in one another.

That night, they lay down and slept together, with Bellero-phon's arm about the neck of Pegasus, not as a caution, but for kindness. And they awoke at peep of day, and bade one another good morning, each in his own language.

In this manner, Bellerophon and the wondrous steed spent several days, and grew better acquainted and fonder of each other, all the time. They went on long aerial journeys, and sometimes ascended so high that the earth looked hardly bigger than the moon. They visited distant countries, and amazed the inhabitants, who thought that the beautiful young man, on the back of the winged horse, must have come down out of the sky. A thousand miles a day was no more than an easy space for the fleet Pegasus to pass over. Bellerophon was delighted with this kind of life, and would have liked nothing better than to live always in the same way, aloft in the clear atmosphere; for it was always sunny weather, up there, how-ever cheerless and rainy it might be in the lower region. But he could not forget the horrible Chimæra, which he had promised King Iobates to slay. So, at last, when he had become well accustomed to feats of horsemanship in the air, and could manage Pegasus with the least motion of his hand, and had taught him to obey his voice, he determined to attempt the performance of this perilous adventure.

At daybreak, therefore, as soon as he unclosed his eyes, he gently pinched the winged horse's ear, in order to arouse him. Pegasus immediately started from the ground, and pranced about a quarter of a mile aloft, and made a grand sweep around the mountain-top, by way of showing that he was wide-awake and ready for any kind of an excursion. During the whole of this little flight, he uttered a loud, brisk, and melodious neigh, and finally came down at Bellerophon's side, as lightly as ever you saw a sparrow hop upon a twig.

"Well done, dear Pegasus! Well done, my sky-skimmer!" cried Bellerophon, fondly stroking the horse's neck. "And now, my fleet and beautiful friend, we must break our fast. To-day, we are to fight the terrible Chimæra!"

As soon as they had eaten their morning-meal, and drank some sparkling water from a spring called Hippocrene, Pegasus held out his head, of his own accord, so that his master might put on the bridle. Then, with a great many playful leaps and airy caperings, he showed his impatience to be gone; while Bellerophon was girding on his sword, and hanging his shield about his neck, and preparing himself for battle. When everything was ready, the rider mounted, and (as was his custom, when going a long distance) ascended five miles perpendicularly, so as the better to see whither he was directing his course. He then turned the head of Pegasus towards the east, and set out for Lycia. In their flight, they overtook an eagle, and came so nigh him, before he could get out of their way, that Bellerophon might easily have caught him by the leg. Hastening onward at this rate, it was still early in the forenoon when they beheld the lofty mountains of Lycia, with their deep and shaggy vallies. If Bellerophon had been told truly, it was in one of those dismal vallies that the hideous Chimæra had taken up its abode.

Being now so near their journey's end, the winged horse gradually descended with his rider; and they took advantage of some clouds, that were floating over the mountain-tops, in order to conceal themselves. Hovering on the upper surface of a cloud, and peeping over its edge, Bellerophon had a pretty distinct view of the mountainous part of Lycia, and could look into all its shadowy vales at once. At first, there appeared to be nothing remarkable. It was a wild, savage, and rocky tract of high and precipitous hills. In the more level part of the country, there were the ruins of houses that had been burnt, and, here and there, the carcasses of dead cattle, strewn about the pastures where they had been feeding.

"The Chimæra must have done this mischief," thought Bellerophon. "But where can the monster be?"

As I have already said, there was nothing remarkable to be detected, at first sight, in any of the vallies and dells that lay among the precipitous heights of the mountains. Nothing at all; unless, indeed, it were three spires of black smoke, which issued from what seemed to be the mouth of a cavern, and clambered sullenly into the atmosphere. Before reaching the mountain-top, these three black smoke-wreaths mingled themselves into one. The cavern was almost directly beneath the winged horse and his rider, at the distance of about a thousand feet. The smoke, as it crept heavily upward, had an ugly, sulphurous, stifling scent, which caused Pegasus to snort and Bellerophon to sneeze. So disagreeable was it to the marvellous steed (who was accustomed to breathe only the purest air) that he waved his wings, and shot half a mile out of the range of this offensive vapor.

But, on looking behind him, Bellerophon saw something that induced him first to draw the bridle, and then to turn

Pegasus about. He made a sign, which the winged horse understood, and sank slowly through the air, until his hoofs were scarcely more than a man's height above the rocky bottom of the valley. In front, as far off as you could throw a stone, was the cavern's mouth, with the three smoke-wreaths oozing out of it. And what else did Bellerophon behold there?

There seemed to be a heap of strange and terrible creatures, curled up within the cavern. Their bodies lay so close together, that Bellerophon could not distinguish them apart; but, judging by their heads, one of these creatures was a huge snake, the second, a fierce lion, and the third, an ugly goat. The lion and the goat were asleep; the snake was broad awake, and kept staring around him with a great pair of fiery eyes. But—and this was the most wonderful part of the matter— the three spires of smoke evidently issued from the nostrils of these three heads! So strange was the spectacle, that, though Bellerophon had been all along expecting it, the truth did not immediately occur to him, that here was the terrible, three-headed Chimæra. He had found out the Chimæra's cavern. The snake, the lion, and the goat, as he supposed them to be, were not three separate creatures, but one monster!

The wicked, hateful thing! Slumbering as two-thirds of it were, it still held, in its abominable claws, the remnant of an unfortunate lamb—or possibly (but I hate to think so) it was a dear little boy—which its three mouths had been gnawing, before two of them fell asleep!

All at once, Bellerophon started as from a dream, and knew it to be the Chimæra. Pegasus seemed to know it, at the same instant, and sent forth a neigh, that sounded like the call of a trumpet to battle. At this sound, the three heads reared themselves erect, and belched out great flashes of flame. Before Bellerophon had time to consider what to do next, the monster flung itself out of the cavern and sprang straight towards him, with its immense claws extended, and its snaky tail twisting itself venomously behind. If Pegasus had not been as nimble as a bird, both he and his rider would have been overthrown by the Chimæra's headlong rush, and thus the battle have been ended before it was well begun. But the winged horse was not to be caught so! In the twinkling of an eye, he was up aloft, half-way to the clouds, snorting with anger. He shuddered, too, not with affright, but with utter disgust at the loathsomeness of this poisonous thing with three heads.

The Chimæra, on the other hand, raised itself up so as to stand absolutely on the tip-end of its tail, with its talons pawing fiercely in the air, and its three heads spluttering fire at Pegasus and his rider. My stars, how it roared, and hissed, and bellowed! Bellerophon, meanwhile, was fitting his shield on his arm, and drawing his sword.

"Now, my beloved Pegasus," he whispered in the winged horse's ear, "thou must help me to slay this insufferable monster; or else thou shalt fly back to thy solitary mountain-peak, without thy friend Bellerophon! For either the Chimæra dies, or its three mouths shall gnaw this head of mine, which has slumbered upon thy neck!"

Pegasus whinnied, and turning back his head, rubbed his nose tenderly against his rider's cheek. It was his way of telling him, that, though he had wings and was an immortal horse, yet he would perish, if it were possible for immortality to perish, rather than leave Bellerophon behind.

"I thank you, Pegasus!" answered Bellerophon. "Now, then, let us make a dash at the monster!"

Uttering these words, he shook the bridle; and Pegasus darted down aslant, as swift as the flight of an arrow, right towards the Chimæra's three-fold head, which, all this time, was poking itself as high as it could into the air. As he came within arm's length, Bellerophon made a cut at the monster, but was carried onward by his steed, before he could see whether the blow had been successful. Pegasus continued his course, but soon wheeled round, at about the same distance from the Chimæra as before. Bellerophon then perceived that he had cut the goat's head of the monster almost off, so that it dangled downward by the skin, and seemed quite dead.

But, to make amends, the snake's head and the lion's head had taken all the fierceness of the dead one into themselves, and spit flame, and hissed, and roared, with a vast deal more fury than before.

"Never mind, my brave Pegasus!" cried Bellerophon. "With another stroke like that, we will stop either its hissing or its roaring."

And again he shook the bridle. Dashing aslantwise, as before, the winged horse made another arrow-flight towards the Chimæra, and Bellerophon aimed another downright stroke at one of the two remaining heads, as he shot by. But, this time, neither he nor Pegasus escaped so well as at first. With one of its claws, the Chimæra had given the young man a deep scratch in his shoulder, and had slightly damaged the left wing of the flying steed, with the other. On his part, Bellerophon had mortally wounded the lion's head of the monster; insomuch that it now hung downward, with its fire almost extinguished, and sending out gasps of thick black smoke. The snake's head, however, (which was the only one now left,) was twice as fierce and venomous as ever before. It belched forth shoots of fire, five hundred yards long, and emitted hisses so loud, so harsh, and so ear-piercing, that King Iobates heard them, fifty miles off, and trembled till the throne shook under him.

"Well-a-day!" thought the poor king. "The Chimæra is certainly coming to devour me!"

Meanwhile, Pegasus had again paused in the air, and neighed angrily, while sparkles of a pure, crystal flame darted out of his eyes. How unlike the lurid fire of the Chimæra! The aerial steed's spirit was all aroused, and so was that of Bellerophon.

"Dost thou bleed, my immortal horse?" cried the young man, caring less for his own hurt than for the anguish of this glorious creature, that ought never to have tasted pain. "The execrable Chimæra shall pay for this mischief, with his last head!"

Then he shook the bridle, shouted loudly, and guided Pegasus, not aslantwise as before, but straight at the monster's hideous front. So rapid was the onset, that it seemed but a dazzle and a flash, before Bellerophon was at close gripes with his enemy.

The Chimæra, by this time, after losing its second head, had got into a red-hot passion of pain and rampant rage. It so flounced about, half on earth and partly in the air, that it was impossible to say which element it rested upon. It opened its snake-jaws to such an abominable width, that Pegasus might almost, I was going to say, have flown right down its throat, wings outspread, rider and all! At their approach, it shot out a tremendous blast of its fiery breath, and enveloped Bellerophon and his steed in a perfect atmosphere of flame; singeing the wings of Pegasus, scorching off one whole side of the young man's golden ringlets, and making them both far hotter than was comfortable, from head to foot.

But this was nothing to what followed.

When the airy rush of the winged horse had brought him within the distance of a hundred yards, the Chimæra gave a spring, and flung its huge, aukward, venomous, and utterly detestable carcass right upon poor Pegasus, clung round him with might and main, and tied up its snaky tail into a knot! Up flew the aerial steed, higher, higher, higher, above the mountain-peaks, above the clouds, and almost out of sight of the solid earth. But still the earth-born monster kept its hold, and was borne upward along with the creature of light and air. Bellerophon, meanwhile, turning about, found himself face to face with the ugly grimness of the Chimæra's visage, and could only avoid being scorched to death, or bitten right in twain, by holding up his shield. Over the upper edge of the shield, he looked sternly into the savage eyes of the monster.

But the Chimæra was so mad and wild with pain, that it did not guard itself so well as might else have been the case. Perhaps, after all, the best way to fight a Chimæra is by getting as close to it as you can. In its efforts to stick its horrible iron claws into its enemy, the creature left its own breast quite exposed; and perceiving this, Bellerophon thrust his sword up to the hilt into its cruel heart. Immediately, the snaky tail untied its knot. The monster let go its hold of Pegasus, and fell from that vast height, downward; while the fire within its bosom, instead of being put out, burned fiercer than ever, and quickly began to consume the dead carcass. Thus it fell out of the sky, all a-flame, and (it being nightfall before it reached the earth) was mistaken for a shooting star or a comet. But, at early sunrise, some cottagers were going to their day's labor, and saw, to their astonishment, that several acres of ground were strewn with black ashes. In the middle of a field, there was a heap of whitened bones, a great deal higher than a haystack. Nothing else was ever seen of the dreadful Chimæra!

And when Bellerophon had won the victory, he bent forward and kissed Pegasus, while the tears stood in his eyes.

"Back now, my beloved steed!" said he. "Back to the Fountain of Pirene!"

Pegasus skimmed through the air, quicker than ever he did before, and reached the fountain in a very short time.

And there he found the old man, leaning on his staff, and the country fellow, watering his cow, and the pretty maiden, filling her pitcher.

"I remember now," quoth the old man, "I saw this winged horse once before, when I was quite a lad. But he was ten times handsomer, in those days!"

"I own a cart-horse, worth three of him!" said the country fellow. "If this pony were mine, the first thing I should do, would be to clip his wings!"

But the poor maiden said nothing; for she had always the luck to be afraid at the wrong time. So she ran away, and let her pitcher tumble down, and broke it.

"Where is the gentle child," asked Bellerophon, "who used to keep me company, and never lost his faith, and never was weary of gazing into the fountain!"

"Here am I, dear Bellerophon!" said the child, softly.

For the little boy had spent day after day, on the margin of Pirene, waiting for his friend to come back; but when he perceived Bellerophon descending through the clouds, mounted on the winged horse, he had shrunk back into the shrubbery. He was a delicate and tender child, and dreaded lest the old man and the country fellow should see the tears gushing from his eyes.

"Thou hast won the victory," said he, joyfully, running to the knee of Bellerophon, who still sat on the back of Pegasus. "I knew thou wouldst!"

"Yes; dear child!" replied Bellerophon, alighting from the winged horse. "But, if thy faith had not helped me, I should never have waited for Pegasus, and never have gone up above the clouds, and never have conquered the terrible Chimæra! Thou, my beloved little friend, hast done it all! And now let us give Pegasus his liberty."

So he slipt off the enchanted bridle from the head of the marvellous steed.

"Be free, forever more, my Pegasus!" cried he, with a shade of sadness in his tone. "Be as free as thou art fleet!"

But Pegasus rested his head on Bellerophon's shoulder, and would not be persuaded to take flight.

"Well, then," said Bellerophon, caressing the airy horse, "thou shalt be with me, as long as thou wilt; and we will go together, forthwith, and tell King Iobates that the Chimæra is destroyed!"

Then Bellerophon embraced the gentle child, and promised to come to him again, and departed. But, in after years, that child took higher flights upon the aerial steed, than ever did Bellerophon, and achieved more honorable deeds than his friend's victory over the Chimæra. For, gentle and tender as he was, he grew to be a mighty Poet!

BALD SUMMIT

AFTER THE STORY

EUSTACE BRIGHT told the legend of Bellerophon with as much fervor and animation as if he had really been taking a gallop on the winged horse. At the conclusion, he was gratified to discern, by the glowing countenances of his auditors, how greatly they had been interested. All their eyes were dancing in their heads, except those of Primrose. In her eyes, there were positively tears; for she was conscious of something in the legend, which the rest of them were not yet old enough to feel. Child's story as it was, the student had contrived to breathe through it the ardor, the generous hope, and the imaginative enterprise of youth.

"I forgive you now, Primrose," said he, "for all your ridicule of myself and my stories. One tear pays for a great deal of laughter."

"Well, Mr. Bright," answered Primrose, wiping her eyes, and giving him another of her mischievous smiles, "it certainly does elevate your ideas, to get your head above the clouds. I advise you never to tell another story, unless it be, as at present, from the top of a mountain!"

"Or from the back of Pegasus," replied Eustace, laughing. "Don't you think that I succeeded pretty well in catching that wonderful pony?"

"It was so like one of your mad-cap pranks!" cried Primrose, clapping her hands. "I think I see you now on his back, two miles high, and with your head downward! It is well that you have not really an opportunity of trying your horsemanship on any wilder steed than our sober Davy, or Old Hundred."

"For my part, I wish I had Pegasus here, at this moment," said the student. "I would mount him, forthwith, and gallop about the country, within a circumference of a few miles, making literary calls on my brother-authors. Dr. Dewey would be within my reach, at the foot of Taconic. In Stockbridge, yonder, is Mr. James, conspicuous to all the world on his mountain-pile of history and romance. Longfellow, I believe, is not yet at the Ox-bow; else the winged horse would neigh at the sight of him. But, here in Lenox, I should find our most truthful novelist, who has made the scenery and life of Berkshire all her own. On the hither side of Pittsfield sits Herman Melville, shaping out the gigantic conception of his 'White Whale,' while the gigantic shape of Graylock looms upon him from his study-window. Another bound of my flying steed would bring me to the door of Holmes, whom I mention last, because Pegasus would certainly unseat me, the next minute, and claim the poet as his rider."

"Have we not an author for our next neighbor?" asked Primrose. "That silent man, who lives in the old red house, near Tanglewood avenue, and whom we sometimes meet, with two children at his side, in the woods or at the lake. I think I have heard of his having written a poem, or a romance, or an arithmetic, or a school-history, or some other kind of a book."

"Hush, Primrose, hush!" exclaimed Eustace, in a thrilling whisper, and putting his finger on his lip. "Not a word about that man, even on a hill-top! If our babble were to reach his ears, and happen not to please him, he has but to fling a quire or two of paper into the stove; and you, Primrose, and I, and Periwinkle, Sweet Fern, Squash Blossom, Blue Eye,

Huckleberry, Clover, Cowslip, Plantain, Milkweed, Dande-lion, and Butter-cup—yes, and wise Mr. Pringle with his unfavorable criticisms on my legends, and poor Mrs. Pringle, too—would all turn to smoke, and go whisking up the funnel! Our neighbor in the red house is a harmless sort of person enough, for aught I know, as concerns the rest of the world; but something whispers me that he has a terrible power over ourselves, extending to nothing short of annihilation."

"And would Tanglewood turn to smoke, as well as we?" asked Periwinkle, quite appalled at the threatened destruc-tion. "And what would become of Ben and Bruin?"

"Tanglewood would remain," replied the student, "looking just as it does now, but occupied by an entirely different family. And Ben and Bruin would be still alive, and would make themselves very comfortable with the bones from the dinner-table, without ever thinking of the good times which they and we have had together!"

"What nonsense you are talking!" exclaimed Primrose.

With idle chat of this kind, the party had already begun to descend the hill, and were now within the shadow of the woods. Primrose gathered some mountain-laurel, the leaf of which, though of last year's growth, was still as verdant and elastic as if the frost and thaw had not alternately tried their force upon its texture. Of these twigs of laurel she twined a wreath, and took off the student's cap, in order to place it on his brow.

"Nobody else is likely to crown you for your stories," observed saucy Primrose. "So take this from me!"

"Do not be too sure," answered Eustace, looking really like a youthful poet, with the laurel among his glossy curls, "that I shall not win other wreaths by these wonderful and admi-rable stories. I mean to spend all my leisure, during the rest of the vacation, and throughout the summer-term at college, in writing them out for the press. Mr. J. T. Fields (with whom I became acquainted when he was in Berkshire, last summer, and who is a poet, as well as a publisher) will see their uncommon merit, at a glance. He will get them illustrated, I hope, by Billings, and will bring them before the world under the very best of auspices, through the eminent house of TICKNOR & CO. In about five months from this moment, I make no doubt of being reckoned among the lights of the age!"

"Poor boy!" said Primrose, half aside. "What a disappointment awaits him!"

Descending a little lower, Bruin began to bark, and was answered by the graver bow-wow of the respectable Ben. They soon saw the good old dog, keeping careful watch over Dandelion, Sweet Fern, Cowslip, and Squash Blossom. These little people, quite recovered from their fatigue, had set about gathering checkerberries, and now came clambering to meet their playfellows. Thus re-united, the whole party went down through Luther Butler's orchard, and made the best of their way home to Tanglewood.

THE END

TANGLEWOOD TALES

THE WAYSIDE

A SHORT TIME AGO, I was favored with a flying visit from my young friend, Eustace Bright, whom I had not before met with, since quitting the breezy mountains of Berkshire. It being the winter-vacation at his college, Eustace was allowing himself a little relaxation, in the hope, he told me, of repairing the inroads which severe application to study had made upon his health; and I was happy to conclude, from the excellent physical condition in which I saw him, that the remedy had already been attended with very desirable success. He had now run up from Boston by the noon-train, partly impelled by the friendly regard with which he is pleased to honor me, and partly, as I soon found, on a matter of literary business.

It delighted me to receive Mr. Bright, for the first time, under a roof, though a very humble one, which I could really call my own. Nor did I fail (as is the custom of landed proprietors, all about the world) to parade the poor fellow up and down over my half-a-dozen acres; secretly rejoicing,

---

Facing: Illustration to "The Dragon's Teeth" in the 1853 first edition of *Tanglewood Tales*. The original caption, "Europa all the while looked down upon her brothers, &c.", has been deleted.

nevertheless, that the disarray of the inclement season, and particularly the six inches of snow, then upon the ground, prevented him from observing the ragged neglect of soil and shrubbery, into which the place has lapsed. It was idle, however, to imagine that an airy guest from Monument Mountain, Bald Summit, and old Graylock, shaggy with primeval forests, could see anything to admire in my poor little hillside, with its growth of frail and insect-eaten locust-trees. Eustace very frankly called the view from my hill-top, tame; and so, no doubt, it was, after rough, broken, rugged, headlong Berkshire, and especially the northern parts of the county, with which his college-residence had made him familiar. But, to me, there is a peculiar, quiet charm in these broad meadows and gentle eminences. They are better than mountains, because they do not stamp and stereotype themselves into the brain, and thus grow wearisome with the same strong impression, repeated day after day. A few summer weeks among mountains; a lifetime among green meadows and placid slopes, with outlines forever new, because continually fading out of the memory. Such would be my sober choice.

I doubt whether Eustace did not internally pronounce the whole thing a bore, until I led him to my predecessor's little ruined, rustic summer-house, mid-way on the hill-side. It is a mere skeleton of slender, decaying, tree-trunks, with neither walls nor a roof; nothing but a tracery of branches and twigs, which the next wintry blast will be very likely to scatter in fragments along the terrace. It looks, and is, as evanescent as a dream; and yet, in its rustic net-work of boughs, it has somehow inclosed a hint of spiritual beauty, and has become a true emblem of the subtile and ethereal mind that planned it. I made Eustace Bright sit down on a snow-bank, which had heaped itself over the mossy seat, and gazing through the arched-window, opposite, he acknowledged that the scene at once grew picturesque.

"Simple as it looks," said he, "this little edifice seems to be the work of magic. It is full of suggestiveness, and, in its way, is as good as a cathedral. Ah, it would be just the spot for one to sit in, of a summer-afternoon, and tell the children some more of those wild stories from the classic myths!"

"It would, indeed," answered I. "The summer-house itself, so airy and so broken, is like one of those old tales, imperfectly remembered; and these living branches of the Baldwin apple-tree, thrusting themselves so rudely in, are like your unwarrantable interpolations. But, by-the-by, have you added any more legends to the series, since the publication of the Wonder Book?"

"Many more;" said Eustace. "Primrose, Periwinkle, and the rest of them, allow me no comfort of my life, unless I tell them a story, every day or two. I have run away from home, partly to escape the importunity of those little wretches! But I have written out six of the new stories, and have brought them for you to look over."

"Are they as good as the first?" I enquired.

"Better chosen, and better handled," replied Eustace Bright. "You will say so, when you read them."

"Possibly not," I remarked. "I know, from my own experience, that an author's last work is always his best one, in his own estimate, until it quite loses the red-heat of composition. After that, it falls into its true place, quietly enough. But let us adjourn to my study, and examine these new stories. It would hardly be doing yourself justice, were you to bring me acquainted with them, sitting here on this snow-bank!"

So we descended the hill to my small, old cottage, and shut ourselves up in the south-eastern room, where the sunshine comes in, warmly and brightly, through the better half of a winter's day. Eustace put his bundle of manuscript into my hands; and I skimmed through it pretty rapidly, trying to find out its merits and demerits by the touch of my fingers, as a veteran story-teller ought to know how to do.

It will be remembered, that Mr. Bright condescended to avail himself of my literary experience by constituting me editor of the Wonder Book. As he had no reason to complain of the reception of that erudite work, by the public, he was now disposed to retain me in a similar position, with respect to the present volume, which he entitled "TANGLEWOOD TALES." Not, as Eustace hinted, that there was any real necessity for my services as introductor, inasmuch as his own name had become established, in some good degree of favor, with the literary world. But the connection with myself, he was kind enough to say, had been highly agreeable; nor was he by any means desirous, as most people are, of kicking away the ladder that had perhaps helped him to reach his present elevation. My young friend was willing, in short, that the fresh verdure of his growing reputation should spread over my straggling, and half-naked boughs; even as I have sometimes thought of training a vine, with its broad leafiness and purple fruitage, over the worm-eaten posts and rafters of the rustic summer-house. I was not insensible to the advantages of his proposal, and gladly assured him of my acceptance.

Merely from the titles of the stories, I saw at once that the subjects were not less rich than those of the former volume; nor did I at all doubt that Mr. Bright's audacity (so far as that endowment might avail) had enabled him to take full advantage of whatever capabilities they offered. Yet, in spite of my experience of his free way of handling them, I did not quite see, I confess, how he could have obviated all the difficulties in the way of rendering them presentable to children. These old legends, so brimming over with everything that is most abhorrent to our Christianized moral-sense—some of them so hideous—others so melancholy and miserable, amid which the Greek Tragedians sought their themes, and moulded them into the sternest forms of grief that ever the world saw;—was such material the stuff that children's playthings should be made of! How were they to be purified? How was the blessed sunshine to be thrown into them?

But Eustace told me that these myths were the most singular things in the world, and that he was invariably astonished, whenever he began to relate one, by the readiness with which it adapted itself to the childish purity of his auditors. The objectionable characteristics seem to be a parasitical growth, having no essential connection with the original fable. They fall away, and are thought of no more, the instant he puts his imagination in sympathy with the innocent little circle, whose wide-open eyes are fixed so eagerly upon him. Thus the stories (not by any strained effort of the narrator's, but in harmony with their inherent germ) transform themselves, and re-assume the shapes which they might be supposed to possess in the pure childhood of the world. When the first poet or romancer told these marvellous legends (such is Eustace Bright's opinion) it was still the Golden Age. Evil had never yet existed; and sorrow, misfortune, crime, were mere shadows which the mind fancifully created for itself, as a shelter against too sunny realities—or, at most, but prophetic dreams, to which the dreamer himself did not yield a waking credence. Children are now the only representatives of the men and women of that happy era; and therefore it is that we must raise the intellect and fancy to the level of childhood, in order to re-create the original myths.

I let the youthful author talk, as much and as extravagantly as he pleased, and was glad to see him commencing life with such confidence in himself and his performances.

A few years will do all that is necessary towards showing him the truth, in both respects. Meanwhile, it is but right to say, he does really appear to have overcome the moral objections against these fables; although at the expence of such liberties with their structure, as must be left to plead their own excuse, without any help from me. Indeed, except that there was a necessity for it—and that the inner life of the legends cannot be come at, save by making them entirely one's own property—there is no defence to be made.

Eustace informed me that he had told his stories to the children in various situations,—in the woods, on the shore of the lake, in the dell of Shadow Brook, in the play-room, at Tanglewood fireside, and in a magnificent palace of snow, with ice-windows, which he helped his little friends to build. His auditors were even more delighted with the contents of the present volume, than with the specimens which have already been given to the world. The classically learned Mr. Pringle, too, had listened to two or three of the tales, and censured them even more bitterly than he did THE THREE GOLDEN APPLES; so that, what with praise, and what with criticism, Eustace Bright thinks that there is good hope of at least as much success with the public, as in the case of the Wonder Book.

I made all sorts of inquiries about the children, not doubting that there would be great eagerness to hear of their welfare, among some good little folks who have written to me, to ask for another volume of myths. They are all, I am happy to say, (unless we except Clover,) in excellent health and spirits. Primrose is now almost a young lady, and, Eustace tells me, is just as saucy as ever. She pretends to consider herself quite beyond the age to be interested by such idle stories as these; but, for all that, whenever a story is to be told, Primrose never fails to be one of the listeners, and to make fun of it, when finished. Periwinkle is very much grown, and is expected to shut up her baby-house and throw away her doll, in a month or two more. Sweet Fern has learned to read and write, and has put on a jacket and pair of pantaloons—all of which improvements I am sorry for. Squash Blossom, Blue Eye, Plantain, and Butter-cup, have had the scarlet-fever, but came easily through it. Huckleberry, Milkweed, and Dandelion, were attacked with the hooping-cough, but bore it bravely, and kept out-of-doors, whenever the sun shone. Cowslip, during the autumn, had either the measles or some eruption that looked very much like it, but was hardly sick a day. Poor Clover has been a good deal troubled with her second teeth, which have made her meagre in aspect and rather fractious in temper; nor, even when she smiles, is the matter much mended, since it discloses a gap, just within her lips, almost as wide as the barn-door. But all this will pass over; and it is predicted that she will turn out a very pretty girl.

As for Mr. Bright himself, he is now in his senior year at Williams College, and has a prospect of graduating with some degree of honorable distinction, at the next Commencement. In his oration for the bachelor's degree, he gives me to understand, he will treat of the Classical Myths, viewed in the aspect of baby-stories, and has a great mind to discuss the expediency of using up the whole of ancient history, for the same purpose. I do not know what he means to do with himself, after leaving college, but trust that, by dabbling so early with the dangerous and seductive business of authorship, he will not be tempted to become an author by profession. If so, I shall be very sorry for the little that I have had to do with the matter, in encouraging these first beginnings.

I wish there were any likelihood of my soon seeing Primrose, Periwinkle, Dandelion, Sweet Fern, Clover, Plantain,

Huckleberry, Milkweed, Cowslip, Butter-cup, Blue Eye, and Squash Blossom, again. But as I do not know when I shall re-visit Tanglewood, and as Eustace Bright probably will not ask me to edit a third Wonder Book, the public of little folks must not expect to hear any more about those dear children, from me. Heaven bless them, and everybody else, whether grown people or children!

THE WAYSIDE, CONCORD, (MASS.)
March 13, 1853.

THE MINOTAUR

I N THE old city of Trœzene, at the foot of a lofty mountain, there lived, a very long time ago, a little boy named Theseus. His grandfather, King Pittheus, was the sovereign of that country, and was reckoned a very wise man; so that Theseus, being brought up in the royal palace, and being naturally a bright lad, could hardly fail of profiting by the old king's instructions. His mother's name was Æthra. As for his father, the boy had never seen him. But, from his earliest remembrance, Æthra used to go with little Theseus into a wood, and sit down upon a moss-grown rock, which was deeply sunken into the earth. Here she often talked with her son about his father, and said that he was called Ægeus, and that he was a great king, and ruled over Attica, and dwelt at Athens, which was as famous a city as any in the world. Theseus was very fond of hearing about King Ægeus, and often asked his good mother Æthra why he did not come and live with them, at Trœzene.

"Ah, my dear son," answered Æthra, with a sigh, "a monarch has his people to take care of. The men and women, over whom he rules, are in the place of children to him; and he can seldom spare time to love his own children, as other parents do. Your father will never be able to leave his kingdom, for the sake of seeing his little boy."

"Well, but, dear mother," asked the boy, "why cannot I go to this famous city of Athens, and tell King Ægeus that I am his son?"

"That may happen, by-and-by," said Æthra. "Be patient, and we shall see. You are not yet big and strong enough to set out on such an errand."

"And how soon shall I be strong enough?" Theseus persisted in inquiring.

"You are but a tiny boy as yet," replied his mother. "See if you can lift this rock on which we are sitting!"

The little fellow had a great opinion of his own strength. So, grasping the rough protuberances of the rock, he tugged and toiled amain, and got himself quite out of breath, without being able to stir the heavy stone. It seemed to be rooted into the ground. No wonder he could not move it; for it would have taken all the force of a very strong man to lift it out of its earthy bed.

His mother stood looking on, with a sad kind of a smile on her lips and in her eyes, to see the zealous, and yet puny efforts of her little boy. She could not help being sorrowful, at finding him already so impatient to begin his adventures in the world.

"You see how it is, my dear Theseus," said she. "You must possess far more strength than now, before I can trust you to go to Athens, and tell King Ægeus that you are his son. But when you can lift this rock, and show me what is hidden beneath it, I promise you my permission to depart!"

Often and often, after this, did Theseus ask his mother whether it was yet time for him to go to Athens; and still his mother pointed to the rock, and told him that, for years to come, he would not be strong enough to move it. And again, and again, the rosy-cheeked and curly-headed boy would tug and strain at the huge mass of stone, striving, child as he was, to do what a giant could hardly have done, without taking both of his great hands to the task. Meanwhile, the rock seemed to be sinking farther and farther into the ground. The moss grew over it, thicker and thicker; until at last it looked almost like a soft green seat, with only a few gray knobs of granite peeping out. The overhanging trees, also, shed their brown leaves upon it, as often as the autumn came; and at its base grew ferns and wild flowers, some of which crept quite over its surface. To all appearance, the rock was as firmly fastened as any other portion of the earth's substance.

But, difficult as the matter looked, Theseus was now growing up to be such a vigorous youth, that, in his own opinion, the time would quickly come, when he might hope to get the upper hand of this ponderous lump of stone.

"Mother, I do believe it has started!" cried he, after one of his attempts. "The earth around it is certainly a little cracked!"

"No, no, child!" his mother hastily answered. "It is not possible you can have moved it, such a boy as you still are!"

Nor would she be convinced, although Theseus showed her the place, where he fancied that the stem of a flower had been partly uprooted by the movement of the rock. But Æthra sighed, and looked disquieted; for, no doubt, she began to be conscious that her son was no longer a child, and that, in a little while hence, she must send him forth among the perils and troubles of the world.

It was not more than a year afterwards, when they were again sitting on the moss-covered stone. Æthra had once more told him the oft-repeated story of his father, and how gladly he would receive Theseus at his stately palace, and how he would present him to his courtiers and the people, and tell them that here was the heir of his dominions. The eyes of Theseus glowed with enthusiasm, and he could hardly sit still to hear his mother speak.

"Dear mother Æthra," he exclaimed, "I never felt half so strong as now! I am no longer a child, nor a boy, nor a mere youth! I feel myself a man! It is now time to make one earnest trial to remove the stone."

"Ah, my dearest Theseus," replied his mother, "not yet!— not yet!"

"Yes, mother," said he resolutely,—"the time has come!"

Then Theseus bent himself in good earnest to the task, and strained every sinew, with manly strength and resolution. He put his whole brave heart into the effort. He wrestled with the big and sluggish stone, as if it had been a living enemy. He heaved; he lifted; he resolved now to succeed, or else to perish there, and let the rock be his monument forever! Æthra stood gazing at him, and clasped her hands, partly with a mother's pride, and partly with a mother's sorrow. The great rock stirred! Yes; it was raised slowly from the bedded moss and earth, uprooting the shrubs and flowers along with it, and was turned upon its side. Theseus had conquered!

While taking breath, he looked joyfully at his mother; and she smiled upon him through her tears.

"Yes, Theseus," she said, "the time has come; and you must stay no longer at my side! See what King Ægeus, your royal father, left for you, beneath the stone, when he lifted it in his mighty arms, and laid it on the spot whence you have now removed it."

Theseus looked, and saw that the rock had been placed over another slab of stone, containing a cavity within it; so that it somewhat resembled a roughly-made chest or coffer, of which the upper mass had served as the lid. Within the cavity lay a sword, with a golden hilt, and a pair of sandals.

"That was your father's sword," said Æthra, "and those were his sandals. When he went to be King of Athens, he bade me treat you as a child, until you should prove yourself a man by lifting this heavy stone. That task being accomplished, you are to put on his sandals, in order to follow in your father's footsteps, and to gird on his sword, so that you may fight giants and dragons, as King Ægeus did in his youth."

"I will set out for Athens, this very day!" cried Theseus.

But his mother persuaded him to stay a day or two longer, while she got ready some necessary articles for his journey. When his grandfather, the wise King Pittheus, heard that Theseus intended to present himself at his father's palace, he earnestly advised him to get on board of a vessel, and go by sea; because he might thus arrive within fifteen miles of Athens, without either fatigue or danger.

"The roads are very bad, by land," quoth the venerable king; "and they are terribly infested with robbers and monsters. A mere lad, like Theseus, is not fit to be trusted on such a perilous journey, all by himself. No, no; let him go by sea!"

But when Theseus heard of robbers and monsters, he pricked up his ears, and was so much the more eager to take the road along which they were to be met with. On the third day, therefore, he bade a respectful farewell to his grandfather, thanking him for all his kindness; and after affectionately embracing his mother, he set forth, with a good many of her tears glistening on his cheeks, and some, if the truth must be told, that had gushed out of his own eyes. But he let the sun and wind dry them, and walked stoutly on, playing with the golden hilt of his sword, and taking very manly strides in his father's sandals.

I cannot stop to tell you hardly any of the adventures that befel Theseus, on the road to Athens. It is enough to say, that he quite cleared that part of the country of the robbers, about whom King Pittheus had been so much alarmed. One of these bad people was named Procrustes; and he was indeed a terrible fellow, and had an ugly way of making fun of the poor travellers who happened to fall into his clutches. In his cavern, he had a bed, on which, with great pretence of hospitality, he invited his guests to lie down; but, if they happened to be shorter than the bed, this wicked villain stretched them out, by main force; or, if they were too tall, he lopt off their heads or feet, and laughed at what he had done, as an excellent joke. Thus, however weary a man might be, he never liked to lie in the bed of Procrustes. Another of these robbers, named Scinis, must likewise have been a very great scoundrel. He was in the habit of flinging his victims off a high cliff into the sea; and, in order to give him exactly his deserts, Theseus tossed him off the very same place. But, if you will believe me, the sea would not pollute itself by receiving such a bad person into its bosom; neither would the earth, having once got rid of him, consent to take him back; so that, between the cliff and the sea, Scinis stuck fast in the air, which was forced to bear the burthen of his naughtiness.

After these memorable deeds, Theseus heard of an enormous sow, which ran wild, and was the terror of all the farmers roundabout; and, as he did not consider himself above doing any good thing that came in his way, he killed this monstrous creature, and gave the carcass to the poor people for bacon. The great sow had been an awful beast, while ramping about the woods and fields, but was a pleasant object enough, when cut up into joints, and smoking on I know not how many dinner-tables.

Thus, by the time he reached his journey's end, Theseus had done many valiant feats with his father's golden-hilted sword, and had gained the renown of being one of the bravest young men of the day. His fame travelled faster than he did, and reached Athens before him. As he entered the city, he heard the inhabitants talking at the street-corners, and saying that Hercules was brave, and Jason too, and Castor and Pollux likewise, but that Theseus, the son of their own king, would turn out as great a hero as the best of them. Theseus took longer strides, on hearing this, and fancied himself sure of a magnificent reception at his father's court; since he came thither with Fame to blow her trumpet before him, and cry to King Ægeus—"Behold your son!"

He little suspected, innocent youth that he was, that here, in this very Athens, where his father reigned, a greater danger awaited him than any which he had encountered on the road. Yet this was the truth. You must understand that the father of Theseus, though not very old in years, was almost worn out with the cares of government, and had thus grown aged before his time. His nephews, not expecting him to live a very great while, intended to get all the power of the king-dom into their own hands. But when they heard that Theseus had arrived in Athens, and learnt what a gallant young man he was, they saw that he would not be at all the kind of person to let them steal away his father's crown and sceptre, which ought to be his own by right of inheritance. Thus, these bad-hearted nephews of King Ægeus, who were the own cousins of Theseus, at once became his enemies. A still more dangerous enemy was Medea, the wicked enchantress; for she was now the king's wife, and wanted to give the kingdom to her son Medus, instead of letting it be given to the son of Æthra, whom she hated.

It so happened that the king's nephews met Theseus, and found out who he was, just as he reached the entrance of the royal palace. With all their evil designs against him, they pretended to be their cousin's best friends, and expressed great joy at making his acquaintance. They proposed to him that he should come into the king's presence as a stranger, in order to try whether Ægeus would discover in the young man's features any likeness either to himself or his mother

Æthra, and thus recognize him for a son. Theseus consented; for he fancied that his father would know him in a moment, by the love that was in his heart. But, while he waited at the door, the nephews ran and told King Ægeus, that a young man had arrived in Athens, who, to their certain knowledge, intended to put him to death, and get possession of his royal crown.

"And he is now waiting for admission to your majesty's presence!" added they.

"Aha!" cried the old king, on hearing this. "Why, he must be a very wicked young fellow, indeed! Pray what would you advise me to do with him?"

In reply to this question, the wicked Medea put in her word. As I have already told you, she was a famous enchantress. According to some stories, she was in the habit of boiling old people in a large cauldron, under pretence of making them young again; but King Ægeus, I suppose, did not fancy such an uncomfortable way of growing young, or perhaps was contented to be old, and therefore would never let himself be popt into the cauldron. If there were time to spare from more important matters, I should be glad to tell you of Medea's fiery chariot, drawn by winged dragons, in which the enchantress used often to take an airing among the clouds. This chariot, in fact, was the vehicle that first brought her to Athens, where she had done nothing but mischief, ever since her arrival. But these, and many other wonders, must be left untold; and it is enough to say, that Medea, amongst a thousand other bad things, knew how to prepare a poison, that was instantly fatal to whomsoever might so much as touch it with his lips.

So, when the king asked what he should do with Theseus, this naughty woman had an answer ready at her tongue's end.

"Leave that to me, please your majesty!" she replied. "Only admit this evil-minded young man to your presence, treat him civilly, and invite him to drink a goblet of wine. Your majesty is well aware that I sometimes amuse myself with distilling very powerful medicines. Here is one of them, in this small phial. As to what it is made of, that is one of my secrets of state. Do but let me put a single drop into the goblet, and, let the young man taste it; and, I will answer for it, he shall quite lay aside the bad designs with which he comes hither!"

As she said this, Medea smiled; but, for all her smiling face, she meant nothing less than to poison the poor innocent Theseus, before his father's eyes. And King Ægeus, like most other kings, thought any punishment mild enough for a person who was accused of plotting against his life. He therefore made little or no objection to Medea's scheme, and, as soon as the poisonous wine was ready, gave orders that the young stranger should be admitted into his presence. The goblet was set on a table beside the king's throne; and a fly, meaning just to sip a little from the brim, immediately tumbled into it, dead. Observing this, Medea looked round at the nephews, and smiled again.

When Theseus was ushered into the royal apartment, the only object, that he seemed to behold, was the white-bearded old king. There he sat on his magnificent throne, a dazzling crown on his head, and a sceptre in his hand. His aspect was stately and majestic, although his years and infirmities weighed heavily upon him; as if each year were a lump of lead, and each infirmity a ponderous stone, and all were bundled up together, and laid upon his weary shoulders. The tears, both of joy and sorrow, sprang into the young man's eyes; for he thought how sad it was to see his dear father so infirm, and how sweet it would be to support him with his own youthful strength, and to cheer him up with the alacrity of his loving spirit. When a son takes his father into his warm heart, it renews the old man's youth in a better way than by the heat of Medea's magic cauldron. And this was what Theseus resolved to do. He could scarcely wait to see whether King Ægeus would recognize him, so eager was he to throw himself into his arms.

Advancing to the foot of the throne, he attempted to make a little speech, which he had been thinking about, as he came up the stairs. But he was almost choked by a great many tender feelings that gushed out of his heart and swelled into his throat, all struggling to find utterance together. And, therefore, unless he could have laid his full, over-brimming heart into the king's hand, poor Theseus knew not what to do or say. The cunning Medea observed what was passing in the young man's mind. She was more wicked, at that moment, than ever she had been before; for (and it makes me tremble to tell you of it) she did her worst to turn all this unspeakable love, with which Theseus was agitated, to his own ruin and destruction.

"Does your majesty see his confusion?" she whispered in the king's ear. "He is so conscious of guilt, that he trembles and cannot speak. The wretch lives too long! Quick!—offer him the wine!"

Now King Ægeus had been gazing earnestly at the young stranger, as he drew near the throne. There was something, he knew not what, either in his white brow, or in the fine expression of his mouth, or in his beautiful and tender eyes, that made him indistinctly feel as if he had seen this youth before; as if, indeed, he had trotted him on his knee when a baby, and had beheld him growing to be a stalwart man, while he himself grew old. But Medea guessed how the king felt, and would not suffer him to yield to these natural sensibilities; although they were the voice of his deepest heart, telling him, as plainly as it could speak, that here was our dear son, and Æthra's son, coming to claim him for a father. The enchantress again whispered in the king's ear, and compelled him, by her witchcraft, to see everything under a false aspect.

He made up his mind, therefore, to let Theseus drink off the poisoned wine.

"Young man," said he, "you are welcome! I am proud to show hospitality to so heroic a youth. Do me the favor to drink the contents of this goblet. It is brimming over, as you see, with delicious wine, such as I bestow only on those who are worthy of it! None is more worthy to quaff it, than yourself."

So saying, King Ægeus took the golden goblet from the table, and was about to offer it to Theseus. But, partly through his infirmities, and partly because it seemed so sad a thing to take away this young man's life, however wicked he might be—and partly, no doubt, because his heart was wiser than his head, and quaked within him at the thought of what he was going to do—for all these reasons, the king's hand trembled so much that a great deal of the wine slopped over. In order to strengthen his purpose, and fearing lest the whole of the precious poison should be wasted, one of his nephews now whispered to him:—

"Has your majesty any doubt of this stranger's guilt? There is the very sword with which he meant to slay you. How sharp, and bright, and terrible it is! Quick!—let him taste the wine; or perhaps he may do the deed even yet!"

At these words, Ægeus drove every thought and feeling out of his breast, except the one idea of how justly the young man deserved to be put to death. He sat erect on his throne, and held out the goblet of wine with a steady hand, and bent on Theseus a frown of kingly severity; for, after all, he had too noble a spirit to murder even a treacherous enemy with a deceitful smile upon his face.

"Drink!" said he, in the stern tone with which he was wont to condemn a criminal to be beheaded. "You have well deserved of me such wine as this!"

Theseus held out his hand to take the wine. But, before he touched it, King Ægeus trembled again. His eyes had fallen on the gold-hilted sword that hung at the young man's side. He drew back the goblet.

"That sword!" he exclaimed. "How came you by it?"

"It was my father's sword!" replied Theseus, with a tremulous voice. "These were his sandals! My dear mother (her name is Æthra) told me his story, while I was yet a little child. But it is only a month since I grew strong enough to lift the heavy stone, and take the sword and sandals from beneath it, and come to Athens to seek my father!"

"My son! my son!" cried King Ægeus, flinging away the fatal goblet, and tottering down from the throne to fall into the arms of Theseus. "Yes; these are Æthra's eyes! It is my son!"

I have quite forgotten what became of the king's nephews. But when the wicked Medea saw this new turn of affairs, she hurried out of the room, and going to her private chamber, lost no time in setting her enchantments at work. In a few moments, she heard a great noise of hissing snakes, outside of the chamber window; and, behold! there was her fiery chariot, and four huge winged serpents, wriggling and twisting in the air, flourishing their tails higher than the top of the palace, and all ready to set off on an aerial journey. Medea staid only long enough to take her son with her, and to steal the crown-jewels, together with the king's best robes, and whatever other valuable things she could lay hands on; and getting into the chariot, she whipped up the snakes, and ascended high over the city.

The king, hearing the hiss of the serpents, scrambled as fast as he could to the window, and bawled out to the abominable enchantress never to come back. The whole people of Athens, too, who had run out of doors to see this wonderful spectacle, set up a shout of joy at the prospect of getting rid of her. Medea, almost bursting with rage, uttered precisely such a hiss as one of her own snakes, only ten times more venomous and spiteful; and, glaring fiercely out of the blaze of the chariot, she shook her hands over the multitude below, as if she were scattering a million of curses among them. In so doing, however, she unintentionally let fall about five hundred diamonds of the first water, together with a thousand great pearls, and two thousand emeralds, rubies, sapphires, opals, and topazes, to which she had helped herself out of the king's strong-box. All these came pelting down, like a shower of many-colored hail-stones, upon the heads of grown people and children, who forthwith gathered them up, and carried them back to the palace. But King Ægeus told them that they were welcome to the whole, and to twice as many more, if he had them, for the sake of his delight at finding his son, and losing the wicked Medea. And, indeed, if you had seen how hateful was her last look, as the flaming chariot flew upward, you would not have wondered that both king and people should think her departure a good riddance.

And now Prince Theseus was taken into great favor by his royal father. The old king was never weary of having him sit beside him on his throne, (which was quite wide enough for two,) and of hearing him tell about his dear mother, and his childhood, and his many boyish efforts to lift the ponderous stone. Theseus, however, was much too brave and active a young man to be willing to spend all his time in relating things which had already happened. His ambition was, to perform other and more heroic deeds, which should be better worth telling in prose and verse. Nor had he been long in Athens, before he caught and chained a terrible mad bull, and made a public show of him, greatly to the wonder and admiration of good King Ægeus and his subjects. But, pretty soon, he undertook an affair that made all his foregone adventures seem like mere boy's play. The occasion of it was as follows.

One morning, when Prince Theseus awoke, he fancied that he must have had a very sorrowful dream, and that it was still running in his mind, even now that his eyes were open. For it appeared as if the air was full of a melancholy wail; and when he listened more attentively, he could hear sobs, and groans, and screams of woe, mingled with deep, quiet sighs, which came from the king's palace, and from the streets, and from the temples, and from every habitation in the city. And all these mournful noises, issuing out of thousands of separate hearts, united themselves into the one great sound of affliction, which had startled Theseus from slumber. He put on his clothes as quickly as he could, (not forgetting his sandals and gold-hilted sword,) and hastening to the king, inquired what it all meant.

"Alas, my son," quoth King Ægeus, heaving a long sigh, "here is a very lamentable matter in hand! This is the woe-fullest anniversary in the whole year. It is the day when we annually draw lots, to see which of the youths and maidens of Athens shall go to be devoured by the horrible Minotaur!"

"The Minotaur!" exclaimed Prince Theseus; and like a brave young prince as he was, he put his hand to the hilt of his sword. "What kind of a monster may that be? Is it not possible, at the risk of one's life, to slay him?"

But King Ægeus shook his venerable head, and, to convince Theseus that it was quite a hopeless case, he gave him an explanation of the whole affair. It seems, that, in the island of Crete, there lived a certain dreadful monster, called a Minotaur, which was shaped partly like a man and partly like a bull, and was altogether such a hideous sort of a creature, that it is really disagreeable to think of him. If he were suffered to exist at all, it should have been on some desert island, or in the duskiness of some deep cavern, where nobody would ever be tormented by his abominable aspect. But King Minos, who reigned over Crete, laid out a vast deal of money in building a habitation for the Minotaur, and took great care of his health and comfort, merely for mischief's sake. A few years before this time, there had been a war between the city of Athens and the island of Crete, in which the Athenians were beaten, and compelled to beg for peace. No peace could they obtain, however, except on condition that they should send seven young men and seven maidens, every year, to be devoured by the pet-monster of the cruel King Minos. For three years past, this grievous calamity had been borne. And the sobs, and groans, and shrieks, with which the city was now filled, were caused by the people's woe, because the fatal day had come again, when the fourteen victims were to be chosen by lot; and the old people feared lest their sons or daughters might be taken, and the youths and damsels dreaded lest they themselves might be destined to glut the ravenous maw of that detestable man-brute.

But when Theseus heard the story, he straightened himself up, so that he seemed taller than ever before; and as for his face, it was indignant, despiteful, bold, tender, and compassionate, all in one look.

"Let the people of Athens, this year, draw lots for only six young men, instead of seven!" said he. "I will myself be the seventh; and let the Minotaur devour me, if he can!"

"Oh, my dear son," cried King Ægeus, "why should you expose yourself to this horrible fate? You are a royal prince, and have a right to hold yourself above the destinies of common men."

"It is because I am a prince, your son, and the rightful heir of your kingdom, that I freely take upon me the calamity of your subjects!" answered Theseus. "And you, my father, being king over this people, and answerable to heaven for their welfare, are bound to sacrifice what is dearest to you, rather than that the son or daughter of the poorest citizen should come to any harm!"

The old king shed tears, and besought Theseus not to leave him desolate in his old age, more especially as he had but just begun to know the happiness of possessing a good and valiant son. Theseus, however, felt that he was in the right, and therefore would not give up his resolution. But he assured his father that he did not intend to be eaten up, unresistingly, like a sheep, and that, if the Minotaur devoured him, it should not be without a battle for his dinner. And finally, since he could not help it, King Ægeus consented to let him go. So a vessel was got ready, and rigged with black sails; and Theseus, with six other young men, and seven tender and beautiful damsels, came down to the harbor to embark. A sorrowful multitude accompanied them to the shore. There was the poor old king, too, leaning on his son's arm, and looking as if his single heart held all the grief of Athens.

Just as Prince Theseus was going on board, his father bethought himself of one last word to say.

"My beloved son," said he, grasping the prince's hand, "you observe that the sails of this vessel are black; as indeed they ought to be, since it goes upon a voyage of sorrow and despair. Now, being weighed down with infirmities, I know not whether I can survive till the vessel shall return. But, as long as I do live, I shall creep daily to the top of yonder cliff, to watch if there be a sail upon the sea. And, dearest Theseus, if, by some happy chance, you should escape the jaws of the Minotaur, then tear down those dismal sails, and hoist others that shall be bright as the sunshine! Beholding them on the horizon, myself and all the people will know that you are coming back victorious, and will welcome you with such a festal uproar as Athens never heard before!"

Theseus promised that he would do so. Then going on board, the mariners trimmed the vessel's black sails to the wind, which blew faintly off the shore, being pretty much made up of the sighs that everybody kept pouring forth, on this melancholy occasion. But, by-and-by, when they had got fairly out to sea, there came a stiff breeze from the north-west, and drove them along as merrily over the white-capt waves, as if they had been going on the most delightful errand imaginable. And, though it was a sad business enough, I rather question whether fourteen young people, without any old persons to keep them in order, could contrive to spend the whole time of the voyage in being miserable. There had been some few dances upon the undulating deck, I suspect, and some hearty bursts of laughter, and other such unseasonable merriment among the victims, before the high, blue mountains of Crete began to show themselves among the far-off clouds. That sight, to be sure, made them all very grave again.

Theseus stood among the sailors, gazing eagerly towards the land; although, as yet, it seemed hardly more substantial than the clouds, amidst which the mountains were looming up. Once or twice, he fancied that he saw a glare of some bright object, a long way off, flinging a gleam across the waves.

"Did you see that flash of light?" he inquired of the master of the vessel.

"No, prince; but I have seen it before," answered the master. "It came from Talus, I suppose."

As the breeze came fresher, just then, the master was busy with trimming his sails, and had no more time to answer questions. But, while the vessel flew faster and faster towards Crete, Theseus was astonished to behold a human figure, gigantic in size, which appeared to be striding, with a measured movement, along the margin of the island. It stept from cliff to cliff, and sometimes from one headland to another; while the sea foamed and thundered on the shore beneath, and dashed its jets of spray over the giant's feet. What was still more remarkable, whenever the sun shone on

this huge figure, it flickered and glimmered; its vast countenance, too, had a metallic lustre, and threw great flashes of
splendor through the air. The folds of its garments, moreover, instead of waving in the wind, fell heavily over its
limbs, as if woven of some kind of metal.

The nigher the vessel came, the more Theseus wondered
what this immense giant could be, and whether it actually
had life or no. For, though it walked, and made other life-
like motions, there yet was a kind of jerk in its gait, which,
together with its brazen aspect, caused the young prince to
suspect that it was no true giant, but only a wonderful piece
of machinery. The figure looked all the more terrible, because
it carried an enormous brass club on its shoulder.

"What is this wonder?" Theseus asked of the master of
the vessel, who was now at leisure to answer him.

"It is Talus, the Man of Brass," said the master.

"And is he a live giant, or a brazen image?" asked Theseus.

"That, truly," replied the master, "is the point which has
always perplexed me. Some say, indeed, that this Talus was
hammered out for King Minos by Vulcan himself, the skilfullest of all workers in metal. But who ever saw a brazen
image that had sense enough to walk round an island, three
times a day, as this giant walks round the island of Crete,
challenging every vessel that comes nigh the shore? And,
on the other hand, what living thing, unless his sinews were
made of brass, would not be weary of marching eighteen
hundred miles in the twenty-four hours, as Talus does, without ever sitting down to rest? He is a puzzler, take him how
you will!"

Still, the vessel went bounding onward; and now Theseus
could hear the brazen clangor of the giant's footsteps, as he
trode heavily upon the sea-beaten rocks, some of which were
seen to crack and crumble into the foamy waves, beneath
his weight. As they approached the entrance of the port, the

giant straddled clear across it, with a foot firmly planted on each headland; and uplifting his club to such a height that its but-end was hidden in a cloud, he stood in that formidable posture, with the sun gleaming all over his metallic surface. There seemed nothing else to be expected, but that, the next moment, he would fetch his great club down, slam-bang, and smash the vessel into a thousand pieces, without heeding how many innocent people he might destroy; for there is seldom any mercy in a giant, you know, and quite as little in a piece of brass clockwork. But, just when Theseus and his companions thought the blow was coming, the brazen lips unclosed themselves, and the figure spoke.

"Whence come you, strangers?"

And when the ringing voice ceased, there was just such a reverberation as you may have heard within a great church-bell, for a moment or two after the stroke of the hammer.

"From Athens!" shouted the master in reply.

"On what errand?" thundered the Man of Brass.

And he whirled his club aloft more threateningly than ever, as if he were about to smite them with a thunder-stroke, right amidships, because Athens, so little while ago, had been at war with Crete.

"We bring the seven youths and the seven maidens," answered the master, "to be devoured by the Minotaur!"

"Pass!" cried the brazen giant.

That one loud word rolled all about the sky, while again there was a booming reverberation within the figure's breast. The vessel glided between the headlands of the port, and the giant resumed his march. In a few moments, this wondrous centinel was far away, flashing in the distant sunshine, and revolving with immense strides around the island of Crete, as it was his never-ceasing task to do.

No sooner had they entered the harbor, than a party of the guards of King Minos came down to the water-side, and took charge of the fourteen young men and damsels. Surrounded by these armed warriors, Prince Theseus and his companions were led to the king's palace, and ushered into his presence. Now, Minos was a stern and pitiless king. If the figure, that guarded Crete, was made of brass, then the monarch, who ruled over it, might be thought to have a still harder metal in his breast, and might have been called a man of iron. He bent his shaggy brows upon the poor Athenian victims. Any other mortal, beholding their fresh and tender beauty, and their innocent looks, would have felt himself sitting on thorns until he had made every soul of them happy, by bidding them go free as the summer-wind. But this immitigable Minos cared only to examine whether they were plump enough to satisfy the Minotaur's appetite. For my part, I wish he himself had been the only victim; and the monster would have found him a pretty tough one!

One after another, King Minos called these pale, frightened youths and sobbing maidens to his footstool, gave them each a poke in the ribs with his sceptre (to try whether they were in good flesh, or no) and dismissed them with a nod to his guards. But when his eyes rested on Theseus, the king looked at him more attentively, because his face was calm and brave.

"Young man," asked he, with his stern voice, "are you not appalled at the certainty of being devoured by this terrible Minotaur?"

"I have offered my life in a good cause," answered Theseus; "and therefore I give it freely and gladly. But thou, King Minos, art thou not thyself appalled, who, year after year, hast perpetrated this dreadful wrong, by giving seven innocent youths and as many maidens to be devoured by a monster? Dost thou not tremble, wicked king, to turn thine eyes inward on thine own heart? Sitting there on thy golden throne, and in thy robes of majesty, I tell thee to thy face, King Minos, thou art a more hideous monster than the Minotaur himself!"

"Aha, do you think me so?" cried the king, laughing in his cruel way. "Tomorrow, at breakfast-time, you shall have an opportunity of judging which is the greater monster, the Minotaur or the king! Take them away, guards; and let this free-spoken youth be the Minotaur's first morsel!"

Near the king's throne (though I had no time to tell you so, before) stood his daughter Ariadne. She was a beautiful and tender-hearted maiden, and looked at these poor doomed captives with very different feelings from those of the iron-breasted King Minos. She really wept, indeed, at the idea of how much human happiness would be needlessly thrown away, by giving so many young people, in the first bloom and rose-blossom of their lives, to be eaten up by a creature who, no doubt, would have preferred a fat ox, or even a large pig, to the plumpest of them. And when she beheld the brave, spirited figure of Prince Theseus, bearing himself so calmly in his terrible peril, she grew a hundred times more pitiful than before. As the guards were taking him away, she flung herself at the king's feet, and besought him to set all the captives free; and especially this one young man.

"Peace, foolish girl!" answered King Minos. "What hast thou to do with an affair like this? It is a matter of state-policy, and therefore quite beyond thy weak comprehension. Go water thy flowers, and think no more of these Athenian caitiffs, whom the Minotaur shall as certainly eat up for breakfast, as I will eat a partridge for my supper!"

So saying, the king looked cruel enough to devour Theseus and all the rest of the captives, himself, had there been no Minotaur to save him the trouble. As he would hear not another word in their favor, the prisoners were now led away and clapt into a dungeon, where the jailer advised them to go to sleep as soon as possible, because the Minotaur was in the habit of calling for breakfast early. The seven maidens, and six of the young men, soon sobbed themselves to slumber. But Theseus was not like them. He felt conscious that he was wiser, and braver, and stronger than his companions, and that therefore he had the responsibility of all their lives upon him, and must consider whether there was no way to save them, even in this last extremity. So he kept himself awake, and paced to-and-fro across the gloomy dungeon in which they were shut up.

Just before midnight, the door was softly unbarred, and the gentle Ariadne showed herself, with a torch in her hand.

"Are you awake, Prince Theseus?" she whispered.

"Yes!" answered Theseus. "With so little time to live, I do not choose to waste any of it in sleep."

"Then follow me," said Ariadne, "and tread softly."

What had become of the jailer and the guards, Theseus never knew. But, however that might be, Ariadne opened all the doors, and led him forth from the darksome prison into the pleasant moonlight.

"Theseus," said the maiden, "you can now get on board your vessel, and sail away for Athens."

"No!" answered the young man. "I will never leave Crete, unless I can first slay the Minotaur, and save my poor companions, and deliver Athens from this cruel tribute!"

"I knew that this would be your resolution," said Ariadne. "Come then with me, brave Theseus! Here is your own sword, which the guards deprived you of. You will need it; and pray Heaven you may use it well!"

Then she led Theseus along, by the hand, until they came to a dark, shadowy grove, where the moonlight wasted itself on the tops of the trees, without shedding hardly so much as a glimmering beam upon their pathway. After going a good way through this obscurity, they reached a high, marble wall, which was overgrown with creeping-plants that made it shaggy with their verdure. The wall seemed to have no door, nor any windows, but rose up, lofty, and massive, and mysterious, and was neither to be clambered over, nor, so far as Theseus could perceive, to be passed through. Neverthe- less, Ariadne did but press one of her soft little fingers against a particular block of marble, and though it looked as solid as any other part of the wall, it yielded to her touch, disclos- ing an entrance just wide enough to admit them. They crept through; and the marble-stone swung back into its place.

"We are now," said Ariadne, "in the famous labyrinth which Dædalus built, before he made himself a pair of wings, and flew away from our island like a bird. That Dædalus was a very cunning workman; but of all his artful contriv- ances, this labyrinth is the most wondrous. Were we to take but a few steps from the doorway, we might wander about, all our lifetime, and never find it again. Yet, in the very centre of this labyrinth is the Minotaur; and, Theseus, you must go thither to seek him!"

"But how shall I ever find him," asked Theseus, "if the labyrinth so bewilders me as you say it will?"

Just as he spoke, they heard a rough and very disagreeable roar, which greatly resembled the lowing of a fierce bull, but yet had some sort of sound like the human voice. Theseus even fancied a rude articulation in it, as if the creature, that uttered it, were trying to shape his hoarse breath into words. It was at some distance, however; and he really could not tell whether it sounded most like a bull's roar or a man's harsh voice.

"That is the Minotaur's noise," whispered Ariadne, closely grasping the hand of Theseus, and pressing one of her own hands to her heart, which was all in a tremble. "You must follow that sound through the windings of the labyrinth, and, by-and-by, you will find him. Stay! Take the end of this silken string. I will hold the other end; and then, if you win the victory, it will lead you again to this spot. Farewell, brave Theseus!"

So the young man took the end of the silken string in his left hand, and his gold-hilted sword, ready drawn from its scabbard, in the other, and trod boldly into the inscrutable labyrinth. How this labyrinth was built, is more than I can tell you. But so cunningly contrived a mizmaze was never seen in the world, before nor since. There can be nothing else so intricate, unless it were the brain of a man like Dædalus, who planned it, or the heart of any ordinary man; which last, to be sure, is ten times as great a mystery as the labyrinth of Crete. Theseus had not taken five steps, before he lost sight of Ariadne; and, in five more, his head was growing dizzy. But still he went on, now creeping through a low arch, now ascending a flight of steps, now in one crooked passage, and now in another, with here a door opening before him, and there one banging behind; until it really seemed as if the walls spun round, and whirled him round along with them. And, all the while, through these hollow avenues, now nearer, now farther off again, resounded the cry of the Minotaur; and the sound was so fierce, so cruel, so ugly—so like a bull's roar, and withal so like a human voice, and yet like neither of them—that the brave heart of Theseus grew sterner and angrier at every step. For he felt it an insult to the moon and sky, and to our affectionate and simple Mother Earth, that such a monster should have the audacity to exist.

As he pressed onward, the clouds gathered over the moon, and the labyrinth grew so dusky that Theseus could no longer discern the bewilderment through which he was passing. He would have felt quite lost, and utterly hopeless of ever again walking in a straight path, if, every little while, he had not been conscious of a gentle twitch at the silken cord. Then he knew that the tender-hearted Ariadne was still holding the other end, and that she was fearing for him, and hoping for him, and giving him just as much of her sympathy as if she were close by his side. Oh, indeed, I can assure you, there was a vast deal of human sympathy running along that slender thread of silk! But still he followed the dreadful roar of the Minotaur, which now grew louder and louder, and finally so very loud, that Theseus fully expected to come close upon him, at every new zig-zag and wriggle of the path. And, at last, in an open space, at the very centre of the labyrinth, he did discern the hideous creature!

Sure enough, what an ugly monster it was! Only his horned head belonged to a bull; and yet, somehow or other, he looked like a bull all over, preposterously waddling on his hind-legs; or, if you happened to view him in another way, he seemed wholly a man, and all the more monstrous for being so. And there he was, the wretched thing, with no society, no companion, no kind of a mate, living only to do mischief, and incapable of knowing what affection means! Theseus hated him, and shuddered at him, and yet could not but be sensible of some sort of pity, and all the more, the uglier and more detestable the creature was. For he kept striding to-and-fro, in a solitary frenzy of rage, continually emitting a hoarse roar, which was oddly mixed up with half-shaped words; and, after listening a while, Theseus understood that the Minotaur was saying to himself how miserable he was, and how hungry, and how he hated everybody, and how he longed to eat up the human race alive!

Ah, the bull-headed villain! And, Oh, my good little people, you will perhaps see, one of these days, as I do now, that every human being, who suffers anything evil to get into his nature, or to remain there, is a kind of Minotaur, an enemy of his fellow-creatures, and separated from all good companionship, as this poor monster was!

Was Theseus afraid? By no means, my dear auditors. What! A hero like Theseus afraid! Not had the Minotaur had twenty bull-heads instead of one. Bold as he was, however, I rather fancy that it strengthened his valiant heart, just at this crisis, to feel a tremulous twitch at the silken cord, which he was still holding in his left hand. It was as if Ariadne were giving him all her might and courage; and, much as he already had, and little as she had to give, it made his own seem twice as much. And, to confess the honest truth, he needed the whole; for now the Minotaur, turning suddenly about, caught sight of Theseus, and instantly lowered his horribly sharp horns, exactly as a mad bull does when he means to rush against an enemy. At the same time, he belched forth a tremendous roar, in which there was something like the words of human language, but all disjointed and shaken to pieces by passing through the gullet of a miserably enraged brute.

Theseus could only guess what the creature intended to say, and that rather by his gestures than his words; for the Minotaur's horns were sharper than his wits, and of a great deal more service to him than his tongue. But probably this was the sense of what he uttered:—

"Ah, wretch of a human being! I'll stick my horns through you, and toss you fifty feet high, and eat you up the moment you come down!"

"Come on, then, and try it!" was all that Theseus deigned to reply; for he was far too magnanimous to assault his enemy with insolent language.

Without more words on either side, there ensued the most awful fight between Theseus and the Minotaur, that ever happened beneath the sun or moon. I really know not how it might have turned out, if the monster, in his first headlong rush against Theseus, had not missed him, by a hair's breadth, and broken one of his horns short off against the stone-wall. On this mishap, he bellowed so intolerably that a part of the labyrinth tumbled down, and all the inhabitants of Crete mistook the noise for an uncommonly heavy thunder-storm. Smarting with the pain, he galloped around the open space

in so ridiculous a way that Theseus laughed at it, long afterwards, though not precisely at the moment. After this, the
two antagonists stood valiantly up to one another, and fought,
sword to horn, for a long while. At last, the Minotaur made
a run at Theseus, grazed his left side with his horn, and
flung him down; and thinking that he had stabbed him to
the heart, he cut a great caper in the air, opened his bull-
mouth from ear to ear, and prepared to snap his head off.
But Theseus, by this time, had leaped up, and caught the
monster off his guard. Fetching a sword-stroke at him, with
all his force, he hit him fair upon the neck, and made his
bull-head skip six yards from his human body, which fell
down flat upon the ground.

So now the battle was ended! Immediately, the moon shone
out as brightly as if all the troubles of the world, and all the
wickedness and the ugliness that infest human life, were
past and gone forever. And Theseus, as he leaned on his
sword, taking breath, felt another twitch of the silken cord;
for, all through the terrible encounter, he had held it fast in
his left hand. Eager to let Ariadne know of his success, he
followed the guidance of the thread, and soon found himself
at the entrance of the labyrinth.

"Thou hast slain the monster!" cried Ariadne, clasping
her hands.

"Thanks to thee, dear Ariadne," answered Theseus, "I
return victorious."

"Then," said Ariadne, "we must quickly summon thy
friends, and get them and thyself on board the vessel, before
dawn. If morning finds thee here, my father will avenge the
Minotaur!"

To make my story short, the poor captives were awakened,
and, hardly knowing whether it was not a joyful dream, were
told of what Theseus had done, and that they must set sail
for Athens before daybreak. Hastening down to the vessel,

they all clambered on board, except Prince Theseus, who lingered behind them, on the strand, holding Ariadne's hand clasped in his own.

"Dear maiden," said he, "thou wilt surely go with us! Thou art too gentle and sweet a child for such an iron-hearted father as King Minos. He cares no more for thee, than a granite-rock cares for the little flower that grows in one of its crevices! But my father, King Ægeus, and my dear mother Æthra, and all the fathers and mothers in Athens, and all the sons and daughters too, will love and honor thee as their benefactress. Come with us, then; for King Minos will be very angry, when he knows what thou hast done!"

Now, some low-minded people, who pretend to tell the story of Theseus and Ariadne, have the face to say that this royal and honorable maiden did really flee away, under cover of the night, with the young stranger whose life she had preserved. They say, too, that Prince Theseus (who would have died, sooner than wrong the meanest creature in the world) ungratefully deserted Ariadne, on a solitary island, where the vessel touched on its voyage to Athens. But, had the noble Theseus heard these falsehoods, he would have served their slanderous authors as he served the Minotaur! Here is what Ariadne answered, when the brave Prince of Athens besought her to accompany him.

"No, Theseus!" the maiden said, pressing his hand, and then drawing back a step or two. "I cannot go with you. My father is old, and has nobody but myself to love him. Hard as you think his heart is, it would break to lose me. At first, King Minos will be angry; but he will soon forgive his only child; and, by-and-by, he will rejoice, I know, that no more youths and maidens must come from Athens, to be devoured by the Minotaur! I have saved you, Theseus, as much for my father's sake as for your own. Farewell! Heaven bless you!"

All this was so true, and so maidenlike, and was spoken with so sweet a dignity, that Theseus would have blushed to urge her any longer. Nothing remained for him, therefore, but to bid Ariadne an affectionate farewell, and to go on board the vessel, and set sail.

In a few moments, the white foam was boiling up before their prow, as Prince Theseus and his companions sailed out of the harbor, with a whistling breeze behind them. Talus, the brazen giant, on his never-ceasing centinel's march, happened to be approaching that part of the coast; and they saw him, by the glimmering of the moonbeams on his polished surface, while he was yet a great way off. As the figure moved like clockwork, however, and could neither hasten his enormous strides nor retard them, he arrived at the port when they were just beyond the reach of his club. Nevertheless, straddling from headland to headland, as his custom was, Talus attempted to strike a blow at the vessel, and, overreaching himself, tumbled at full length into the sea, which splashed high over his gigantic shape, as when an iceberg turns a somerset. There he lies yet; and whoever desires to enrich himself by means of brass, had better go thither with a diving-bell, and fish up Talus!

On the homeward voyage, the fourteen youths and damsels were in excellent spirits, as you will easily suppose. They spent most of their time in dancing, unless when the sidelong breeze made the deck slope too much. In due season, they came within sight of the coast of Attica, which was their native country. But here, I am grieved to tell you, happened a sad misfortune.

You will remember (what Theseus unfortunately forgot) that his father, King Ægeus, had enjoined it upon him to hoist sunshiny sails, instead of black ones, in case he should overcome the Minotaur, and return victorious. In the joy of their success, however, and amidst the sports, dancing, and other merriment, with which these young folks wore away the time, they never once thought whether their sails were black, white, or rainbow-colored, and, indeed, left it entirely to the mariners whether they had any sails at all. Thus, the vessel returned, like a raven, with the same sable wings that had wafted her away. But poor King Ægeus, day after day, infirm as he was, had clambered to the summit of a cliff that overhung the sea, and there sat watching for Prince Theseus, homeward bound; and no sooner did he behold the fatal blackness of the sails, than he concluded that his dear son, whom he loved so much, and felt so proud of, had been eaten by the Minotaur. He could not bear the thought of living any longer; so, first flinging his crown and sceptre into the sea, (useless baubles that they were to him, now!) King Ægeus merely stooped forward, and fell headlong over the cliff, and was drowned, poor soul, in the waves that foamed at its base!

This was melancholy news for Prince Theseus, who, when he stept ashore, found himself king of all the country, whether he would or no; and such a turn of fortune was enough to make any young man feel very much out of spirits. However, he sent for his dear mother to Athens, and, by taking her advice in matters of state, became a very excellent monarch, and was greatly beloved by his people.

THE PYGMIES

A GREAT while ago, when the world was full of wonders, there lived an earth-born giant, named Antæus, and a million or more of curious little earth-born people, who were called Pygmies. This giant and these Pygmies, being children of the same mother, (that is to say, our good old Grandmother Earth,) were all brethren, and dwelt together in a very friendly and affectionate manner, far, far off, in the middle of hot Africa. The Pygmies were so small, and there were so many sandy deserts and such high mountains between them and the rest of mankind, that nobody could get a peep at them oftener than once in a hundred years. As for the giant, being of a very lofty stature, it was easy enough to see him, but safest to keep out of his sight.

Among the Pygmies, I suppose, if one of them grew to the height of six or eight inches, he was reckoned a prodigiously tall man. It must have been very pretty to behold their little cities, with streets two or three feet wide, paved with the smallest pebbles, and bordered by habitations about as big as a squirrel's cage. The king's palace attained to the stupendous magnitude of Periwinkle's baby-house, and stood in the centre of a spacious square, which could hardly have been covered by our hearth-rug. Their principal temple, or cathedral, was as lofty as yonder bureau, and was looked upon as a wonderfully sublime and magnificent edifice. All these structures were built neither of stone nor wood. They were neatly plastered together by the Pygmy-workmen, pretty much like birds' nests, out of straw, feathers, egg-shells, and other small bits of stuff, with stiff clay instead of mortar; and when the hot sun had dried them, they were just as snug and comfortable as a Pygmy could desire.

The country roundabout was conveniently laid out in fields, the largest of which was nearly of the same extent as one of Sweet Fern's flower-beds. Here the Pygmies used to plant wheat and other kinds of grain, which, when it grew up and ripened, overshadowed these tiny people, as the pines, and the oaks, and the walnut and chestnut-trees, overshadow you and me, when we walk in our own tracts of woodland. At harvest-time, they were forced to go with their little axes and cut down the grain, exactly as a wood-cutter makes a clearing in the forest; and when a stalk of wheat, with its over-burthened top, chanced to come crashing down upon an unfortunate Pygmy, it was apt to be a very sad affair. If it did not smash him all to pieces, at least, I am sure, it must have made the poor little fellow's head ache! And, Oh, my stars! If the fathers and mothers were so small, what must the children and babies have been? A whole family of them might have been put to bed in a shoe, or have crept into an old glove, and played at hide-and-seek in its thumb and fingers! You might have hidden a year-old baby under a thimble!

Now these funny Pygmies, as I told you before, had a giant for their neighbor and brother, who was bigger, if possible, than they were little. He was so very tall that he carried a pine-tree, which was eight feet through the but, for a walking-stick. It took a far-sighted Pygmy, I can assure you, to discern his summit without the help of a telescope; and sometimes, in misty weather, they could not see his upper half, but only his long legs, which seemed to be striding about by themselves. But at noon-day, in a clear atmosphere, when the sun shone brightly over him, the giant Antæus presented a very grand spectacle. There he used to stand, a perfect mountain of a man, with his great countenance smiling down upon his little brothers, and his one vast eye (which was as big as a cart-wheel, and placed right in the centre of his forehead) giving a friendly wink to the whole nation at once.

The Pygmies loved to talk with Antæus; and fifty times a day, one or another of them would turn up his head, and shout through the hollow of his fists—"Halloo, brother Antæus! How are you, my good fellow?"—And when the small, distant squeak of their voices reached his ear, the giant would make answer—"Pretty well, brother Pygmy, I thank you!"—in a thunderous roar that would have shaken down the walls of their strongest temple, only that it came from so far aloft.

It was a happy circumstance that Antæus was the Pygmy people's friend; for there was more strength in his little finger, than in ten million of such bodies as theirs. If he had been as ill-natured to them as he was to everybody else, he might have beaten down their biggest city at one kick, and hardly have known that he did it. With the tornado of his breath, he could have stript the roofs from a hundred dwellings, and sent thousands of the inhabitants whirling through the air. He might have set his immense foot upon a multitude; and when he took it up again, there would have been a pitiful sight, to be sure! But, being the son of Mother Earth, as they likewise were, the giant gave them his brotherly kindness, and loved them with as big a love, as it was possible to feel for creatures so very small. And, on their parts, the Pygmies loved Antæus with as much affection as their tiny hearts could hold. He was always ready to do them any good offices that lay in his power; as, for example, when they wanted a breeze to turn their wind-mills, the giant would set all the sails a-going with the mere natural respiration of his lungs. When the sun was too hot, he often sat himself down and let his shadow fall over the kingdom, from one frontier to the other; and as for matters in general, he was wise enough to let them alone, and leave the Pygmies to manage their own affairs— which, after all, is about the best thing that great people can do for little ones.

In short, as I said before, Antæus loved the Pygmies, and the Pygmies loved Antæus. The giant's life being as long as his body was large, while the lifetime of a Pygmy was but a span, this friendly intercourse had been going on for innumerable generations and ages. It was written about, in the Pygmy histories, and talked about, in their ancient traditions. The most venerable and white-bearded Pygmy had never heard of a time, even in his greatest of grandfather's days, when the giant was not their enormous friend. Once, to be sure, (as was recorded on an obelisk, three feet high, erected on the place of the catastrophe,) Antæus sat down upon about five thousand Pygmies, who were assembled at a military review. But this was one of those unlucky accidents for which nobody is to blame; so that the small folks never took it to heart, and only requested the giant to be careful, forever afterwards, to examine the acre of ground where he intended to squat himself.

It is a very pleasant picture to imagine Antæus standing among the Pygmies, like the spire of the tallest cathedral that ever was built, while they ran about like pismires at his feet; and to think that, in spite of their difference in size, there was affection and sympathy between them and him! Indeed, it has always seemed to me that the giant needed the little people, more than the Pygmies needed the giant. For, unless they had been his neighbors and well-wishers, and, as we may say, his playfellows, Antæus would not have had a single friend in the world. No other being, like himself, had ever been created. No creature of his own size had ever talked with him, in thunder-like accents, face to face. When he stood with his head among the clouds, he was quite alone, and had been so, for hundreds of years, and would be so, forever! Even if he had met another giant, Antæus would have fancied the world not big enough for two such vast personages, and, instead of being friends with him, would have fought him till one of the two was killed. But, with the Pygmies, he was the most sportive, and humorous, and merryhearted, and sweet-tempered old giant, that ever washed his face in a wet cloud!

His little friends, like all other small people, had a great opinion of their own importance, and used to assume quite a patronizing air towards the giant.

"Poor creature!" they said one to another. "He has a very dull time of it, all by himself; and we ought not to grudge wasting a little of our precious time to amuse him. He is not half so bright as we are, to be sure; and, for that reason, he needs us to look after his comfort and happiness. Let us be kind to the old fellow! Why, if Mother Earth had not been very kind to ourselves, we might all have been giants too!"

On all their holidays, the Pygmies had excellent sport with Antæus. He often stretched himself out at full length on the ground, where he looked like the long ridge of a hill; and it was a good hour's walk, no doubt, for a short-legged Pygmy to journey from head to foot of the giant. He would lay down his great hand flat on the grass, and challenge the tallest of them to clamber upon it, and straddle from finger to finger. So fearless were they, that they made nothing of creeping in among the folds of his garments. When his head lay sideways on the earth, they would march boldly up and peep into the great cavern of his mouth, and take it all as a joke (as, indeed, it was meant) when Antæus gave a sudden snap with his jaws, as if he were going to swallow fifty of them at once. You would have laughed to see the children dodging in and out among his hair, or swinging from his beard. It is impossible to tell half of the funny tricks that they played with their huge comrade; but I do not know that anything was more curious, than when a party of boys were seen running races on his forehead, to try which of them could get first round the circle of his one, great eye. It was another favorite feat with them, to march along the bridge of his nose, and jump down upon his upper lip!

If the truth must be told, they were sometimes as troublesome to the giant as a swarm of ants or musquitoes; especially as they had a fondness for mischief, and liked to prick his skin with their little swords and lances, to see how thick and tough it was. But Antæus took it all kindly enough; although, once in a while, when he happened to be sleepy, he would grumble out a peevish word or two, like the muttering of a tempest, and ask them to have done with their nonsense. A great deal oftener, however, he watched their merriment and gambols, until his huge, heavy, clumsy wits were completely stirred up by them; and then would he roar out such a tremendous volume of immeasurable laughter, that the whole nation of Pygmies had to put their hands to their ears—else it would certainly have deafened them.

"Ho! Ho! Ho!" quoth the giant, shaking his mountainous sides. "What a funny thing it is to be little! If I were not Antæus, I should like to be a Pygmy, just for the joke's sake!"

The Pygmies had but one thing to trouble them in the world. They were constantly at war with the cranes, and had always been so, ever since the long-lived giant could remember. From time to time, very terrible battles had been fought, in which sometimes the little men won the victory, and sometimes the cranes. According to some historians, the Pygmies used to go to the battle, mounted on the backs of goats and rams; but such animals as these must have been far too big for Pygmies to ride upon; so that, I rather suppose, they rode on squirrel-back, or rabbit-back, or rat-back, or, perhaps, got upon hedge-hogs, whose prickly quills would be very terrible to the enemy. However this might be, and whatever creatures the Pygmies rode upon, I do not doubt that they made a formidable appearance, armed with sword and spear, and bow and arrow, blowing their tiny trumpet, and shouting their little war-cry. They never failed to exhort one another to fight bravely, and recollect that the world had its eyes upon them; although, in simple truth, the only spectator was the giant Antæus, with his one, great, stupid eye, in the middle of his forehead.

When the two armies joined battle, the cranes would rush forward, flapping their wings and stretching out their necks, and would perhaps snatch up some of the Pygmies crosswise in their beaks. Whenever this happened, it was truly an awful spectacle to see those little men of might kicking and sprawling in the air, and at last disappearing down the crane's long, crooked throat, swallowed up alive! A hero, you know, must hold himself in readiness for any kind of fate; and, doubtless, the glory of the thing was a consolation to him, even in the crane's gizzard. If Antæus observed that the battle was going hard against his little allies, he generally stopped laughing, and ran with mile-long strides to their assistance, flourishing his club aloft and shouting at the cranes, who quacked and croaked, and retreated as fast as they could. Then the Pygmy army would march homeward in triumph, attributing the victory entirely to their own valor, and to the warlike skill and strategy of whomsoever happened to be captain-general; and, for a tedious while afterwards, nothing would be heard of but grand processions, and public banquets, and brilliant illuminations, and shows of wax-work, with likenesses of the distinguished officers, as small as life!

In the above-described warfare, if a Pygmy chanced to pluck out a crane's tail-feather, it proved a very great feather in his cap. Once or twice, if you will believe me, a little man was made chief-ruler of the nation, for no other merit in the world than bringing home such a feather!

But I have now said enough to let you see what a gallant little people these were, and how happily they and their fore-fathers, for nobody knows how many generations, had lived with the immeasurable giant Antæus. In the remaining part of the story, I shall tell you of a far more astonishing battle than any that was fought between the Pygmies and the cranes.

One day, the mighty Antæus was lolling at full length among his little friends. His pine-tree walking-stick lay on the ground, close by his side. His head was in one part of the kingdom, and his feet extended across the boundaries of another part; and he was taking whatever comfort he could get, while the Pygmies scrambled over him, and peeped into his cavernous mouth, and played among his hair. Sometimes, for a minute or two, the giant dropped asleep, and snored like the rush of a whirlwind. During one of these little bits of slumber, a Pygmy chanced to climb upon his shoulder, and took a view around the horizon, as from the summit of a hill; and he beheld something, a long way off, which made him rub the bright specks of his eyes, and look sharper than before. At first, he mistook it for a mountain, and wondered how it had grown up so suddenly out of the earth. But, soon, he saw the mountain move. As it came nearer and nearer, what should it turn out to be, but a human shape, not so big as Antæus, it is true, although a very enormous figure, in com-parison with Pygmies, and a vast deal bigger than the men whom we see, now-a-days!

When the Pygmy was quite satisfied that his eyes had not deceived him, he scampered, as fast as his legs would carry him, to the giant's ear, and stooping over its cavity, shouted lustily into it.

"Halloo, brother Antæus! Get up, this minute, and take your pine-tree walking-stick in your hand. Here comes another giant to have a tustle with you!"

"Poh, poh!" grumbled Antæus, only half awake. "None of your nonsense, my little fellow! Don't you see I'm sleepy. There is not a giant on earth for whom I would take the trouble to get up!"

But the Pygmy looked again, and now perceived that the stranger was coming directly towards the prostrate form of Antæus. With every step, he looked less like a blue mountain, and more like an immensely large man. He was soon so nigh, that there could be no possible mistake about the matter. There he was, with the sun flaming on his golden helmet, and flashing from his polished breastplate; he had a sword by his side, and a lion's skin over his back, and on his right shoulder he carried a club, which looked bulkier and heavier than the pine-tree walking-stick of Antæus.

By this time, the whole nation of Pygmies had seen the new wonder, and a million of them set up a shout, all together; so that it really made quite an audible squeak.

"Get up, Antæus! Bestir yourself, you lazy old giant! Here comes another giant, as strong as you are, to fight with you!"

"Nonsense, nonsense!" growled the sleepy giant. "I'll have my nap out, come who may!"

Still, the stranger drew nearer; and now the Pygmies could plainly discern, that, if his stature were less lofty than the giant's, yet his shoulders were even broader. And, in truth, what a pair of shoulders they must have been! As I told you, a long while ago, they once upheld the sky! The Pygmies, being ten times as vivacious as their great numskull of a brother, could not abide the giant's slow movements, and were determined to have him on his feet. So they kept shouting to him, and even went so far as to prick him with their swords.

"Get up, get up, get up!" they cried. "Up with you, lazy-bones! The strange giant's club is bigger than your own, his shoulders are the broadest, and we think him the stronger of the two!"

Antæus could not endure to have it said, that any mortal was half so mighty as himself. This latter remark of the Pygmies pricked him deeper than their swords; and sitting up, in rather a sulky humor, he gave a gape of several yards wide, rubbed his eyes, and finally turned his stupid head in the direction whither his little friends were eagerly pointing.

No sooner did he set eyes on the stranger, than, leaping on his feet and seizing his walking-stick, he strode a mile or two to meet him; all the while, brandishing the sturdy pine-tree, so that it whistled through the air.

"Who are you?" thundered the giant. "And what do you want in my dominions?"

There was one strange thing about Antæus, of which I have not yet told you; lest, hearing of so many wonders all in a lump, you might not believe much more than half of them. You are to know, then, that, whenever this redoubtable giant touched the ground, either with his hand, his foot, or any other part of his body, he grew stronger than ever he had been before. The Earth, you remember, was his mother, and was very fond of him, as being almost the biggest of her children; and so she took this method of keeping him always in full vigor. Some persons affirm, that he grew ten times stronger, at every touch; others say, that it was only twice as strong. But, only think of it! Whenever Antæus took a walk, supposing it were but ten miles, and that he stepped a hundred yards at a stride, you may try to cypher out how much mightier he was, on sitting down again, than when he first started. And whenever he flung himself on the earth, to take a little repose, even if he got up the very next instant, he would be as strong as exactly ten just such giants as his former self! It was well for the world that Antæus happened to be of a sluggish disposition, and liked ease better than exercise; for, if he had frisked about like the Pygmies, and touched the earth as often as they did, he would long ago have been strong enough to pull down the sky about people's ears! But these great lubberly fellows resemble mountains, not only in bulk, but in their disinclination to move.

Any other mortal man, except the very one whom Antæus had now encountered, would have been half frightened to death by the giant's ferocious aspect and terrible voice. But the stranger did not seem at all disturbed. He carelessly lifted his club and balanced it in his hand, measuring Antæus with his eye, from head to foot, not as if wonder-smitten at his stature, but as if he had seen a great many giants before, and this was by no means the biggest of them. In fact, if the giant had been no bigger than the Pygmies, (who stood pricking up their ears, and looking and listening to what was going forward,) the stranger could not have been less afraid of him.

"Who are you, I say?" roared Antæus again. "What's your name? Why do you come hither? Speak, you vagabond; or I'll try the thickness of your skull, with my walking-stick!"

"You are a very discourteous giant," answered the stranger, quietly; "and I shall probably have to teach you a little civility, before we part. As for my name, it is Hercules. I have come hither, because this is my most convenient road to the garden of the Hesperides, whither I am going to get three of the golden apples for King Eurystheus."

"Caitiff, you shall go no farther!" bellowed Antæus, putting on a grimmer look than before; for he had heard of the mighty Hercules, and hated him because he was said to be so strong. "Neither shall you go back whence you came!"

"How will you prevent me," asked Hercules, "from going whither I please?"

"By hitting you a rap with this pine-tree here!" shouted Antæus, scowling so, that he made himself the ugliest monster in Africa. "I am fifty times stronger than you; and, now that I stamp my foot upon the ground, I am five hundred times stronger! I am ashamed to kill such a puny little dwarf as you seem to be. I will make a slave of you; and you shall likewise be the slave of my brethren, here, the Pygmies. So throw down your club and your other weapons; and as for that lion's skin, I intend to have a pair of gloves made of it!"

"Come and take it off my shoulders, then!" answered Hercules, lifting his club.

Then the giant, grinning with rage, strode tower-like towards the stranger, (ten times strengthened at every step,) and fetched a monstrous blow at him with his pine-tree, which Hercules caught upon his club; and being more skilful than Antæus, he paid him back such a rap upon the sconce, that down tumbled the great lumbering man-mountain, flat upon the ground. The poor little Pygmies (who really never dreamed that anybody in the world was half so strong as their brother Antæus) were a good deal dismayed at this. But no sooner was the giant down, than up he bounced again, with tenfold might, and such a furious visage as was horrible to behold. He aimed another blow at Hercules, but struck awry, being blinded with wrath, and only hit his poor innocent Mother Earth, who groaned and trembled at the stroke. His pine-tree went so deep into the ground, and stuck there so fast, that, before Antæus could get it out, Hercules brought down his club across his shoulders with a mighty thwack, which made the giant roar, as if all sorts of intolerable noises had come screeching and rumbling out of his immeasurable lungs, in that one cry! Away it went, over mountains and vallies, and, for aught I know, was heard on the other side of the African deserts.

As for the Pygmies, their capital city was laid in ruins by the concussion and vibration of the air; and, though there was uproar enough without their help, they all set up a shriek out of three million of little throats, fancying, no doubt, that they swelled the giant's bellow by at least ten times as much. Meanwhile, Antæus had scrambled upon his feet again, and pulled his pine-tree out of the earth; and, all a-flame with fury, and more outrageously strong than ever, he ran at Hercules and brought down another blow.

"This time, rascal," shouted he, "you shall not escape me!"

But, once more, Hercules warded off the stroke with his club; and the giant's pine-tree was shattered into a thousand splinters, most of which flew among the Pygmies, and did them more mischief than I like to think about. Before Antæus could get out of the way, Hercules let drive again and gave him another knock-down blow, which sent him heels over head, but served only to increase his already enormous and insufferable strength. As for his rage, there is no telling what a fiery furnace it had now got to be. His one eye was nothing but a circle of red flame. Having now no weapons but his fists, he doubled them up, (each bigger than a hogshead,) smote one against the other, and danced up and down with absolute frenzy, flourishing his immense arms about, as if he meant not merely to kill Hercules, but to smash the whole world to pieces!

"Come on!" roared this thundering giant. "Let me hit you but one box on the ear, and you'll never have the headache again!"

Now Hercules (though strong enough, as you already know, to hold the sky up) began to be sensible that he should never win the victory, if he kept on knocking Antæus down. For, by-and-by, if he hit him such hard blows, the giant would inevitably, by the help of his Mother Earth, become stronger than the mighty Hercules himself. So, throwing down his club, with which he had fought so many dreadful battles, the hero stood ready to receive his antagonist with naked arms.

"Step forward!" cried he. "Since I've broken your pine-tree, we'll try which is the better man at a wrestling-match!"

"Aha, then, I'll soon satisfy you!" shouted the giant; for, if there was one thing on which he prided himself more than another, it was his skill in wrestling. "Villain, I'll fling you where you can never pick yourself up again!"

On came Antæus, hopping and capering with the scorching heat of his rage, and getting new vigor wherewith to wreak his passion, every time he hopped. But Hercules, you must understand, was wiser than this numskull of a giant, and had thought of a way to fight him—huge, earth-born monster that he was!—and to conquer him, too, in spite of all that his Mother Earth could do for him. Watching his opportunity, as the mad giant made a rush at him, Hercules caught him round the middle with both hands, lifted him high into the air, and held him aloft overhead.

Just imagine it, my dear little friends! What a spectacle it must have been, to see this monstrous fellow sprawling in the air, face downward, kicking out his long legs and wriggling his whole vast body, like a baby when its father holds it at arm's length towards the ceiling!

But the most wonderful thing was, that, as soon as Antæus was fairly off the earth, he began to lose the vigor which he had gained by touching it. Hercules very soon perceived that his troublesome enemy was growing weaker, both because he struggled and kicked with less violence, and because the thunder of his big voice subsided into a grumble. The truth was, that, unless the giant touched Mother Earth as often as once in five minutes, not only his overgrown strength, but the very breath of his life, would depart from him. Hercules had guessed this secret; and it may be well for us all to remember it, in case we should ever have to fight a battle with a fellow like Antæus. For these earth-born creatures are only difficult to conquer on their own ground, but may easily be managed, if we can contrive to lift them into a loftier and purer region. So it proved with the poor giant, whom I am really a little sorry for, notwithstanding his uncivil way of treating strangers who came to visit him.

When his strength and breath were quite gone, Hercules gave his huge body a toss, and flung it about a mile off, where it fell heavily, and lay with no more motion than a sand-hill. It was too late for the giant's Mother Earth to help him now; and I should not wonder if his ponderous bones were lying on the same spot, to this very day, and were mistaken for those of an uncommonly large elephant.

But, alas me! what a wailing did the poor little Pygmies set up, when they saw their enormous brother treated in this terrible manner! If Hercules heard their shrieks, however, he took no notice, and perhaps fancied them only the shrill, plaintive twittering of small birds, that had been frightened from their nests by the uproar of the battle between himself and Antæus. Indeed, his thoughts had been so much taken up with the giant, that he had never once looked at the Pygmies, nor even knew that there was such a funny little nation in the world. And now, as he had travelled a good way, and was also rather weary with his exertions in the fight, he spread out his lion's skin on the ground, and reclining himself upon it, fell fast asleep.

As soon as the Pygmies saw Hercules preparing for a nap, they nodded their little heads at one another, and winked with their little eyes. And, when his deep, regular breathing gave them notice that he was asleep, they assembled together in an immense crowd, spreading over a space of about twenty-seven feet square. One of their most eloquent orators (and a valiant warrior enough, besides, though hardly so good at any other weapon as he was with his tongue) climbed upon a toad-stool, and, from that elevated position, addressed the multitude. His sentiments were pretty much as follows; or, at all events, something like this was probably the upshot of his speech.

"Tall Pygmies and mighty little-men! You and all of us have seen what a public calamity has been brought to pass, and what an insult has here been offered to the majesty of our nation. Yonder lies Antæus, our great friend and brother, slain, within our territory, by a miscreant who took him at disadvantage, and fought him (if fighting it can be called) in a way that neither man, nor giant, nor Pygmy, ever dreamed of fighting, until this hour. And, adding a grievous contumely to the wrong already done us, the miscreant has now fallen asleep, as quietly as if nothing were to be dreaded from our wrath! It behooves you, fellow-countrymen, to consider in what aspect we shall stand before the world, and what will be the verdict of impartial history, should we suffer these accumulated outrages to go unavenged.

"Antæus was our brother, born of that same beloved parent to whom we owe the thews and sinews, as well as the courageous hearts, which made him proud of our relationship. He was our faithful ally, and fell fighting as much for our national rights and immunities, as for his own personal ones. We and our forefathers have dwelt in friendship with him, and held affectionate intercourse, as man to man, through immemorial generations. You remember how often our entire people have reposed in his great shadow, and how our little ones have played at hide-and-seek in the tangles of his hair, and how his mighty footsteps have familiarly gone to-and-fro among us, and never trodden upon any of our toes. And there lies this dear brother—this sweet and amiable friend—

this brave and faithful ally—this virtuous giant—this blame-
less and excellent Antæus—dead! Dead! Silent! Powerless!
A mere mountain of clay! Forgive my tears! Nay; I behold
your own! Were we to drown the world with them, could
the world blame us?

"But, to resume! Shall we, my countrymen, suffer this
wicked stranger to depart, unharmed, and triumph in his
treacherous victory, among distant communities of the earth?
Shall we not, rather, compel him to leave his bones here on
our soil, by the side of our slain brother's bones?—so that,
while one skeleton shall remain as the everlasting monument
of our sorrow, the other shall endure as long, exhibiting to
the whole human race a terrible example of Pygmy vengeance! Such is the question! I put it to you in full confidence
of a response that shall be worthy of our national character,
and calculated to increase, rather than diminish, the glory
which our ancestors have transmitted to us, and which we
ourselves have proudly vindicated in our warfare with
the cranes."

The orator was here interrupted by a burst of irrepressible
enthusiasm; every individual Pygmy crying out that the national honor must be preserved, at all hazards. He bowed, and
making a gesture for silence, wound up his harangue in the
following admirable manner.

"It only remains for us, then, to decide whether we shall
carry on the war in our national capacity, one united people
against a common enemy—or whether some champion,
famous in former fights, shall be selected to defy the slayer
of our brother Antæus to single combat. In the latter case,
though not unconscious that there may be taller men among
you, I hereby offer myself for that enviable duty. And believe
me, dear countrymen, whether I live or die, the honor of
this great country, and the fame bequeathed us by our heroic
progenitors, shall suffer no diminution in my hands! Never,
while I can wield this sword, of which I now fling away the

scabbard! Never, never, never, even if the crimson hand, that slew the great Antæus, shall lay me prostrate, like him, on the soil which I give my life to defend!"

So saying, this valiant Pygmy drew out his weapon, (which was terrible to behold, being as long as the blade of a pen-knife,) and sent the scabbard whirling over the heads of the multitude. His speech was followed by an uproar of applause, as its patriotism and self-devotion unquestionably deserved; and the shouts and clapping of hands would have been greatly prolonged, had they not been rendered quite inaudible by a deep respiration, vulgarly called a snore, from the sleeping Hercules.

It was finally decided, that the whole nation of Pygmies should set to work to destroy Hercules; not, be it understood, from any doubt that a single champion would be capable of putting him to the sword, but because he was a public enemy, and all were desirous of sharing in the glory of his defeat. There was a debate whether the national honor did not demand, that a herald should be sent with a trumpet, to stand over the ear of Hercules, and, after blowing a blast right into it, to defy him to the combat by formal proclama-tion. But two or three venerable and sagacious Pygmies, well versed in state-affairs, gave it as their opinion that war already existed, and that it was their rightful privilege to take the enemy by surprise. Moreover, if awakened, and allowed to get upon his feet, Hercules might happen to do them a mis-chief, before he could be beaten down again. For, as these sage counsellors remarked, the stranger's club was really very big, and had rattled like a thunderbolt against the skull of Antæus. So the Pygmies resolved to set aside all foolish punctilios, and assail their antagonist at once.

Accordingly, all the fighting men of the nation took their weapons, and went boldly up to Hercules, who still lay fast asleep, little dreaming of the harm which the Pygmies meant to do him. A body of twenty thousand archers marched in front, with their little bows all ready, and the arrows on the string. The same number were ordered to clamber upon Hercules, some with spades, to dig his eyes out, and others with bundles of hay, and all manner of rubbish, with which they intended to plug up his mouth and nostrils, so that he might perish for lack of breath. These last, however, could by no means perform their appointed duty; inasmuch as the enemy's breath rushed out of his nose in an obstreperous hurricane and whirlwind, which blew the Pygmies away as fast as they came nigh. It was found necessary, therefore, to hit upon some other method of carrying on the war.

After holding a council, the captains ordered their troops to collect sticks, straws, dry weeds, and whatever combustible stuff they could find, and make a pile of it, heaping it high around the head of Hercules. As a great many thousand Pygmies were employed in this task, they soon brought together several bushels of inflammatory matter, and raised so tall a heap, that, mounting on its summit, they were quite upon a level with the sleeper's face. The archers, meanwhile, were stationed within bow-shot, with orders to let fly at Hercules, the instant that he stirred. Everything being in readiness, a torch was applied to the pile, which immediately burst into flames, and soon waxed hot enough to roast the enemy, had he but chosen to lie still. A Pygmy, you know, though so very small, might set the world on fire, just as easily as a giant could; so that this was certainly the very best way of dealing with their foe, provided they could have kept him quiet while the conflagration was going forward.

But no sooner did Hercules begin to be scorched, than up he started, with his hair in a red blaze.

"What's all this?" he cried, bewildered with sleep, and staring about him, as if he expected to see another giant.

At that moment, the twenty thousand archers twanged their bowstrings, and the arrows came whizzing, like so many winged musquitoes, right into the face of Hercules. But I doubt whether more than half-a-dozen of them punctured the skin, which was remarkably tough; as, you know, the skin of a hero has good need to be.

"Villain!" shouted all the Pygmies at once. "You have killed the giant Antæus, our great brother, and the ally of our nation. We declare bloody war against you, and will slay you on the spot!"

Surprised at the shrill piping of so many little voices, Hercules, after putting out the conflagration of his hair, gazed all roundabout, but could see nothing. At last, however, looking narrowly on the ground, he espied the innumerable assemblage of Pygmies at his feet. He stooped down, and taking up the nearest one between his thumb and finger, set him on the palm of his left hand, and held him at a proper distance for examination. It chanced to be the very identical Pygmy, who had spoken from the top of the toad-stool, and had offered himself as a champion to meet Hercules in single combat.

"What in the world, my little fellow," ejaculated Hercules, "may you be?"

"I am your enemy!" answered the valiant Pygmy, in his mightiest squeak. "You have slain the enormous Antæus, our brother by the mother's side, and, for ages, the faithful ally of our illustrious nation. We are determined to put you to death; and, for my own part, I challenge you to instant battle, on equal ground!"

Hercules was so tickled with the Pygmy's big words and warlike gestures, that he burst into a great explosion of laughter, and almost dropped the poor little mite of a creature off the palm of his hand, through the ecstasy and convulsion of his merriment.

"Upon my word," cried he, "I thought I had seen wonders before to-day;—hydras with nine heads, stags with golden horns, six-legged men, three-headed dogs, giants with furnaces in their stomachs, and nobody knows what besides! But here, on the palm of my hand, stands a wonder that outdoes them all! Your body, my little friend, is about the size of an ordinary man's finger. Pray how big may your soul be?"

"As big as your own!" said the Pygmy.

Hercules was touched with the little man's dauntless courage, and could not help acknowledging such a brotherhood with him, as one hero feels for another.

"My good little people," said he, making a low obeisance to the grand nation, "not for all the world, would I do an intentional injury to such brave fellows as you! Your hearts seem to me so exceedingly great, that, upon my honor, I marvel how your small bodies can contain them. I sue for peace, and, as a condition of it, will take five strides, and be out of your kingdom at the sixth. Good bye! I shall pick my steps carefully, for fear of treading upon some fifty of you, without knowing it. Ha, Ha, Ha! Ho, Ho, Ho! For once, Hercules acknowledges himself vanquished!"

Some writers say, that Hercules gathered up the whole race of Pygmies in his lion's skin, and carried them home to Greece, for the children of King Eurystheus to play with. But this is a mistake. He left them, one and all, within their own territory, where, for aught I can tell, their descendants are alive, to the present day, building their little houses, cultivating their little fields, spanking their little children, waging their little warfare with the cranes, doing their little business, whatever it may be, and reading their little histories of ancient times. In those histories, perhaps, it stands recorded, that, a great many centuries ago, the valiant Pygmies avenged the death of the giant Antæus, by scaring away the mighty Hercules!

THE DRAGON'S TEETH

CADMUS, Phœnix, and Cilix, the three sons of King Agenor, and their little sister Europa, (who was a very beautiful child,) were at play together, near the sea-shore, in their father's kingdom of Phœnicia. They had rambled to some distance from the palace where their parents dwelt, and were now in a verdant meadow, on one side of which lay the sea, all sparkling and dimpling in the sunshine, and murmuring gently against the beach. The three boys were very happy gathering flowers, and twining them into garlands, with which they adorned the little Europa. Seated on the grass, the child was almost hidden under an abundance of buds and blossoms, whence her rosy face peeped merrily out, and, as Cadmus said, was the prettiest of all the flowers.

Just then, there came a splendid butterfly, fluttering along the meadow; and Cadmus, Phœnix, and Cilix, set off in pursuit of it, crying out that it was a flower with wings. Europa, who was a little wearied with playing, all day long, did not chase the butterfly with her brothers, but sat still where they had left her, and closed her eyes. For a while, she listened to the pleasant murmur of the sea, which was like a voice saying "Hush!" and bidding her go to sleep. But the pretty child, if she slept at all, could not have slept more than a moment, when she heard something trample on the grass, not far from her, and peeping out from the heap of flowers, beheld a snow-white bull.

And whence could this bull have come? Europa and her brothers had been a long time playing in the meadow, and had seen no cattle nor other living thing, either there, or on the neighboring hills.

"Brother Cadmus!" cried Europa, starting up out of the midst of the roses and lilies. "Phœnix! Cilix! Where are you all? Help! Help! Come and drive away this bull!"

But her brothers were too far off to hear; especially as the fright took away Europa's voice, and hindered her from calling very loudly. So there she stood, with her pretty mouth wide open, as pale as the white lilies that were twisted among the other flowers in her garlands.

Nevertheless, it was the suddenness with which she had perceived the bull, rather than anything frightful in his appearance, that caused Europa so much alarm. On looking at him more attentively, she began to see that he was a beautiful animal, and even fancied a particularly amiable expression in his face. As for his breath, (the breath of cattle, you know, is always sweet,) it was as fragrant as if he had been grazing on no other food than rosebuds, or, at least, the most delicate of clover-blossoms. Never before did a bull have such bright and tender eyes, and such smooth horns of ivory, as this one. And the bull ran little races, and capered sportively around the child; so that she quite forgot how big and strong he was, and, from the gentleness and playfulness of his actions, soon came to consider him as innocent a creature as a pet-lamb.

Thus, frightened as she at first was, you might by-and-by have seen Europa stroking the bull's forehead with her small white hand, and taking the garlands off her own head to hang them on his neck and ivory horns. Then she pulled up some blades of grass, and he ate them out of her hand, not as if he were hungry, but because he wanted to be friends with the child, and took pleasure in eating what she had touched. Well, my stars! Was there ever such a gentle, sweet, pretty, and amiable creature, as this bull, and ever such a nice playmate for a little girl?

When the animal saw, (for the bull had so much intelligence that it is really wonderful to think of,) when he saw that Europa was no longer afraid of him, he grew overjoyed, and could hardly contain himself for delight. He frisked about the meadow, now here, now there, making sprightly leaps, with as little effort as a bird expends in hopping from twig to twig. Indeed, his motion was as light as if he were flying through the air, and his hoofs seemed hardly to leave their print in the grassy soil over which he trod. With his spotless hue, he resembled a snow-drift, wafted along by the wind. Once, he galloped so far away that Europa feared lest she might never see him again; so, setting up her childish voice, she called him back.

"Come back, pretty creature!" she cried. "Here is a nice clover-blossom!"

And then it was delightful to witness the gratitude of this amiable bull, and how he was so full of joy and thankfulness that he capered higher than ever! He came running, and bowed his head before Europa, as if he knew her to be a king's daughter, or else recognized the important truth, that a little girl is everybody's queen. And not only did the bull bend his neck. He absolutely knelt down at her feet, and made such intelligent nods, and other inviting gestures, that Europa understood what he meant, just as well as if he had put it in so many words.

"Come, dear child!"—was what he wanted to say—"Let me give you a ride on my back!"

At the first thought of such a thing, Europa drew back. But then she considered, in her wise little head, that there could be no possible harm in taking just one gallop on the back of this docile and friendly animal, who would certainly set her down, the very instant she desired it. And how it would surprise her brothers, to see her riding across the green meadow! And what merry times they might have, either taking turns for a gallop, or clambering on the gentle creature, all four children together, and careering round the field, with shouts of laughter that would be heard as far off as King Agenor's palace!

"I think I will do it!" said the child to herself.

And, indeed, why not? She cast a glance around, and caught a glimpse of Cadmus, Phœnix, and Cilix, who were still in pursuit of the butterfly, almost at the other end of the meadow. It would be the quickest way of rejoining them, to get upon the white bull's back. She came a step nearer to him, therefore; and—sociable creature that he was!—he showed so much joy at this mark of her confidence, that the child could not find in her heart to hesitate any longer. Making one bound, (for this little princess was active as a squirrel,) there sat Europa on the beautiful bull, holding an ivory horn in each hand, lest she should fall off.

"Softly, pretty bull, softly!" she said, rather frightened at what she had done. "Do not gallop too fast!"

Having got the child on his back, the animal gave a leap into the air, and came down so like a feather that Europa did not know when his hoofs touched the ground. He then began a race to that part of the flowery plain where her three brothers were, and where they had just caught their splendid butterfly. Europa screamed with delight; and Phœnix, Cilix, and Cadmus, stood gaping at the spectacle of their sister mounted on a white bull, not knowing whether to be frightened, or to wish the same good luck for themselves. The gentle and innocent creature (for who could possibly doubt that he was so?) pranced round among the children as sportively as a kitten. Europa, all the while, looked down upon her brothers, nodding and laughing, but yet with a sort of stateliness in her rosy little face. As the bull wheeled about, to take another gallop across the meadow, the child waved her hand and said "Good bye!"—playfully pretending that she was now bound on a distant journey, and might not see her brothers again for nobody could tell how long.

"Good bye!" shouted Cadmus, Phœnix, and Cilix, all in one breath.

But, together with her enjoyment of the sport, there was still a little remnant of fear in the child's heart; so that her last look at the three boys was a troubled one, and made them feel as if their dear sister were really leaving them forever. And what do you think the snowy bull did next? Why, he set off, as swift as the wind, straight down to the sea-shore, scampered across the sand, took an airy leap, and plunged right in among the foaming billows! The white spray rose in a shower over him and little Europa, and fell spattering down upon the water.

Then what a scream of terror did the poor child send forth! The three brothers screamed manfully, likewise, and ran to the shore as fast as their legs would carry them, with Cadmus at their head. But it was too late! When they reached the margin of the sand, the treacherous animal was already far away in the wide blue sea, with only his snowy head and tail emerging, and poor little Europa between them, stretching out one hand towards her dear brothers, while she grasped the bull's ivory horn with the other. And there stood Cadmus, Phœnix, and Cilix, gazing at this sad spectacle, through their tears; until they could no longer distinguish the bull's snowy head from the white-capt billows that seemed to boil up out of the sea's depths, around him. Nothing more was ever seen of the white bull; nothing more of the beautiful child!

This was a mournful story, as you may well think, for the three boys to carry home to their parents. King Agenor, their father, was the ruler of the whole country; but he loved his little daughter Europa better than his kingdom, or than all his other children, or than anything else in the world. Therefore, when Cadmus and his two brothers came crying home, and told him how that a white bull had carried off their sister, and swum with her over the sea, the king was quite beside himself with grief and rage. Although it was now twilight, and fast growing dark, he bade them set out instantly in search of her.

"Never shall you see my face again," he cried, "unless you bring me back my little Europa, to gladden me with her smiles and her pretty ways. Begone, and enter my presence no more, till you come leading her by the hand!"

As King Agenor said this, his eyes flashed fire, (for he was a very passionate king,) and he looked so terribly angry that the poor boys did not even venture to ask for their suppers, but slunk away out of the palace, and only paused on the steps, a moment, to consult whither they should go first. While they were standing there, all in dismay, their mother, Queen Telephassa, (who happened not to be by, when they told the story to the king,) came hurrying after them, and said that she, too, would go in quest of her daughter.

"Oh no, mother!" cried the boys. "The night is dark; and there is no knowing what troubles and perils we may meet with!"

"Alas, my dear children," answered poor Queen Telephassa, weeping bitterly, "that is only another reason why I should go with you! If I should lose you, too, as well as my little Europa, what would become of me!"

"And let me go, likewise!" said their playfellow Thasus, who came running to join them.

Thasus was the son of a sea-faring person, in the neighborhood; he had been brought up with the young princes, and was their intimate friend, and loved Europa very much; so they consented that he should accompany them. The whole party, therefore, set forth together. Cadmus, Phœnix, Cilix, and Thasus, clustered round Queen Telephassa, grasping her skirts, and begging her to lean upon their shoulders, whenever she felt weary. In this manner, they went down the palace-steps, and began a journey, which turned out to be a great deal longer than they dreamed of. The last that they saw of King Agenor, he came to the door, with a servant holding a torch beside him, and called after them into the gathering darkness:—

"Remember! Never ascend these steps again, without the child!"

"Never!" sobbed Queen Telephassa; and the three brothers and Thasus answered, "Never! Never! Never! Never!"

And they kept their word! Year after year, King Agenor sat in the solitude of his beautiful palace, listening in vain for their returning footsteps, hoping to hear the familiar voice of the queen, and the cheerful talk of his sons and their playfellow Thasus, entering the door together, and the sweet, childish accents of little Europa in the midst of them. But so long a time went by, that, at last, if they had really come, the king would not have known that this was the voice of Telephassa, and these the younger voices that used to make such joyful echoes, when the children were playing about the palace. We must now leave King Agenor to sit on his throne, and must go along with Queen Telephassa and her four youthful companions.

They went on and on, and travelled a long way, and passed over mountains and rivers, and sailed over seas. Here, and there, and everywhere, they made continual inquiry if any person could tell them what had become of Europa. The rustic people, of whom they asked this question, paused a little while from their labors in the field, and looked very much surprised. They thought it strange to behold a woman in the garb of a queen, (for Telephassa, in her haste, had forgotten to take off her crown and her royal robes,) roaming about the country, with four lads around her, on such an errand as this seemed to be. But nobody could give them any tidings of Europa; nobody had seen a little girl dressed like a princess, and mounted on a snow-white bull, which galloped as swiftly as the wind.

I cannot tell you how long Queen Telephassa, and Cadmus, Phœnix, and Cilix, her three sons, and Thasus, their play-fellow, went wandering along the highways and by-paths, or through the pathless wildernesses of the earth, in this manner. But, certain it is, that, before they reached any place of rest, their splendid garments were quite worn out. They all looked very much travel-stained, and would have had the dust of many countries on their shoes, if the streams, through which they waded, had not washed it all away. When they had been gone a year, Telephassa threw away her crown, because it chafed her forehead.

"It has given me many a head-ache," said the poor queen; "and it cannot cure my heart-ache!"

As fast as their princely robes got torn and tattered, they exchanged them for such mean attire as ordinary people wore. By-and-by, they came to have a wild and homeless aspect; so that you would much sooner have taken them for a gipsey family, than a queen, and three princes, and a young nobleman, who had once a palace for their home, and a train of servants to do their bidding. The four boys grew up to be tall young men, with sun-burned faces. Each of them girded on a sword, to defend themselves against the perils of the way. When the husbandmen, at whose farm-houses they sought hospitality, needed their assistance in the harvest-field, they gave it willingly; and Queen Telephassa (who had done no work, in her palace, save to braid silk threads with

golden ones) came behind them to bind the sheaves. If pay-
ment was offered, they shook their heads, and only asked
for tiding of Europa.

"There are bulls enough in my pasture," the old farmers
would reply; "but I never heard of one like this you tell
me of! A snow-white bull with a little princess on his back!
Ho! Ho! I ask your pardon, good folks; but there never was
such a sight seen hereabouts!"

At last, when his upper lip began to have the down on
it, Phœnix grew weary of rambling hither and thither, to no
purpose. So, one day, when they happened to be passing
through a pleasant and solitary tract of country, he sat himself down on a heap of moss.

"I can go no farther!" said Phœnix. "It is a mere foolish
waste of life to spend it, as we do, in always wandering up
and down, and never coming to any home at nightfall. Our
sister is lost, and never will be found. She probably perished
in the sea; or, to whatever shore the white bull may have
carried her, it is now so many years ago, that there would be
neither love nor acquaintance between us, should we meet
again. My father has forbidden us to return to his palace;
so I shall build me a hut of branches, and dwell here!"

"Well, son Phœnix," replied Telephassa, sorrowfully, "you
have grown to be a man, and must do as you judge best.
But, for my part, I will still go in quest of my poor child!"

"And we three will go along with you!" cried Cadmus and
Cilix, and their faithful friend Thasus.

But, before setting out, they all helped Phœnix to build
a habitation. When completed, it was a sweet, rural bower,
roofed overhead with an arch of living boughs. Inside, there
were two pleasant rooms, one of which had a soft heap of
moss, for a bed, while the other was furnished with a rustic
seat or two, curiously fashioned out of the crooked roots of
trees. So comfortable and home-like did it seem, that Tele-

phassa and her three companions could not help sighing, to think that they must still roam about the world, instead of spending the remainder of their lives in some such cheerful abode as they had here built for Phœnix. But, when they bade him farewell, Phœnix shed tears, and probably regretted that he was no longer to keep them company.

However, he had fixed upon an admirable place to dwell in. And, by-and-by, there came other people, who chanced to have no homes; and seeing how pleasant a spot it was, they built themselves huts in the neighborhood of Phœnix's habitation. Thus, before many years went by, a city had grown up there, in the centre of which was seen a stately palace of marble, wherein dwelt Phœnix, clothed in a purple robe, and wearing a golden crown upon his head. For the inhabitants of the new city, finding that he had royal blood in his veins, had chosen him to be their king. The very first decree of state, which King Phœnix issued, was, that, if a maiden happened to arrive in the kingdom, mounted on a snow-white bull, and calling herself Europa, his subjects should treat her with the greatest kindness and respect, and immediately bring her to the palace. You may see, by this, that Phœnix's conscience never quite ceased to trouble him, for giving up the quest of his dear sister, and sitting himself down to be comfortable, while his mother and her companions went onward.

But, often and often, at the close of a weary day's journey, did Telephassa, and Cadmus, Cilix, and Thasus, remember the pleasant spot in which they had left Phœnix. It was a sorrowful prospect for these wanderers, that, on the morrow, they must again set forth, and that, after many nightfalls, they would perhaps be no nearer the close of their toilsome pilgrimage, than now. These thoughts made them all melancholy, at times, but appeared to torment Cilix more than the rest of the party. At length, one morning, when they were taking their staffs in hand, to set out, he thus addressed them:—

"My dear mother, and you, good brother Cadmus, and my friend Thasus, methinks we are like people in a dream! There is no substance in the life which we are leading. It is such a dreary length of time since the white bull carried off my sister Europa, that I have quite forgotten how she looked, and the tones of her voice, and, indeed, almost doubt whether such a little girl ever lived in the world! And whether she once lived or no, I am convinced that she no longer survives, and that therefore it is the merest folly to waste our own lives and happiness in seeking her. Were we to find her, she would now be a woman grown, and would look upon us all as strangers. So, to tell you the truth, I have resolved to take up my abode here; and I entreat you, mother, and brother, and friend, to follow my example!"

"Not I, for one!" said Telephassa; although the poor queen, firmly as she spoke, was so travel-worn that she could hardly put her foot to the ground. "Not I, for one! In the depths of my heart, little Europa is still the rosy child, who ran to gather flowers, so many years ago. She has not grown to womanhood, nor forgotten me. At noon, at night, journeying onward, sitting down to rest, her childish voice is always in my ears, calling 'Mother! Mother!' Stop here who may, there is no repose for me!"

"Nor for me," said Cadmus, "while my dear mother pleases to go onward!"

And the faithful Thasus, too, was resolved to bear them company. They remained with Cilix a few days, however, and helped him to build a rustic bower, closely resembling the one which they had formerly built for Phœnix.

When they were bidding him farewell, Cilix burst into tears, and told his mother that it seemed just as melancholy a dream, to stay there, in solitude, as to go onward. If she really believed that they would ever find Europa, he was willing to continue the search with them, even now. But Telephassa bade him remain there, and be happy, if his own heart would let him. So the pilgrims took their leave of him, and departed, and were hardly out of sight, before some other wandering people came along that way, and saw Cilix's habitation, and were greatly delighted with the appearance of the place. There being abundance of unoccupied ground, in the neighborhood, these strangers built huts for themselves, and were soon joined by a multitude of new settlers, who quickly formed a city. In the middle of it, was seen a magnificent palace of colored marble, on the balcony of which, every noontide, appeared Cilix, in a long purple robe, and with a jewelled crown upon his head; for the inhabitants, when they found out that he was a king's son, had considered him the fittest of all men to be a king, himself.

One of the first acts of King Cilix's government was to send out an expedition, consisting of a grave ambassador and an escort of bold and hardy young men, with orders to visit the principal kingdoms of the earth, and inquire whether a young maiden had passed through those regions, galloping swiftly on a white bull. It is therefore plain to my mind, that Cilix secretly blamed himself for giving up the search for Europa, as long as he was able to put one foot before the other.

As for Telephassa, and Cadmus, and the good Thasus, it grieves me to think of them, still keeping up that weary pilgrimage! The two young men did their best for the poor queen, helping her over the rough places, often carrying her across rivulets in their faithful arms, and seeking to shelter her at nightfall, even when they themselves lay on the ground. Sad, sad it was to hear them asking of every-passer-by, if he had seen Europa, so long after the white bull had carried her away! But, though the gray years thrust themselves between, and made the child's figure dim in their remembrance, neither of these true-hearted three ever dreamed of giving up the search.

One morning, however, poor Thasus found that he had sprained his ancle, and could not possibly go a step farther.

"After a few days, to be sure," said he, mournfully, "I might make shift to hobble along with a stick. But that would only delay you, and perhaps hinder you from finding dear little Europa, after all your pains and trouble! Do you go forward, therefore, my beloved companions, and leave me to follow as I may."

"Thou hast been a true friend, dear Thasus!" said Queen Telephassa, kissing his forehead. "Being neither my son, nor the brother of our lost Europa, thou hast shown thyself truer to me and her, than Phœnix and Cilix did, whom we have left behind us. Without thy loving help, and that of my son Cadmus, my limbs could not have borne me half so far as this. Now, take thy rest, and be at peace! For—and it is the first time I have owned it to myself—I begin to question whether we shall ever find my beloved daughter, in this world!"

Saying this, the poor queen shed tears, because it was a grievous trial to the mother's heart, to confess that her hopes were growing faint. From that day forward, Cadmus noticed that she never travelled with the same alacrity of spirit that had heretofore supported her. Her weight was heavier upon his arm.

Before setting out, Cadmus helped Thasus build a bower; while Telephassa, being too infirm to give any great assistance, advised them how to fit it up and furnish it, so that it might be as comfortable as a hut of branches could. Thasus, however, did not spend all his days in this green bower. For it happened to him, as to Phœnix and Cilix, that other homeless people visited the spot, and liked it, and built themselves habitations in the neighborhood. So here, in the course of a few years, was another thriving city, with a red freestone palace in the centre of it, where Thasus sat upon a throne, doing justice to the people, with a purple robe over his shoulders, a sceptre in his hand, and a crown upon his head. The inhabitants had made him king, not for the sake of any royal blood, (for none was in his veins,) but because Thasus was an upright, true-hearted, and courageous man, and therefore fit to rule.

But, when the affairs of his kingdom were all settled, King Thasus laid aside his purple robe, and crown and sceptre, and bade his worthiest subject distribute justice to the people, in his stead. Then, grasping the pilgrim's staff that had supported him so long, he set forth again, hoping still to discover some hoof-mark of the snow-white bull; some trace of the vanished child! He returned, after a lengthened absence, and sat down wearily upon his throne. To his latest hour, nevertheless, King Thasus showed his true-hearted remembrance of Europa, by ordering that a fire should always be kept burning in his palace, and a bath steaming-hot, and food ready to be served up, and a bed with snow-white sheets, in case the maiden should arrive, and require immediate refreshment. And though Europa never came, the good Thasus had the blessings of many a poor traveller, who profited by the food and lodging which were meant for the little playmate of the king's boyhood.

Telephassa and Cadmus were now pursuing their weary way, with no companion but each other. The queen leaned heavily upon her son's arm, and could walk only a few miles a day. But, for all her weakness and weariness, she would not be persuaded to give up the search. It was enough to bring tears into the eyes of bearded men, to hear the melancholy tone with which she inquired of every stranger, whether he could tell her any news of the lost child.

"Have you seen a little girl—no, no, I mean a young maiden of full growth!—passing by this way, mounted on a snow-white bull, which gallops as swiftly as the wind?"

"We have seen no such wondrous sight!" the people would reply; and very often, taking Cadmus aside, they whispered to him, "Is this stately and sad-looking woman your mother? Surely, she is not in her right mind; and you ought to take her home, and make her comfortable, and do your best to get this dream out of her fancy!"

"It is no dream!" said Cadmus. "Everything else is a dream, save that!"

But, one day, Telephassa seemed feebler than usual, and leaned almost her whole weight on the arm of Cadmus, and walked more slowly than ever before. At last, they reached a solitary spot, where she told her son that she must needs lie down, and take a good, long rest.

"A good, long rest!" she repeated, looking Cadmus tenderly in the face. "A good, long rest, thou dearest one!"

"As long as you please, dear mother," answered Cadmus.

Telephassa bade him sit down on the turf beside her, and then she took his hand.

"My son," said she, fixing her dim eyes most lovingly upon him, "this rest, that I speak of, will be very long indeed! You must not wait till it is finished. Dear Cadmus, you do not comprehend me! You must make a grave here, and lay your mother's weary frame into it. My pilgrimage is over!"

Cadmus burst into tears, and, for a long time, refused to believe that his dear mother was now to be taken from him. But Telephassa reasoned with him, and kissed him, and, at length, made him discern that it was better for her spirit to pass away, out of the toil, the weariness, the grief, and disappointment, which had burdened her, on earth, ever since the child was lost. He therefore repressed his sorrow, and listened to her last words.

"Dearest Cadmus," said she, "thou hast been the truest son that ever mother had, and faithful, to the very last! Who else would have borne with my infirmities, as thou hast! It is owing to thy care, thou tenderest child, that my grave was not dug, long years ago, in some valley or on some hill-side, that lies far, far behind us. It is enough! Thou shalt wander no more on this hopeless search. But, when thou hast laid thy mother in the earth, then go, my son, to Delphi, and inquire of the oracle what thou shalt do next."

"Oh, mother, mother," cried Cadmus, "couldst thou but have seen my sister, before this hour!"

"It matters little, now!" answered Telephassa; and there was a smile upon her face. "I go now to the better world, and, sooner or later, shall find my daughter there!"

I will not sadden you, my little hearers, with telling how Telephassa died and was buried, but will only say, that her dying smile grew brighter, instead of vanishing from her dead face; so that Cadmus felt convinced, that, at her very first step into the better world, she had caught Europa in her arms. He planted some flowers on his mother's grave, and left them to grow there and make the place beautiful, when he should be far away.

After performing this last sorrowful duty, he set forth alone, and took the road towards the famous oracle of Delphi, as Telephassa had advised him. On his way thither, he still inquired of most people whom he met, whether they had seen Europa; for, to say the truth, Cadmus had grown so accustomed to ask the question, that it came to his lips as readily as a remark about the weather. He received various answers. Some told him one thing, and some another. Among the rest, a mariner affirmed, that, many years before, in a distant country, he had heard a rumor about a white bull, which came swimming across the sea with a child on his back, dressed up in flowers that were blighted by the sea-

water. He did not know what had become of the child or
the bull; and Cadmus suspected, indeed, by a queer twinkle
in the mariner's eyes, that he was putting a joke upon him,
and had never really heard anything about the matter.

Poor Cadmus found it more wearisome to travel alone,
than to bear all his dear mother's weight, while she had kept
him company. His heart, you will understand, was now so
heavy, that it seemed impossible, sometimes, to carry it any
farther. But his limbs were strong and active, and well accustomed to exercise. He walked swiftly along, thinking of King
Agenor, and Queen Telephassa, and his brothers, and the
friendly Thasus, all of whom he had left behind him, at
one point of his pilgrimage or another, and never expected
to see them any more. Full of these remembrances, he came
within sight of a lofty mountain, which, the people thereabouts told him, was called Parnassus. On the slope of Mount
Parnassus was the famous Delphi, whither Cadmus was going.

This Delphi was supposed to be the very midmost spot
of the whole world. The place of the oracle was a certain
cavity in the mountain-side, over which, when Cadmus came
thither, he found a rude bower of branches. It reminded him
of those which he had helped to build for Phœnix and Cilix,
and afterwards for Thasus. In later times, when multitudes
of people came, from great distances, to put questions to the
oracle, a spacious temple of marble was erected over the spot.
But, in the days of Cadmus, as I have told you, there was only
this rustic bower, with its abundance of green foliage, and a
tuft of shrubbery, that ran wild over the mysterious hole in
the hill-side.

When Cadmus had thrust a passage through the tangled
boughs, and made his way into the bower, he did not at first
discern the half-hidden cavity. But, soon, he felt a cold
stream of air rushing out of it, with so much force that it
shook the ringlets on his cheek. Pulling away the shrubbery,
which clustered over the hole, he bent forward, and spoke

in a distinct, but reverential tone, as if addressing some unseen personage, inside of the mountain.

"Sacred Oracle of Delphi," said he, "whither shall I go next, in quest of my dear sister Europa?"

There was at first a deep silence, and then a rushing sound, or a noise like a long sigh, proceeding out of the interior of the earth. This cavity, you must know, was looked upon as a sort of fountain of truth, which sometimes gushed out in audible words; although, for the most part, these words were such a riddle that they might just as well have staid at the bottom of the hole. But Cadmus was more fortunate than many others, who went to Delphi in search of truth. By-and-by, the rushing noise began to sound like articulate language. It repeated, over and over again, the following sentence, which, after all, was so like the vague whistle of a blast of air, that Cadmus really did not quite know whether it meant anything, or not:—

"Seek her no more! Seek her no more! Seek her no more!"

"What, then, shall I do?" asked Cadmus.

For, ever since he was a child you know, it had been the great object of his life to find his sister. From the very hour that he left following the butterfly, in the meadow, near his father's palace, he had done his best to follow Europa, over land and sea. And, now, if he must give up the search, he seemed to have no more business in the world.

But, again, the sighing gust of air grew into something like a hoarse voice.

"Follow the cow!" it said. "Follow the cow! Follow the cow!"

And when these words had been repeated until Cadmus was tired of hearing them, (especially as he could not imagine what cow it was, or why he was to follow her,) the gusty hole gave vent to another sentence.

"Where the stray cow lies down, there is your home!"

These words were pronounced but a single time, and died away into a whisper before Cadmus was fully satisfied that he had caught the meaning. He put other questions, but received no answer; only the gust of wind sighed continually out of the cavity, and blew the withered leaves rustling along the ground, before it.

"Did there really come any words out of the hole?" thought Cadmus. "Or have I been dreaming, all this while?"

He turned away from the oracle, and thought himself no wiser than when he came thither. Caring little what might happen to him, he took the first path that offered itself, and went along at a sluggish pace; for, having no object in view, nor any reason to go one way more than another, it would certainly have been foolish to make haste. Whenever he met anybody, the old question was at his tongue's end:—

"Have you seen a beautiful maiden, dressed like a king's daughter, and mounted on a snow-white bull, that gallops as swiftly as the wind?"

But, remembering what the oracle had said, he only half uttered the words, and then mumbled the rest indistinctly; and, from his confusion, people must have imagined that this handsome young man had lost his wits.

I know not how far Cadmus had gone, nor could he himself have told you, when, at no great distance before him, he beheld a brindled cow. She was lying down by the wayside, and quietly chewing her cud; nor did she take any notice of the young man, until he had approached pretty nigh. Then getting leisurely upon her feet, and giving her head a gentle toss, she began to move along at a moderate pace, often pausing, just long enough to crop a mouthful of grass. Cadmus loitered behind, whistling idly to himself, and scarcely noticing the cow; until the thought occurred to him, whether this could possibly be the animal, which, according to the oracle's response, was to serve him for a guide. But he smiled at himself for fancying such a thing! He could not seriously think that this was the cow, because she went along so quietly, behaving just like any other cow. Evidently, she neither knew nor cared so much as a wisp of hay about Cadmus, and was only thinking how to get her living along the wayside, where the herbage was green and fresh. Perhaps she was going home to be milked.

"Cow, cow, cow!" cried Cadmus. "Hey, Brindle, hey! Stop, my good cow!"

He wanted to come up with the cow, so as to examine her, and see if she would appear to know him, or whether there were any peculiarities to distinguish her from a thousand other cows, whose only business is to fill the milk-pail, and sometimes kick it over. But still the brindled cow trudged on, whisking her tail to keep the flies away, and taking as little notice of Cadmus as she well could. If he walked slowly, so did the cow, and seized the opportunity to graze. If he quickened his pace, the cow went just so much the faster; and once, when Cadmus tried to catch her by running, she threw out her heels, stuck her tail straight on end, and set off at a gallop, looking as queerly as cows generally do, while putting themselves to their speed.

When Cadmus saw that it was impossible to come up with her, he walked on moderately, as before. The cow, too, went leisurely on, without looking behind. Wherever the grass was greenest, there she nibbled a mouthful or two. Where a brook glistened brightly across the path, there the cow drank, and breathed a comfortable sigh, and drank again, and trudged onward, at the pace that best suited herself and Cadmus.

"I do believe," thought Cadmus, "that this may be the cow that was foretold me! If it be the one, I suppose she will lie down, somewhere hereabouts."

Whether it were the oracular cow, or some other one, it did not seem reasonable that she should travel a great way farther. So, whenever they reached a particularly pleasant spot, on a breezy hill-side, or in a sheltered vale or flowery meadow, on the shore of a calm lake, or along the bank of a clear stream, Cadmus looked eagerly around, to see if the situation would suit him for a home. But still, whether he liked the place or no, the brindled cow never offered to lie down. On she went, at the quiet pace of a cow going home-ward to the barn-yard; and, every moment, Cadmus expected to see a milkmaid approaching with a pail, or a herdsman running to head the stray animal, and turn her back towards the pasture. But no milkmaid came; no herdsman drove her back; and Cadmus followed the stray brindle, till he was almost ready to drop down with fatigue.

"Oh, brindled cow," cried he, in a tone of despair, "do you never mean to stop!"

He had now grown too intent on following her, to think of lagging behind, however long the way, and whatever might be his fatigue. Indeed, it seemed as if there were something about the animal, that bewitched people. Several persons, who happened to see the brindled cow, and Cadmus following behind, began to trudge after her, precisely as he did. Cadmus was glad of somebody to converse with, and therefore talked very freely to these good people. He told them all his adven-tures, and how he had left King Agenor in his palace, and Phœnix at one place, and Cilix at another, and Thasus at a third, and his dear mother, Queen Telephassa, under a flowery sod; so that now he was quite alone, both friendless and homeless. He mentioned, likewise, that the oracle had bidden him be guided by a cow, and inquired of the strangers, whether they supposed that this brindled animal could be the one.

"Why, 'tis a very wonderful affair!" answered one of his new companions. "I am pretty well acquainted with the ways of cattle; and I never knew a cow, of her own accord, to go so far without stopping. If my legs will let me, I'll never leave following the beast, till she lies down!"

"Nor I!" said a second.

"Nor I!" cried a third. "If she goes a hundred miles farther, I'm determined to see the end of it!"

The secret of it was, you must know, that the cow was an enchanted cow, and that, without their being conscious of it, she threw some of her enchantment over everybody that took so much as half-a-dozen steps behind her. They could not possibly help following her, though, all the time, they fancied themselves doing it of their own accord. The cow was by no means very nice in choosing her path; so that sometimes they had to scramble over rocks, or wade through mud and mire, and were all in a terribly be-draggled condition, and tired to death, and very hungry, into the bargain. What a weary business it was!

But still they kept trudging stoutly forward, and talking as they went. The strangers grew very fond of Cadmus, and resolved never to leave him, but to help him build a city, wherever the cow might lie down. In the centre of it, there should be a noble palace, in which Cadmus might dwell, and be their king, with a throne, a crown and sceptre, a purple robe, and everything else that a king ought to have; for, in him, there was the royal blood and the royal heart, and the head that knew how to rule.

While they were talking of these schemes, and beguiling the tediousness of the way with laying out the plan of the new city, one of the company happened to look at the cow.

"Joy! Joy!" cried he, clapping his hands. "Brindle is going to lie down!"

They all looked; and, sure enough, the cow had stopt, and was staring leisurely about her, as other cows do, when on the point of lying down. And slowly, slowly, did she recline herself on the soft grass, first bending her fore-legs, and then crouching her hind ones. When Cadmus and his companions came up with her, there was the brindled cow taking her ease, chewing her cud, and looking them quietly in the face; as if this was just the spot she had been seeking for, and as if it were all a matter of course!

"This, then," said Cadmus, gazing around him, "this is to be my home!"

It was a fertile and lovely plain, with great trees flinging their sun-speckled shadows over it, and hills fencing it in from the rough weather. At no great distance, they beheld a river gleaming in the sunshine. A home-feeling stole into the heart of poor Cadmus. He was very glad to know, that here he might awake in the morning, without the necessity of putting on his dusty sandals to travel farther and farther. The days and the years would pass over him, and find him still in this pleasant spot. If he could have had his brothers with him, and his friend Thasus, and could have seen his dear mother under a roof of his own, he might here have been happy, after all their disappointments. Some day or other, too, his sister Europa might have come quietly to the door of his home, and smiled round upon the familiar faces! But, indeed, since there was no hope of regaining the friends of his boyhood, or ever seeing his dear sister again, Cadmus resolved to make himself happy with these new companions, who had grown so fond of him while following the cow.

"Yes, my friends!" said he to them. "This is to be our home. Here we will build our habitations. The brindled cow, which has led us hither, will supply us with milk. We will cultivate the neighboring soil, and lead an innocent and happy life."

His companions joyfully assented to this plan; and, in the first place, being very hungry and thirsty, they looked about them for the means of providing a comfortable meal. Not far off, they saw a tuft of trees, which appeared as if there might be a spring of water beneath them. They went thither to fetch some, leaving Cadmus stretched on the ground, along with the brindled cow; for, now that he had found a place of rest, it seemed as if all the weariness of his pilgrimage, ever since he left King Agenor's palace, had fallen upon him at once. But his new friends had not long been gone, when he was suddenly startled by cries, shouts, and screams, and the noise of a terrible struggle, and, in the midst of it all, a most awful hissing, which went right through his ears like a rough saw!

Running towards the tuft of trees, he beheld the head and fiery eyes of an immense serpent or dragon, with the widest jaws that ever a dragon had, and a vast many rows of horribly sharp teeth. Before Cadmus could reach the spot, this pitiless reptile had killed his poor companions, and was busily devouring them, making but a mouthful of each man.

It appears that the fountain of water was enchanted, and that the dragon had been set to guard it, so that no mortal might ever quench his thirst there. As the neighboring inhabitants carefully avoided the spot, it was now a long time (not less than a hundred years, or thereabouts) since the monster had broken his fast; and, as was natural enough, his appetite had grown to be enormous, and was not half satisfied by the poor people whom he had just eaten up. When he caught sight of Cadmus, therefore, he set up another abominable hiss, and flung back his immense jaws, until his mouth looked like a great red cavern, at the farther end of which were seen the legs of his last victim, whom he had hardly had time to swallow.

But Cadmus was so enraged at the destruction of his friends, that he cared neither for the size of the dragon's jaws, nor for his hundreds of sharp teeth. Drawing his sword, he rushed at the monster, and flung himself right into his cavernous mouth. This bold method of attacking him took the dragon by surprise; for, in fact, Cadmus had leaped so far down into his throat, that the rows of terrible teeth could not close upon him, nor do him the least harm in the world. Thus, though the struggle was a tremendous one, and though the dragon shattered the tuft of trees into small splinters by the lashing of his tail, yet, as Cadmus was all the while slashing and stabbing at his very vitals, it was not long before the scaly wretch bethought himself of slipping away. He had not gone his length, however, when the brave Cadmus gave him a sword-thrust that finished the battle; and, creeping out of the gateway of the creature's jaws, there he beheld him, still wriggling his vast bulk, although there was no longer life enough in him to harm a little child.

But do not you suppose that it made Cadmus sorrowful, to think of the melancholy fate which had befallen those poor, friendly people, who had followed the cow along with him? It seemed as if he were doomed to lose everybody whom he loved, or to see them perish, in one way or another. And here he was, after all his toils and troubles, in a solitary place, with not a single human being to help him build a hut.

"What shall I do!" cried he aloud. "It were better for me to have been devoured by the dragon, as my poor companions were!"

"Cadmus!" said a voice—but whether it came from above or below him, or whether it spoke within his own breast, the young man could not tell—"Cadmus, pluck out the dragon's teeth, and plant them in the earth!"

This was a strange thing to do; nor was it very easy, I should imagine, to dig out all those deep-rooted fangs from the dead dragon's jaws. But Cadmus toiled and tugged, and after pounding the monstrous head almost to pieces with a great stone, he at last collected as many teeth as might have filled a bushel or two. The next thing was to plant them. This, likewise, was a tedious piece of work, especially as Cadmus was already exhausted with killing the dragon and knocking his head to pieces, and had nothing to dig the earth with, that I know of, unless it were his sword-blade. Finally, however, a sufficiently large tract of ground was turned up, and sown with this new kind of seed; although half of the dragon's teeth still remained, to be planted some other day.

Cadmus, quite out of breath, stood leaning upon his sword, and wondering what was to happen next. He had waited but a few moments, when he began to see a sight, which was as great a marvel as the most marvellous thing I ever told you about.

The sun was shining aslantwise over the field, and showed all the moist, dark soil, just like any other newly planted piece of ground. All at once, Cadmus fancied he saw something glisten very brightly, first at one spot, then at another, and then at a hundred and a thousand spots together. Soon, he perceived them to be the steel-heads of spears, sprouting up everywhere, like so many stalks of grain, and continually growing taller and taller. Next appeared a vast number of bright sword-blades, thrusting themselves up in the same way. A moment afterwards, the whole surface of the ground was broken by a multitude of polished brass helmets, coming up like a crop of enormous beans! So rapidly did they grow, that Cadmus now discerned the fierce countenance of a man, beneath every one. In short, before he had time to think what a wonderful affair it was, he beheld an abundant harvest of what looked like human beings, armed with helmets and breastplates, shields, swords, and spears; and, before they were well out of the earth, they brandished their weapons and clashed them one against another, seeming to think, little while as they had yet lived, that they had wasted too much of life without a battle. Every tooth of the dragon had produced one of these sons of deadly mischief!

Up-sprouted, also, a great many trumpeters; and, with the first breath that they drew, they put their brazen trumpets to their lips, and sounded a tremendous and ear-shattering blast;

so that the whole space, just now so quiet and solitary, reverberated with the clash and clang of arms, the bray of warlike music, and the shouts of angry men. So enraged did they all look, that Cadmus fully expected them to put the whole world to the sword. How fortunate would it be for a great conqueror, if he could get a bushel of the dragon's teeth to sow!

"Cadmus!" said the same voice which he had before heard. "Throw a stone into the midst of the armed men!"

So Cadmus seized a large stone, and flinging it into the middle of the earth-army, saw it strike the breastplate of a gigantic and fierce-looking warrior. Immediately on feeling the blow, he seemed to take it for granted that somebody had struck him; and uplifting his weapon, he smote his next neighbor a blow that cleft his helmet asunder, and stretched him on the ground. In an instant, those nearest the fallen warrior began to strike at one another with their swords, and stab with their spears. The confusion spread wider and wider. Each man smote down his brother, and was himself smitten down, before he had time to exult in his victory. The trumpeters, all the while, blew their blasts shriller and shriller; each soldier shouted a battle-cry, and often fell with it on his lips. It was the strangest spectacle of causeless wrath, and of mischief for no good end, that had ever been witnessed; but, after all, it was neither more foolish nor more wicked than a thousand battles that have since been fought, in which men have slain their brothers with just as little reason as these children of the dragon's teeth. It ought to be considered, too, that the dragon-people were made for nothing else; whereas, other mortals were born to love and help one another.

Well; this memorable battle continued to rage, until the ground was strewn with helmeted heads that had been cut off. Of all the thousands that began the fight, there were only five left standing. These now rushed from different parts of the field, and, meeting in the middle of it, clashed their swords, and struck at each other's hearts as fiercely as ever.

"Cadmus!" said the voice again. "Bid those five warriors sheathe their swords. They will help you to build the city."

Without hesitating an instant, Cadmus stepped forward, with the aspect of a king and a leader, and extending his drawn sword amongst them, spoke to the warriors in a stern and commanding voice.

"Sheathe your weapons!" said he.

And forthwith, feeling themselves bound to obey him, the five remaining sons of the dragon's teeth made him a military salute with their swords, returned them to the scabbards, and stood before Cadmus in a rank, eyeing him as soldiers eye their captain, while awaiting the word of command.

These five men had probably sprung from the biggest of the dragon's teeth, and were the boldest and strongest of the whole army. They were almost giants, indeed, and had good need to be so; else they never could have lived through so terrible a fight. They still had a very furious look, and, if Cadmus happened to glance aside, would glare at one another, with fire flashing out of their eyes. It was strange, too, to observe how the earth, out of which they had so lately grown, was incrusted, here-and-there, on their bright breastplates, and even begrimed their faces; just as you may have seen it clinging to beets and carrots, when pulled out of their native soil. Cadmus hardly knew whether to consider them as men, or some odd kind of vegetable; although, on the whole, he concluded that there was human nature in them, because they were so fond of trumpets and weapons, and so ready to shed blood.

They looked him earnestly in the face, waiting for his next order, and evidently desiring no other employment than to follow him from one battle-field to another, all over the wide world. But Cadmus was wiser than these earth-born creatures, with the dragon's fierceness in them, and knew better how to use their strength and hardihood.

"Come!" said he. "You are sturdy fellows. Make yourselves

useful! Quarry some stones with those great swords of yours, and help me to build a city!"

The five soldiers grumbled a little, and muttered that it was their business to overthrow cities, not to build them up. But Cadmus looked at them with a stern eye, and spoke to them in a tone of authority; so that they knew him for their master, and never again thought of disobeying his commands. They set to work in good earnest, and toiled so diligently, that, in a very short time, a city began to make its appearance. At first, to be sure, the workmen showed a quarrelsome disposition. Like savage beasts, they would doubtless have done one another a mischief, if Cadmus had not kept watch over them, and quelled the fierce old serpent that lurked in their hearts, when he saw it gleaming out of their wild eyes. But, in course of time, they got accustomed to honest labor, and had sense enough to feel that there was more true enjoyment in living at peace, and doing good to one's neighbor, than in striking at him with a two-edged sword. It may not be too much to hope, that the rest of mankind will by-and-by grow as wise and peaceable, as these five earth-begrimed warriors, who sprang from the dragon's teeth!

And now the city was built, and there was a home in it for each of the workmen. But the palace of Cadmus was not yet erected, because they had left it till the last, meaning to introduce all the new improvements of architecture, and make it very commodious, as well as stately and beautiful. After finishing the rest of their labors, they all went to bed betimes, in order to rise in the gray of the morning, and get at least the foundation of the edifice laid, before nightfall. But, when Cadmus arose, and took his way towards the site where the palace was to be built, followed by his five sturdy workmen, marching all in a row—what do you think he saw?

What should it be, but the most magnificent palace that had ever been seen in the world. It was built of marble, and other beautiful kinds of stone, and rose high into the air, with a splendid dome, and a portico along the front, and carved pillars, and everything else that befitted the habitation of a mighty king. It had grown up out of the earth, in almost as short a time as it had taken the armed host to spring from the dragon's teeth; and what made the matter more strange, no seed of this stately edifice had ever been planted!

When the five workmen beheld the dome, with the morning sunshine making it look golden and glorious, they gave a great shout.

"Long live King Cadmus," they cried, "in his beautiful palace!"

And the new king, with his five faithful followers at his heels, shouldering their pickaxes and marching in a rank, (for they still had a soldierlike sort of behavior, as their nature was,) ascended the palace-steps. Halting at the entrance, they gazed through a long vista of lofty pillars, that were ranged from end to end of a great hall. At the farther extremity of this hall, approaching slowly towards him, Cadmus beheld a female figure, wonderfully beautiful, and adorned with a royal robe, and a crown of diamonds over her golden ringlets, and the richest necklace that ever a queen wore. His heart thrilled with delight. He fancied it his long-lost sister Europa, now grown to womanhood, coming to make him happy, and to repay him, with her sweet sisterly affection, for all those weary wanderings in quest of her, since he left King Agenor's palace!—for the tears that he had shed, on parting with Phœnix, and Cilix, and Thasus!—for the heart-break that had made the whole world seem dismal to him, over his dear mother's grave!

But, as Cadmus advanced to meet the beautiful stranger, he saw that her features were unknown to him, although, in the little time that it required to tread along the hall, he had already felt a sympathy betwixt himself and her.

"No, Cadmus!" said the same voice that had spoken to him in the field of the armed men. "This is not that dear sister

Europa, whom you have sought so faithfully, all over the wide world. This is Harmonia, a daughter of the sky, who is given you instead of sister, and brothers, and friend, and mother. You will find all those dear ones in her alone!"

So King Cadmus dwelt in the palace, with his new friend Harmonia, and found a great deal of comfort in his magnificent abode, but would doubtless have found as much, if not more, in the humblest cottage by the wayside. Before many years went by, there was a group of rosy little children (but how they came thither, has always been a mystery to me) sporting in the great hall, and on the marble steps of the palace, and running joyfully to meet King Cadmus, when affairs of state left him at leisure to play with them. They called him father, and Queen Harmonia, mother. The five old soldiers of the dragon's teeth grew very fond of these small urchins, and were never weary of showing them how to shoulder sticks, flourish wooden swords, and march in military order, blowing a penny-trumpet, or beating an abominable rub-a-dub upon a little drum.

But King Cadmus, lest there should be too much of the dragon's tooth in his children's disposition, used to find time from his kingly duties to teach them their A.B.C.;—which he invented for their benefit, and for which many little people, I am afraid, are not half so grateful to him as they ought to be!

CIRCE'S PALACE

SOME of you have heard, no doubt, of the wise King Ulysses, and how he went to the siege of Troy, and how, after that famous city was taken and burnt, he spent ten long years in trying to get back again to his own little kingdom of Ithaca. At one time, in the course of this weary voyage, he arrived at an island that looked very green and pleasant, but the name of which was unknown to him. For, only a little while before he came thither, he had met with a terrible hurricane, or, rather, a great many hurricanes at once, which drove his fleet of vessels into a strange part of the sea, where neither himself nor any of his mariners had ever sailed. This misfortune was entirely owing to the foolish curiosity of his shipmates, who, while Ulysses lay asleep, had untied some very bulky leathern bags, in which they supposed a valuable treasure to be concealed. But, in each of these stout bags, King Æolus, the ruler of the winds, had tied up a tempest, and had given it to Ulysses to keep, in order that he might be sure of a favorable passage homeward to Ithaca; and when the strings were loosened, forth rushed the whistling blasts, like air out of a blown bladder, whitening the sea with foam, and scattering the vessels nobody could tell whither!

Immediately after escaping from this peril, a still greater one had befallen him. Scudding before the hurricane, he reached a place which, as he afterwards found, was called Læstrygonia, where some monstrous giants had eaten up many of his companions, and had sunk every one of his vessels, except that in which he himself sailed, by flinging great masses of rock at them, from the cliffs along the shore. After going through such troubles as these, you cannot wonder that King Ulysses was glad to moor his tempest-beaten bark in a quiet cove of the green island, which I began with telling you about. But he had encountered so many dangers from giants, and one-eyed Cyclopes, and monsters of the sea and land, that he could not help dreading some mischief, even in this pleasant and seemingly solitary spot. For two days, therefore, the poor weather-worn voyagers kept quiet, and either staid on board of their vessel, or merely crept along under the cliffs that bordered the shore; and, to keep themselves alive, they dug shell-fish out of the sand, and sought for any little rill of fresh water that might be running towards the sea.

Before the two days were spent, they grew very weary of this kind of life; for the followers of King Ulysses, as you will find it important to remember, were terrible gormandizers, and pretty sure to grumble if they missed their regular meals, and their irregular ones, besides. Their stock of provisions was quite exhausted, and even the shell-fish began to get scarce; so that they had now to choose between starving to death, or venturing into the interior of the island, where perhaps some huge three-headed dragon or other horrible monster had his den. Such mis-shapen creatures were very numerous, in those days; and nobody ever expected to make a voyage, or take a journey, without running more or less risk of being devoured by them.

But King Ulysses was a bold man, as well as a prudent one; and, on the third morning, he determined to discover what sort of a place the island was, and whether it were possible to obtain a supply of food for the hungry mouths of his companions. So, taking a spear in his hand, he clambered to the summit of a cliff, and gazed roundabout him. At a distance, towards the centre of the island, he beheld the stately towers of what seemed to be a palace, built of snow-white marble, and rising in the midst of a grove of lofty trees. The thick branches of these trees stretched across the front of the edifice, and more than half concealed it; although, from the portion which he saw, Ulysses judged it to be spacious and exceedingly beautiful, and probably the residence of some great nobleman or prince. A blue smoke went curling up from the chimney, and was almost the pleasantest part of the spectacle to Ulysses. For, from the abundance of this smoke, it was reasonable to conclude that there was a good fire in the kitchen, and that, at dinner time, a plentiful banquet would be served up to the inhabitants of the palace, and to whatever guests might happen to drop in.

With so agreeable a prospect before him, Ulysses fancied that he could not do better than to go straight to the palace-gate, and tell the master of it that there was a crew of poor shipwrecked mariners, not far off, who had eaten nothing, for a day or two, save a few clams and oysters, and would therefore be thankful for a little food. And the prince or nobleman must be a very stingy curmudgeon, to be sure, if, at least, when his own dinner was over, he would not bid them welcome to the broken victuals from the table!

Pleasing himself with this idea, King Ulysses had made a few steps in the direction of the palace, when there was a great twittering and chirping from the branch of a neighboring tree. A moment afterwards, a bird came flying towards him, and hovered in the air, so as almost to brush his face with its wings. It was a very pretty little bird, with purple wings and body, and yellow legs, and a circle of golden feathers round its neck, and on its head a golden tuft, which looked like a king's crown in miniature. Ulysses tried to catch the bird. But it fluttered nimbly out of his reach, still chirping in a piteous tone, as if it could have told a lamentable story, had it only been gifted with human language. And when he attempted to drive it away, the bird flew no farther than the bough of the next tree, and again came fluttering about his head, with its doleful chirp, as soon as he showed a purpose of going forward.

"Have you any thing to tell me, little bird?" asked Ulysses.

And he was ready to listen attentively to whatever the bird might communicate; for, at the siege of Troy, and elsewhere, he had known such odd things to happen, that he would not have considered it much out of the common run, had this little feathered creature talked as plainly as himself.

"Peep!" said the bird. "Peep, peep, pe—weep!"

And nothing else would it say, but only 'peep, peep, pe—weep!' in a melancholy cadence, and over and over, and over again. As often as Ulysses moved forward, however, the bird showed the greatest alarm, and did its best to drive him back, with the anxious flutter of its purple wings. Its unaccountable behavior made him conclude, at last, that the bird knew of some danger that awaited him, and which must needs be very terrible, beyond all question, since it moved even a little fowl to feel compassion for a human being. So he resolved, for the present, to return to the vessel, and tell his companions what he had seen.

This appeared to satisfy the bird. As soon as Ulysses turned back, it ran up the trunk of a tree, and began to pick insects out of the bark with its long, sharp bill; for it was a kind of woodpecker, you must know, and had to get its living in the same manner as other birds of that species. But, every little while, as it pecked at the bark of the tree, the purple bird bethought itself of some secret sorrow, and repeated its plaintive note of 'peep, peep, pe—weep!'

On his way to the shore, Ulysses had the good luck to kill a large stag by thrusting his spear into its back. Taking it on his shoulders, (for he was a remarkably strong man,) he lugged it along with him, and flung it down before his hungry companions. I have already hinted to you what gormandizers some of the comrades of King Ulysses were. From what is related of them, I reckon that their favorite diet was pork, and that they had lived upon it until a good part of their physical substance was swine's flesh, and their tempers and dispositions were very much akin to the hog. A dish of venison, however, was no unacceptable meal to them, especially after feeding so long on oysters and clams. So, beholding the dead stag, they felt of its ribs, in a knowing way, and lost no time in kindling a fire of drift-wood, to cook it. The rest of the day was spent in feasting; and if these enormous eaters got up from table, at sunset, it was only because they could not scrape another morsel off the poor animal's bones.

The next morning, their appetites were as sharp as ever. They looked at Ulysses, as if they expected him to clamber up the cliff again, and come back with another fat deer upon his shoulders. Instead of setting out, however, he summoned the whole crew together, and told them it was in vain to hope that he could kill a stag every day, for their dinner, and therefore it was advisable to think of some other mode of satisfying their hunger.

"Now," said he, "when I was on the cliff, yesterday, I discovered that this island is inhabited. At a considerable distance from the shore, stood a marble palace, which appeared to be very spacious, and had a great deal of smoke curling out of one of its chimneys."

"Aha!" muttered some of his companions, smacking their lips. "That smoke must have come from the kitchen-fire. There was a good dinner on the spit; and, no doubt, there will be as good a one, to-day!"

"But," continued the wise Ulysses, "you must remember, my good friends, our mis-adventure in the cavern of one-eyed Polyphemus, the Cyclops! Instead of his ordinary milk-diet, did he not eat up two of our comrades for his supper, and a couple more for breakfast, and two at his supper again? Methinks I see him yet, the hideous monster, scanning us with that great red eye, in the middle of his forehead, to single out the fattest! And then, again, only a few days ago, did we not fall into the hands of the king of the Læstrygons, and those other horrible giants, his subjects, who devoured a great many more of us than are now left? To tell you the truth, if we go to yonder palace, there can be no question that we shall make our appearance at the dinner-table; but whether seated as guests, or served up as food, is a point to be seriously considered."

"Either way," murmured some of the hungriest of the crew, "it will be better than starvation; particularly if one could be sure of being well fattened beforehand, and daintily cooked afterwards!"

"That is a matter of taste," said King Ulysses, "and, for my own part, neither the most careful fattening nor the daintiest of cookery would reconcile me to being dished at last. My proposal is, therefore, that we divide ourselves into two equal parties, and ascertain, by drawing lots, which of the two shall go to the palace, and beg for food and assistance. If these can be obtained, all is well. If not, and if the inhabitants prove as inhospitable as Polyphemus or the Læstrygons, then there will but half of us perish, and the remainder may set sail and escape."

As nobody objected to this scheme, Ulysses proceeded to count the whole band, and found that there were forty-six men, including himself. He then numbered off twenty-two of them, and put Eurylochus (who was one of his chief-officers, and second only to himself in sagacity) at their head. Ulysses took command of the remaining twenty-two men, in person. Then, taking off his helmet, he put two shells into it, on one of which was written, 'Go,' and on the other, 'Stay.' Another person now held the helmet, while Ulysses and Eurylochus drew out each a shell; and the word 'Go' was found written on that which Eurylochus had drawn. In this manner, it was decided that Ulysses and his twenty-two men were to remain at the sea-side, until the other party should have found out what sort of treatment they might expect, at the mysterious palace. As there was no help for it, Eurylochus immediately set forth, at the head of his twenty-two followers, who went off in a very melancholy state of mind, leaving their friends in hardly better spirits than themselves.

No sooner had they clambered up the cliff, than they discerned the tall marble towers of the palace, ascending, as white as snow, out of the lovely green shadow of the trees which surrounded it. A gush of smoke came from a chimney in the rear of the edifice. This vapor rose high in the air, and, meeting with a breeze, was wafted seaward, and made to pass over the heads of the hungry mariners. When people's appetites are keen, they have a very quick scent for anything savory in the wind.

"That smoke comes from the kitchen!" cried one of them, turning up his nose as high as he could, and snuffing eagerly. "And, as sure as I'm a half-starved vagabond, I smell roast-meat in it!"

"Pig! Roast pig!" said another. "Ah, the dainty little porker! My mouth waters for him!"

"Let us make haste," cried the others, "or we shall be too late for the good cheer!"

But scarcely had they made half-a-dozen steps from the edge of the cliff, when a bird came fluttering to meet them. It was the same pretty little bird, with the purple wings and body, the yellow legs, the golden collar round its neck, and the crown-like tuft upon its head, whose behavior had so much surprised Ulysses. It hovered about Eurylochus, and almost brushed his face with its wings.

"Peep, peep, pe—weep!" chirped the bird.

So plaintively intelligent was the sound, that it seemed as if the little creature were going to break its heart, with some mighty secret that it had to tell, and only this one poor note to tell it with.

"My pretty bird," said Eurylochus, for he was a wary person, and let no token of harm escape his notice, "my pretty bird, who sent you hither? And what is the message which you bring?"

"Peep, peep, pe—weep!" replied the bird, very sorrowfully.

Then it flew towards the edge of the cliff, and looked round at them, as if exceedingly anxious that they should return whence they came. Eurylochus and a few of the others were inclined to turn back. They could not help suspecting that the purple bird must be aware of something mischievous that would befal them, at the palace, and the knowledge of which affected its airy spirit with a human sympathy and sorrow. But the rest of the voyagers, snuffing up the smoke from the palace-kitchen, ridiculed the idea of returning to the vessel. One of them (more brutal than his fellows, and the most notorious gormandizer in the whole crew) said such a cruel and wicked thing, that I wonder the mere thought did not turn him into a wild beast, in shape, as he already was in his nature.

"This troublesome and impertinent little fowl," said he, "would make a delicate tit-bit to begin dinner with! Just one plump morsel, melting away between the teeth! If he comes within my reach, I'll catch him, and give him to the palace-cook to be roasted on a skewer!"

The words were hardly out of his mouth, before the purple bird flew away, crying 'Peep, peep, pe—weep,' more dolorously than ever.

"That bird," remarked Eurylochus, "knows more than we do about what awaits us at the palace!"

"Come on, then," cried his comrades; "and we'll soon know as much as he does!"

The party, accordingly, went onward through the green and pleasant wood. Every little while, they caught new glimpses of the marble palace, which looked more and more beautiful, the nearer they approached it. They soon entered a broad pathway, which seemed to be very neatly kept, and which went winding along, with streaks of sunshine falling across it, and specks of light quivering among the deepest shadows that fell from the lofty trees. It was bordered, too, with a great many sweet-smelling flowers, such as the mariners had never seen before. So rich and beautiful they were, that, if the shrubs grew wild here, and were native in the soil, then this island was surely the flower-garden of the whole earth; or, if transplanted from some other clime, it must have been from the Happy Islands that lay towards the golden sunset.

"There has been a great deal of pains foolishly wasted on these flowers!" observed one of the company; and I tell you what he said, that you may keep in mind what gormandizers they were. "For my part, if I were the owner of the palace, I would bid my gardener cultivate nothing but savory pot-herbs, to make a stuffing for roast-meat, or to flavor a stew with."

"Well said!" cried the others. "But, I'll warrant you, there's a kitchen garden in the rear of the palace."

At one place, they came to a crystal spring, and paused to drink at it, for want of liquor which they liked better. Looking into its bosom, they beheld their own faces dimly reflected, but so extravagantly distorted by the gush and motion of the water, that each one of them appeared to be laughing at himself and all his companions. So ridiculous were these images of themselves, indeed, that they did really laugh aloud, and could hardly be grave again as soon as they wished. And after they had drunk, they grew still merrier than before.

"It has a twang of the wine-cask in it!" said one, smacking his lips.

"Make haste!" cried his fellows. "We'll find the wine-cask itself at the palace; and that will be better than a hundred crystal fountains!"

Then they quickened their pace, and capered for joy at the thought of the savory banquet at which they hoped to be guests. But Eurylochus told them, that he felt as if he were walking in a dream.

"If I am really awake," continued he, "then, in my opinion, we are on the point of meeting with some stranger adventure than any that befel us in the cave of Polyphemus, or among the gigantic man-eating Læstrygons, or in the windy palace of King Æolus, which stands on a brazen-walled island. This kind of dreamy feeling always comes over me, before any wonderful occurrence. If you take my advice, you will turn back."

"No, no!" answered his comrades, snuffing the air, in which the scent from the palace-kitchen was now very perceptible. "We would not turn back, though we were certain that the king of the Læstrygons, as big as a mountain, would sit at the head of the table, and huge Polyphemus, the one-eyed Cyclops, at its foot!"

At length, they came within full sight of the palace, which proved to be very large and lofty, with a great number of airy pinnacles upon its roof. Though it was now mid-day, and the sun shone brightly over the marble front, yet its snowy white-ness, and its fantastic style of architecture, made it look unreal, like the frost-work on a window-pane, or like the shapes of castles which one sees among the clouds, by moonlight. But, just then, a puff of wind brought down the smoke of the kitchen-chimney among them, and caused each man to smell the odor of the dish that he liked best; and, after scenting it, they thought everything else moonshine, and nothing real save this palace, and save the banquet that was evidently ready to be served up in it.

So they hastened their steps towards the portal, but had not got half-way across the wide lawn, when a pack of lions, tigers, and wolves, came bounding to meet them. The terrified mariners started back, expecting no better fate than to be torn to pieces and devoured. To their surprise and joy, however, these wild beasts merely capered around them, wagging their tails, offering their heads to be stroked and patted, and behaving just like so many well-bred house-dogs, when they wish to express their delight at meeting their master, or their master's friends. The biggest lion licked the feet of Eurylochus; and every other lion, and every wolf and tiger, singled out one of his two-and-twenty followers, whom the beast fondled as if he loved him better than a beef-bone.

But, for all that, Eurylochus imagined that he saw something fierce and savage in their eyes; nor would he have been surprised, at any moment, to feel the big lion's terrible claws, or to see each of the tigers make a deadly spring, or each wolf leap at the throat of the man whom he had fondled. Their mildness seemed unreal, and a mere freak; but their savage nature was as true as their teeth and claws.

Nevertheless, the men went safely across the lawn, with the wild beasts frisking about them, and doing no manner of harm; although, as they mounted the steps of the palace, you might possibly have heard a low growl, particularly from the wolves; as if they thought it a pity, after all, to let the strangers pass without so much as tasting what they were made of.

Eurylochus and his followers now passed under a lofty portal, and looked through the open doorway into the interior of the palace. The first thing that they saw was a spacious hall, and a fountain in the middle of it, gushing up towards the ceiling out of a marble basin, and falling back into it with a continual plash. The water of this fountain, as it spouted upward, was constantly taking new shapes, not very distinctly, but plainly enough for a nimble fancy to recognize what they were. Now it was the shape of a man in a long robe, the fleecy whiteness of which was made out of the fountain's spray; now it was a lion, or a tiger, or a wolf, or an ass, or, as often as anything else, a hog, wallowing in the marble basin as if it were his sty. It was either magic or some very curious machinery that caused the gushing water-spout to assume all these forms. But, before the strangers had time to look closely at this wonderful sight, their attention was drawn off by a very sweet and agreeable sound. A woman's voice was singing melodiously in another room of the palace; and with her voice was mingled the noise of a loom, at which she was probably seated, weaving a rich texture of cloth, and intertwining the high and low sweetness of her voice into a rich tissue of harmony.

By-and-by, the song came to an end; and then, all at once, there were several feminine voices, talking airily and cheer-fully, with now-and-then a merry burst of laughter, such as you may always hear, when three or four young women sit at work together.

"What a sweet song that was!" exclaimed one of the voyagers.

"Too sweet, indeed!" answered Eurylochus, shaking his head. "Yet it was not so sweet as the song of the Sirens, those bird-like damsels, who wanted to tempt us on the rocks, so that our vessel might be wrecked and our bones left whitening along the shore!"

"But just listen to the pleasant voices of those maidens, and that buzz of the loom, as the shuttle passes to-and-fro!" said another comrade. "What a domestic, household, home-like sound it is! Ah, before that weary siege of Troy, I used to hear the buzzing loom and the women's voices, under my own roof! Shall I never hear them again?—nor taste those nice, little savory dishes, which my dearest wife knew how to serve up?"

"Tush! we shall fare better here," said another. "But how innocently those women are babbling together, without guessing that we overhear them! And mark that richest voice of all, so pleasant and familiar, but which yet seems to have the authority of a mistress among them! Let us show ourselves, at once. What harm can the lady of the palace and her maidens do to mariners and warriors, like us?"

"Remember," said Eurylochus, "that it was a young maiden who beguiled three of our friends into the palace of the king of the Læstrygons, who ate up one of them in the twinkling of an eye!"

No warning or persuasion, however, had any effect on his companions. They went up to a pair of folding-doors, at the farther end of the hall, and throwing them wide open, passed into the next room. Eurylochus, meanwhile, had stept behind a pillar. In the short moment, while the folding-doors opened and closed again, he caught a glimpse of a very beautiful woman rising from the loom, and coming to meet the poor weather-beaten wanderers, with a hospitable smile, and her hand stretched out in welcome. There were four other young women, who joined their hands and danced merrily forward, making gestures of obeisance to the strangers. They were only less beautiful than the lady who seemed to be their mistress. Yet Eurylochus fancied that one of them had sea-green hair, and that the close-fitting boddice of a second looked like the bark of a tree, and that both the others had something odd in their aspect; although he could not quite determine what it was, in the little while that he had to examine them.

The folding-doors swung quickly back, and left him standing behind the pillar, in the solitude of the outer hall. There Eurylochus waited until he was quite weary, and listened eagerly to every sound, but without hearing anything that could help him to guess what had become of his friends. Footsteps, it is true, seemed to be passing and re-passing, in other parts of the palace. Then there was a clatter of silver dishes, or golden ones, which made him imagine a rich feast in a splendid banquetting-hall. But, by-and-by, he heard a tremendous grunting and squealing, and then a sudden scampering, like that of small, hard hoofs over a marble floor; while the voices of the mistress and her four handmaidens were screaming all together, in tones of anger and derision. Eurylochus could not conceive what had happened, unless a drove of swine had broken into the palace, attracted by the smell of the feast. Chancing to cast his eyes at the fountain, he saw that it did not shift its shape, as formerly, nor looked either like a long-robed man, or a lion, a tiger, a wolf, or an ass. It looked like nothing but a hog, which lay wallowing in the marble basin, and filled it from brim to brim.

But we must leave the prudent Eurylochus waiting in the outer hall, and follow his friends into the inner secrecy of the palace. As soon as the beautiful woman saw them, she arose from the loom, as I have told you, and came forward, smiling, and stretching out her hand. She took the hand of the foremost among them, and bade him and the whole party welcome.

"You have been long expected, my good friends!" said she. "I and my maidens are well acquainted with you, although you do not appear to recognize us. Look at this piece of tapestry, and judge if your faces must not have been familiar to us!"

So the voyagers examined the web of cloth, which the beautiful woman had been weaving in her loom; and, to their vast astonishment, they saw their own figures perfectly represented in different-colored threads. It was a life-like picture of their recent adventures, showing them in the cave of

Polyphemus, and how they had put out his one, great, moony eye; while, in another part of the tapestry, they were untying the leathern bags, puffed out with contrary winds; and, further on, they beheld themselves scampering away from the gigantic king of the Læstrygons, who had caught one of them by the leg. Lastly, there they were, sitting on the desolate shore of this very island, hungry and downcast, and looking ruefully at the bare bones of the stag which they devoured yesterday. This was as far as the work had yet proceeded; but when the beautiful woman should again sit down at her loom, she would probably make a picture of what had since happened to the strangers, and of what was now going to happen.

"You see," she said, "that I know all about your troubles; and you cannot doubt that I desire to make you happy, for as long a time as you may remain with me. For this purpose, my honored guests, I have ordered a banquet to be prepared. Fish, fowl, and flesh, roasted, and in luscious stews, and seasoned, I trust, to all your tastes, are ready to be served up. If your appetites tell you it is dinner-time, then come with me to the festal saloon!"

At this kind invitation, the hungry mariners were quite overjoyed; and one of them, taking upon himself to be spokesman, assured their hospitable hostess that any hour of the day was dinner-time with them, whenever they could get flesh to put in the pot, and fire to boil it with. So the beautiful woman led the way; and the four maidens (one of them had sea-green hair, another a boddice of oak bark, a third sprinkled a shower of water-drops from her fingers' ends, and the fourth had some other oddity, which I have forgotten)— all these followed behind, and hurried the guests along, until they entered a magnificent saloon. It was built in a perfect oval, and lighted from a crystal dome above. Around the walls were ranged two-and-twenty thrones, overhung by canopies of crimson and gold, and provided with the softest of cushions, which were tasselled and fringed with gold cord. Each of the strangers was invited to sit down; and there they were, two-and-twenty storm-beaten mariners, in worn and tattered garb, sitting on two-and-twenty cushioned and canopied thrones, so rich and gorgeous that the proudest monarch had nothing more splendid, in his stateliest hall.

Then you might have seen the guests nodding, winking with one eye, and leaning from one throne to another, to communicate their satisfaction in hoarse whispers.

"Our good hostess has made kings of us all!" said one. "Ha! Do you smell the feast? I'll engage, it will be fit to set before two-and-twenty kings!"

"I hope," said another, "it will be, mainly, good, substantial joints, sirloins, spare-ribs, and hinder quarters, without too many kick-shaws! If I thought the good lady would not take it amiss, I should call for a fat slice of fried bacon, to begin with!"

Ah, the gluttons and gormandizers! You see how it was with them. In the loftiest seats of dignity, on royal thrones, they could think of nothing but their greedy appetite, which was the portion of their nature that they shared with wolves and swine; so that they resembled those vilest of animals far more than they did kings—if, indeed, kings were what they ought to be!

But the beautiful woman now clapt her hands; and immediately there entered a train of two-and-twenty serving-men, bringing dishes of the richest food, all hot from the kitchen-fire, and sending up such a steam that it hung like a cloud below the crystal dome of the saloon. An equal number of attendants brought great flagons of wine, of various kinds, some of which sparkled as it was poured out, and went bubbling down the throat; while, of other sorts, the purple liquor was so clear that you could see the wrought figures at the bottom of the goblet. While the servants supplied the two-and-twenty guests with food and drink, the hostess and her four maidens went from one throne to another, exhorting them to eat their fill, and to quaff wine abundantly, and thus to recompense themselves, at this one banquet, for the many days when they had gone without a dinner. But, whenever the mariners were not looking at them, (which was pretty often, as they looked chiefly into the basins and platters,) the beautiful woman and her damsels turned aside, and laughed. Even the servants, as they knelt down to present the dishes, might be seen to grin and sneer, while the guests were helping themselves to the offered dainties.

And, once in a while, the strangers seemed to taste something that they did not like.

"Here is an odd kind of a spice in this dish!" said one. "I can't say it quite suits my palate. Down it goes, however!"

"Send a good draught of wine down your throat!" said his comrade on the next throne. "That is the stuff to make this sort of cookery relish well. Though, I must needs say, the wine has a queer taste too! But the more I drink of it, the better I like the flavor."

Whatever little fault they might find with the dishes, they sat at dinner a prodigiously long while; and it would really have made you ashamed, to see how they swilled down the liquor and gobbled up the food. They sat on golden thrones, to be sure; but they behaved like pigs in a sty; and, if they had had their wits about them, they might have guessed that this was the opinion of their beautiful hostess and her maidens. It brings a blush into my face, to reckon up, in my own mind, what mountains of meat and pudding, and what gallons of wine, these two-and-twenty guzzlers and gormandizers ate and drank. They forgot all about their homes, and their wives and children, and all about Ulysses, and everything else, except this banquet, at which they wanted to keep feasting forever! But at length they began to give over, from mere incapacity to hold any more.

"That last bit of fat is too much for me!" said one.

"And I have not room for another morsel!" said his next neighbor, heaving a sigh. "What a pity. My appetite is as sharp as ever!"

In short, they all left off eating, and leaned back on their thrones, with such a stupid and helpless aspect as made them ridiculous to behold. When their hostess saw this, she laughed aloud; so did her four damsels; so did the two-and-twenty serving-men that bore the dishes, and their two-and-twenty fellows that poured out the wine. And the louder they all laughed, the more stupid and helpless did the two-and-twenty gormandizers look. Then the beautiful woman took her stand in the middle of the saloon, and stretching out a slender rod, (it had been all the while in her hand, although they never noticed it till this moment,) she turned it from one guest to another, until each had felt it pointed at himself. Beautiful as her face was, and though there was a smile on it, it looked just as wicked and mischievous as the ugliest serpent that ever was seen; and, fat-witted as the voyagers had made themselves, they began to suspect that they had fallen into the power of an evil-minded enchantress.

"Wretches," cried she, "you have abused a lady's hospitality; and, in this princely saloon, your behavior has been suited to a hog-pen! You are already swine in everything but the human form, which you disgrace, and which I myself should be ashamed to keep a moment longer, were you to share it with me. But it will require only the slightest exercise of magic, to make the exterior conform to the hoggish disposition. Assume your proper shapes, gormandizers, and begone to the sty!"

Uttering these last words, she waved her wand; and stamping her foot imperiously, each of the guests was struck aghast at beholding, instead of his comrades in human shape, one-and-twenty hogs sitting on the same number of golden thrones! Each man (as he still supposed himself to be) essayed to give a cry of surprise, but found that he could merely grunt, and that, in a word, he was just such another beast as his companions. It looked so intolerably absurd to see hogs on cushioned thrones, that they made haste to wallow down upon all-fours, like other swine. They tried to groan and beg for mercy, but forthwith emitted the most awful grunting and squealing, that ever came out of swinish throats. They would have wrung their hands in despair, but, attempting to do so, grew all the more desperate for seeing themselves squatted on their hams, and pawing the air with their fore-trotters! Dear me, what pendulous ears they had; what little red eyes, half-buried in fat; and what long snouts, instead of Grecian noses!

But, brutes as they certainly were, they yet had enough of human nature in them to be shocked at their own hideousness; and, still intending to groan, they uttered a viler grunt and squeal than before. So harsh and ear-piercing it was, that you would have fancied a butcher sticking his knife into each of their throats, or, at the very least, that somebody was pulling every hog by his funny little twist of a tail!

"Begone to your sty!" cried the enchantress, giving them some smart strokes with her wand; and then she turned to the serving-men. "Drive out these swine, and throw down some acorns for them to eat!"

The door of the saloon being flung open, the drove of hogs ran in all directions save the right one, in accordance with their hoggish perversity, but were finally driven into the back-yard of the palace. It was a sight to bring tears into one's eyes, (and I hope none of you will be cruel enough to laugh at it,) to see the poor creatures go snuffing along, picking up here a cabbage-leaf, and there a turnip-top, and rooting their noses in the earth for whatever they could find. In their sty, moreover, they behaved more piggishly than the pigs that had been born so; for they bit and snorted at one another, put their feet in the trough, and gobbled up their victuals in a ridiculous hurry; and, when there was nothing more to be had, they made a great pile of themselves among some unclean straw, and fell fast asleep. If they had any human reason left, it was just enough to keep them wondering when they should be slaughtered, and what quality of bacon they should make!

Meantime, as I told you before, Eurylochus had waited, and waited, and waited, in the entrance-hall of the palace, without being able to comprehend what had befallen his friends. At last, when the swinish uproar resounded through the palace, and when he saw the image of a hog in the marble basin, he thought it best to hasten back to the vessel, and inform the wise Ulysses of these marvellous occurrences. So he ran as fast as he could down the steps, and never stopped to draw breath till he reached the shore.

"Why do you come alone?" asked King Ulysses, as soon as he saw him. "Where are your two-and-twenty comrades?"

At these questions, Eurylochus burst into tears.

"Alas!" cried he, "I greatly fear that we shall never see one of their faces again!"

Then he told Ulysses all that had happened, as far as he knew it, and added that he suspected the beautiful woman to be a vile enchantress, and the marble palace, magnificent as it looked, to be only a dismal cavern in reality. As for his companions, he could not imagine what had become of them, unless they had been given to the swine, to be devoured alive. At this intelligence, all the voyagers were greatly affrighted. But Ulysses lost no time in girding on his sword, and hanging his bow and quiver over his shoulders, and taking a spear in his right hand. When his followers saw their wise leader making these preparations, they inquired whither he was going, and earnestly besought him not to leave them.

"You are our king," cried they; "and what is more, you are the wisest man in the whole world; and nothing but your wisdom and courage can get us out of this danger. If you desert us, and go to the enchanted palace, you will suffer the same fate as our poor companions; and not a soul of us will ever see our dear Ithaca again!"

"As I am your king," answered Ulysses, "and wiser than any of you, it is therefore the more my duty to see what has befallen our comrades, and whether anything can yet be done to rescue them. Wait for me here, until tomorrow. If I do not then return, you must hoist sail, and endeavor to find your way to our native land. For my part, I am answerable for the fate of these poor mariners, who have stood by my side in battle, and been so often drenched to the skin, along with me, by the same tempestuous surges. I will either bring them back with me, or perish!"

Had his followers dared, they would have detained him by force. But King Ulysses frowned sternly on them, and shook his spear, and bade them stop him at their peril. Seeing him so determined, they let him go, and sat down on the sand, as disconsolate a set of people as could be, waiting and praying for his return.

It happened to Ulysses, just as before, that, when he had gone a few steps from the edge of the cliff, the purple bird came fluttering towards him, crying, "Peep, peep, pe—weep!" and using all the art it could, to persuade him to go no farther.

"What mean you, little bird?" cried Ulysses. "You are arrayed like a king, in purple and gold, and wear a golden crown upon your head. Is it because I too am a king, that you desire so earnestly to speak with me? If you can talk in human language, say what you would have me do!"

"Peep!" answered the purple bird, very dolorously. "Peep, peep, pe—wee—ep!"

Certainly, there lay some heavy anguish at the little bird's heart; and it was a sorrowful predicament, that he could not, at least, have the consolation of telling what it was. But Ulysses had no time to waste in trying to get at the mystery. He therefore quickened his pace, and had gone a good way along the pleasant wood-path, when there met him a young man of very brisk and intelligent aspect, and clad in a rather singular garb. He wore a short cloak, and a sort of cap that seemed to be furnished with a pair of wings; and, from the lightness of his step, you would have supposed that there might likewise be wings on his feet. To enable him to walk still better, (for he was always on one journey or another,) he carried a winged staff, around which two serpents were wriggling and twisting. In short, I have said enough to make you guess that it was Quicksilver; and Ulysses (who knew him of old, and had learned a great deal of his wisdom from him) recognized him in a moment.

"Whither are you going in such a hurry, wise Ulysses?" asked Quicksilver. "Do you not know that this island is enchanted? The wicked enchantress (whose name is Circe, the sister of King Æetes) dwells in the marble palace, which you see yonder among the trees. By her magic arts, she changes every human being into the brute beast or fowl, whom he happens most to resemble."

"That little bird, which met me at the edge of the cliff!" exclaimed Ulysses. "Was he a human being once?"

"Yes!" answered Quicksilver. "He was once a king, named Picus, and a pretty good sort of a king too, only rather too proud of his purple robe, and his crown, and the golden chain about his neck; so he was forced to take the shape of a gaudy-feathered bird. The lions, and wolves, and tigers, who will come running to meet you, in front of the palace, were formerly fierce and cruel men, resembling in their dispositions the wild beasts, whose forms they now rightfully wear."

"And my poor companions!" said Ulysses. "Have they undergone a similar change, through the arts of this wicked Circe?"

"You well know what gormandizers they were," replied Quicksilver; and, rogue that he was, he could not help laughing at the joke. "So you will not be surprised to hear that they have all taken the shapes of swine! If Circe had never done anything worse, I really should not think her so very much to blame."

"But can I do nothing to help them?" inquired Ulysses.

"It will require all your wisdom," said Quicksilver, "and a little of my own, into the bargain, to keep your royal and sagacious self from being transformed into a fox! But, do as I bid you; and the matter may end better than it has begun."

While he was speaking, Quicksilver seemed to be in search of something; he went stooping along the ground, and soon laid his hand on a little plant with a snow-white flower, which he plucked and smelt of. Ulysses had been looking at that very spot, only just before; and it appeared to him that the plant had burst into full flower, the instant when Quicksilver touched it with his fingers.

"Take this flower, King Ulysses!" said he. "Guard it as you do your eyesight; for, I can assure you, it is exceedingly rare and precious, and you might seek the whole earth over, without ever finding another like it. Keep it in your hand, and smell of it frequently after you enter the palace, and while you are talking with the enchantress. Especially when she offers you food, or a draught of wine out of her goblet, be careful to fill your nostrils with the flower's fragrance! Follow these directions, and you may defy her magic arts to change you into a fox!"

Quicksilver then gave him some further advice how to behave, and, bidding him be bold and prudent, again assured him, that, powerful as Circe was, he would have a fair prospect of coming safely out of her enchanted palace. After listening attentively, Ulysses thanked his good friend, and resumed his way. But he had taken only a few steps, when, recollecting some other questions which he wished to ask, he turned round again, and beheld nobody on the spot where Quicksilver had stood; for that winged cap of his, and those winged shoes, with the help of the winged staff, had carried him quickly out of sight.

When Ulysses reached the lawn, in front of the palace, the lions and other savage animals came bounding to meet him, and would have fawned upon him and licked his feet. But the wise king struck at them with his long spear, and sternly bade them begone out of his path; for he knew that they had once been blood-thirsty men, and would now tear him limb from limb, instead of fawning upon him, could they do the mischief that was in their hearts. The wild beasts yelped and glared at him, and stood at a distance, while he ascended the palace steps.

On entering the hall, Ulysses saw the magic fountain in the centre of it. The up-gushing water had now again taken the shape of a man in a long, white, fleecy robe, who appeared to be making gestures of welcome. The king likewise heard the noise of the shuttle in the loom, and the sweet melody of the beautiful woman's song, and then the pleasant voices of herself and the four maidens talking together, with peals of merry laughter intermixed. But Ulysses did not waste much time in listening to the laughter or the song. He leaned his spear against one of the pillars of the hall, and then, after loosening his sword in the scabbard, stepped boldly forward, and threw the folding-doors wide open. The moment she beheld his stately figure, standing in the door-way, the beautiful woman rose from the loom and ran to meet him, with a glad smile throwing its sunshine over her face, and both her hands extended.

"Welcome, brave stranger!" cried she. "We were expecting you!"

And the nymph with the sea-green hair made a courtesy down to the ground, and likewise bade him welcome; so did her sister, with the boddice of oaken bark, and she that sprinkled dew-drops from her fingers' ends, and the fourth one, with some oddity which I cannot remember. And Circe, as the beautiful enchantress was called, (who had deluded so many persons, that she did not doubt of being able to delude Ulysses, not imagining how wise he was,) again addressed him.

"Your companions," said she, "have already been received into my palace, and have enjoyed the hospitable treatment to which the propriety of their behavior so well entitles them. If such be your pleasure, you shall first take some refreshment, and then join them in the elegant apartment which they now occupy. See! I and my maidens have been weaving their figures into this piece of tapestry."

She pointed to the web of beautifully woven cloth, in the loom. Circe and the four nymphs must have been very diligently at work, since the arrival of the mariners; for a great many yards of tapestry had now been wrought, in addition to what I before described. In this new part, Ulysses saw his two-and-twenty friends represented as sitting on cushioned and canopied thrones, greedily devouring dainties, and quaffing deep draughts of wine. The work had not yet gone any further. Oh no, indeed! The enchantress was far too cunning to let Ulysses see the mischief which her magic arts had since brought upon the gormandizers.

"As for yourself, valiant Sir," said Circe, "judging by the dignity of your aspect, I take you to be nothing less than a king. Deign to follow me, and you shall be treated as befits your rank."

So Ulysses followed her into the oval saloon, where his two-and-twenty comrades had devoured the banquet, which ended so disastrously for themselves. But, all this while, he had held the snow-white flower in his hand, and had constantly smelt of it while Circe was speaking; and as he crossed the threshold of the saloon, he took good care to inhale several long and deep snuffs of its fragrance. Instead of two-and-twenty thrones, which had before been ranged around the wall, there was now only a single throne, in the centre of the apartment. But this was surely the most magnificent seat that ever a king or an emperor reposed himself upon, all made of chased gold, studded with precious stones, with a cushion that looked like a soft heap of living roses, and overhung by a canopy of sunlight, which Circe knew how to weave into drapery. The enchantress took Ulysses by the hand, and made him sit down upon this dazzling throne. Then, clapping her hands, she summoned the chief-butler.

"Bring hither," said she, "the goblet that is set apart for kings to drink out of! And fill it with the same delicious wine which my royal brother, King Æetes, praised so highly, when he last visited me with his fair daughter Medea. That good and amiable child! Were she now here, it would delight her to see me offering this wine to my honored guest!"

But Ulysses, while the butler was gone for the wine, held the snow-white flower to his nose.

"Is it a wholesome wine?" he asked.

At this, the four maidens tittered; whereupon, the enchantress looked round at them, with an aspect of severity.

"It is the wholesomest juice that ever was squeezed out of the grape," said she; "for, instead of disguising a man, as other liquor is apt to do, it brings him to his true self, and shows him as he ought to be!"

The chief-butler liked nothing better than to see people turned into swine, or making any kind of a beast of themselves; so he made haste to bring the royal goblet, filled with a liquid as bright as gold, and which kept sparkling upward and throwing a sunny spray over the brim. But, delightfully as the wine looked, it was mingled with the most potent enchantments that Circe knew how to concoct. For every drop of the pure grape-juice, there were two drops of the pure mischief; and the danger of the thing was, that the mischief made it taste all the better. The mere smell of the bubbles, which effervesced at the brim, was enough to turn a man's beard into pig's bristles, or make a lion's claws grow out of his fingers, or a fox's brush behind him!

"Drink, my noble guest!" said Circe, smiling as she presented him with the goblet. "You will find in this draught a solace for all your troubles!"

King Ulysses took the goblet with his right hand, while, with his left, he held the snow-white flower to his nostrils, and drew in so long a breath that his lungs were quite filled with its pure and simple fragrance. Then, drinking off all the wine, he looked the enchantress calmly in the face.

"Wretch," cried Circe, giving him a smart stroke with her wand, "how dare you keep your human shape a moment longer? Take the form of the brute whom you most resemble! If a hog, go join your fellow-swine in the sty; if a lion, a wolf, a tiger, go howl with the wild beasts on the lawn; if a fox, go exercise your craft in stealing poultry! Thou hast quaffed off my wine, and canst be man no longer!"

But, such was the virtue of the snow-white flower, instead of wallowing down from his throne in swinish shape, or taking any other brutal form, Ulysses looked even more manly and kinglike than before. He gave the magic goblet a toss, and sent it clashing over the marble floor, to the farthest end of the saloon. Then drawing his sword, he seized the enchantress by her beautiful ringlets, and made a gesture as if he meant to strike off her head at one blow.

"Wicked Circe," cried he, in a terrible voice, "this sword shall put an end to thy enchantments! Thou shalt die, vile witch, and do no more mischief in the world, by tempting human beings into the vices which make beasts of them!"

The tone and countenance of Ulysses were so awful, and his sword gleamed so brightly, and seemed to have so intolerably keen an edge, that Circe was almost killed by the mere fright, without waiting for a blow. The chief-butler scrambled out of the saloon, picking up the golden goblet as he went; and the enchantress and the four maidens fell on their knees, wringing their hands and screaming for mercy.

"Spare me!" cried Circe. "Spare me, royal and wise Ulysses! For now I know that thou art he of whom Quicksilver forewarned me, the most prudent of mortals, against whom no enchantments can prevail. Thou only couldst have conquered Circe! Spare me, wisest of men! I will show thee true hospitality, and even give myself to be thy slave, and this magnificent palace to be henceforth thy home!"

The four nymphs, meanwhile, were making a most piteous ado; and especially the ocean-nymph, with the sea-green hair, wept a great deal of salt-water, and the fountain-nymph, besides scattering dew-drops from her fingers' ends, nearly melted away into tears. But Ulysses would not be pacified, until Circe had taken a solemn oath to change back his companions, and as many others as he should direct, from their present forms of beast or bird, into their former shapes of men.

"On these conditions," said he, "I consent to spare your life. Otherwise, you must die upon the spot!"

With a drawn sword hanging over her, the enchantress would readily have consented to do as much good as she had hitherto done mischief, however little she might like such employment. She therefore led Ulysses out of the back-entrance of the palace, and showed him the swine in their sty. There were about fifty of these unclean beasts, in the whole herd; and though the greater part were hogs by birth and education, there was wonderfully little difference to be seen betwixt them and their new brethren, who had so recently worn the human shape. To speak critically, indeed, the latter rather carried the thing to excess, and seemed to make it a point to wallow in the miriest part of the sty, and otherwise to outdo the original swine in their own natural vocation. When men once turn to brutes, the trifle of man's wit, that remains in them, adds tenfold to their brutality.

The comrades of Ulysses, however, had not quite lost the remembrance of having formerly stood erect. When he approached the sty, two-and-twenty enormous swine separated themselves from the herd, and scampered towards him, with such a chorus of horrible squealing as made him clap both hands to his ears. And yet they did not seem to know what they wanted, nor whether they were merely hungry, or miserable from some other cause. It was curious, in the midst of their distress, to observe them thrusting their noses into the mire, in quest of something to eat. The nymph with the boddice of oaken bark (she was the hamadryad of an oak) threw a handful of acorns among them; and the two-and-twenty hogs scrambled and fought for the prize, as if they had tasted not so much as a noggin of sour milk for a twelvemonth.

"These must certainly be my comrades," said Ulysses. "I recognize their dispositions. They are hardly worth the trouble of changing them into the human form again. Nevertheless, we will have it done, lest their bad example should corrupt the other hogs! Let them take their original shapes, therefore, Dame Circe, if your skill is equal to the task. It will require greater magic, I trow, than it did to make swine of them!"

So Circe waved her wand again, and repeated a few magic words, at the sound of which the two-and-twenty hogs pricked up their pendulous ears. It was a wonder to behold how their snouts grew shorter and shorter, and their mouths (which they seemed to be sorry for, because they could not gobble so expeditiously) smaller and smaller, and how one and another began to stand upon his hind-legs, and scratch his nose with his fore-trotters! At first, the spectators hardly knew whether to call them hogs or men, but, by-and-by, came to the conclusion that they rather resembled the latter. Finally, there stood the twenty-two comrades of Ulysses, looking pretty much the same as when they left the vessel.

You must not imagine, however, that the swinish quality had entirely gone out of them. When once it fastens itself into a person's character, it is very difficult getting rid of it. This was proved by the hamadryad, who, being exceedingly fond of mischief, threw another handful of acorns before the twenty-two newly restored people; whereupon, down they wallowed, in a moment, and gobbled them up in a very shameful way. Then, recollecting themselves, they scrambled to their feet, and looked more than commonly foolish.

"Thanks, noble Ulysses!" they cried. "From brute beasts, you have restored us to the condition of men again!"

"Do not put yourselves to the trouble of thanking me," said the wise king. "I fear I have done but little for you!"

To say the truth, there was a suspicious kind of a grunt in their voices, and, for a long time afterwards, they spoke gruffly, and were apt to set up a squeal.

"It must depend on your own future behavior," added Ulysses, "whether you do not find your way back to the sty!"

At this moment, the note of a bird sounded from the branch of a neighboring tree.

"Peep, peep, pe—wee—ep!"

It was the purple bird, who, all this while, had been sitting over their heads, watching what was going forward, and hoping that Ulysses would remember how he had done his utmost to keep him and his followers out of harm's way. Ulysses ordered Circe instantly to make a king of this good little fowl, and leave him exactly as she found him. Hardly were the words spoken, and before the bird had time to utter another 'pe—weep,' King Picus leaped down from the bough of the tree, as majestic a sovereign as any in the world, dressed in a long purple robe and gorgeous yellow stockings, with a splendidly wrought collar about his neck, and a golden crown upon his head. He and King Ulysses exchanged with one another the courtesies which belong to their elevated rank. But, from that time forth, King Picus was no longer proud of his crown and his trappings of royalty, nor of the fact of his being a king; he felt himself merely the upper servant of his people, and that it must be his life-long labor to make them better and happier.

As for the lions, tigers, and wolves, (though Circe would have restored them to their former shapes, at his slightest word,) Ulysses thought it advisable that they should remain as they now were, and thus give warning of their cruel dispositions; instead of going about under the guise of men, and pretending to human sympathies, while their hearts had the blood-thirstiness of wild beasts. So he let them howl as much as they liked, but never troubled his head about them. And, when everything was settled according to his pleasure, he sent to summon the remainder of his comrades, whom he had left at the sea-shore. These being arrived, with the prudent Eurylochus at their head, they all made themselves comfortable in Circe's enchanted palace, until quite rested and refreshed from the toils and hardships of their voyage.

THE POMEGRANATE-SEEDS

MOTHER CERES was exceedingly fond of her daughter Proserpina, and seldom let her go alone into the fields. But, just at the time when my story begins, the good lady was very busy, because she had the care of the wheat, and the Indian corn, and the rye and barley, and, in short, of the crops of every kind, all over the earth; and as the season had thus far been uncommonly backward, it was necessary to make the harvest ripen more speedily than usual. So she put on her turban, made of poppies, (a kind of flower which she was always noted for wearing,) and got into her car, drawn by a pair of winged dragons, and was just ready to set off.

"Dear mother," said Proserpina, "I shall be very lonely, while you are away. May I not run down to the shore, and ask some of the sea-nymphs to come up out of the waves and play with me?"

"Yes, child," answered Mother Ceres. "The sea-nymphs are good creatures, and will never lead you into any harm. But you must take care not to stray away from them, nor go wandering about the fields by yourself. Young girls, without their mothers to take care of them, are very apt to get into mischief."

The child promised to be as prudent as if she were a grown-up woman; and, by the time the winged dragons had whirled the car out of sight, she was already on the shore, calling to the sea-nymphs to come and play with her. They knew Proserpina's voice, and were not long in showing their glistening faces and sea-green hair above the water, at the bottom of which was their home. They brought along with them a great many beautiful shells; and sitting down on the moist sand, where the surf-wave broke over them, they busied themselves in making a necklace, which they hung round Proserpina's neck. By way of showing her gratitude, the child besought them to go with her a little way into the fields, so that they might gather abundance of flowers, with which she would make each of her kind playmates a wreath.

"Oh no, dear Proserpina," cried the sea-nymphs, "we dare not go with you upon the dry land. We are apt to grow faint, unless, at every breath, we can snuff up the salt breeze of the ocean. And don't you see how careful we are to let the surf-wave break over us, every moment or two, so as to keep ourselves comfortably moist. If it were not for that, we should soon look like bunches of uprooted sea-weed, dried in the sun!"

"It is a great pity!" said Proserpina. "But do you wait for me here, and I will run and gather my apronful of flowers, and be back again before the surf-wave has broken ten times over you. I long to make you some wreaths that shall be as lovely as this necklace of many-colored shells."

"We will wait, then," answered the sea-nymphs. "But, while you are gone, we may as well lie down on a bank of soft sponge, under the water. The air to-day is a little too dry for our comfort. But we will pop up our heads, every few minutes, to see if you are coming."

The young Proserpina ran quickly to a spot, where, only the day before, she had seen a great many flowers. These, however, were now a little past their bloom; and, wishing to give her friends the freshest and loveliest blossoms, she strayed farther into the fields, and found some that made her scream with delight. Never had she met with such exquisite flowers before—violets so large and fragrant—roses, with so rich and delicate a blush—such superb hyacinths and such aromatic pinks—and many others, some of which seemed to be of new shapes and colors. Two or three times, moreover, she could not help thinking that a tuft of most splendid flowers had suddenly sprouted out of the earth, before her very eyes, as if on purpose to tempt her a few steps farther. Proserpina's apron was soon filled and brimming over with delightful blossoms. She was on the point of turning back, in order to rejoin the sea-nymphs and sit with them on the moist sands, all twining wreaths together. But, a little farther on, what should she behold? It was a large shrub, completely covered with the most magnificent flowers in the world!

"The darlings!" cried Proserpina; and then she thought to herself, "I was looking at that spot, only a moment ago. How strange it is that I did not see the flowers!"

The nearer she approached the shrub, the more attractive it looked, until she came quite close to it; and then, although its beauty was richer than words can tell, she hardly knew whether to like it or not. It bore above a hundred flowers, of the most brilliant hues, and each different from the others, but all having a kind of resemblance among themselves, which showed them to be sister-blossoms. But there was a deep, glossy lustre on the leaves of the shrub, and on the petals of the flowers, that made Proserpina doubt whether they might not be poisonous. To tell you the truth, foolish as it may seem, she was half-inclined to turn round and run away.

"What a silly child I am!" thought she, taking courage. "It is really the most beautiful shrub that ever sprang out of the earth. I will pull it up by the roots, and carry it home, and plant it in my mother's garden."

Holding up her apronful of flowers with her left hand, Proserpina seized the large shrub with the other, and pulled, and pulled, but was hardly able to loosen the soil about its roots. What a deep-rooted plant it was! Again the girl pulled, with all her might, and observed that the earth began to stir and crack, to some distance around the stem. She gave another pull, but relaxed her hold, fancying that there was a rumbling sound right beneath her feet. Did the roots extend down into some enchanted cavern? Then, laughing at herself for so childish a notion, she made another effort—up came the shrub!—and Proserpina staggered back, holding the stem triumphantly in her hand, and gazing at the deep hole which its roots had left in the soil.

Much to her astonishment, this hole kept spreading wider and wider, and growing deeper and deeper, until it really seemed to have no bottom; and, all the while, there came a rumbling noise out of its depths, louder and louder, and nearer and nearer, and sounding like the tramp of horses' hoofs and the rattling of wheels. Too much frightened to run away, she stood straining her eyes into this wonderful cavity, and soon saw a team of four sable horses, snorting smoke out of their nostrils and tearing their way out of the earth, with a splendid golden chariot whirling at their heels. They leaped out of the bottomless hole, chariot and all; and there they were, tossing their black manes, flourishing their black tails, and curvetting with every one of their hoofs off the ground at once, close by the spot where Proserpina stood. In the chariot sat the figure of a man, richly dressed, with a crown on his head, all flaming with diamonds. He was of a noble aspect, and rather handsome, but looked sullen and discontented; and he kept rubbing his eyes and shading them with his hand, as if he did not live enough in the sunshine to be very fond of its light.

As soon as this personage saw the affrighted Proserpina, he beckoned her to come a little nearer.

"Do not be afraid!" said he, with as cheerful a smile as he knew how to put on. "Come! Will not you like to ride a little way with me, in my beautiful chariot?"

But Proserpina was so alarmed, that she wished for nothing but to get out of his reach. And no wonder! The stranger did not look remarkably good-natured, in spite of his smile; and as for his voice, its tones were deep and stern, and sounded as much like the rumbling of an earthquake, under ground, as anything else. As is always the case with children in trouble, Proserpina's first thought was to call for her mother.

"Mother! Mother Ceres!" cried she, all in a tremble. "Come quickly and save me!"

But her voice was too faint for her mother to hear. Indeed, it is most probable that Ceres was then a thousand miles off, making the corn grow, in some far distant country. Nor could it have availed her poor daughter, even had she been within hearing; for no sooner did Proserpina begin to cry out, than the stranger leaped to the ground, caught the child in his arms, and again mounting the chariot, shook the reins, and shouted to the four black horses to set off. They immediately broke into so swift a gallop, that it seemed rather like flying through the air than running along the earth. In a moment, Proserpina lost sight of the pleasant vale of Enna, in which she had always dwelt. Another instant; and even the summit of Mount Ætna, had become so blue in the distance, that she could scarcely distinguish it from the smoke that gushed out of its crater. But still the poor child screamed, and scattered her apronful of flowers along the way, and left a long cry trailing behind the chariot; and many mothers, to whose ears it came, ran quickly to see if any mischief had befallen their children. But Mother Ceres was a great way off, and could not hear the cry.

As they rode on, the stranger did his best to soothe her.

"Why should you be so frightened, my pretty child?" said he, trying to soften his rough voice. "I promise not to do you any harm. What! You have been gathering flowers? Wait till we come to my palace, and I will give you a garden full of prettier flowers than those, all made of pearls, and diamonds, and rubies. Can you guess who I am? They call my name Pluto; and I am the king of diamonds and all other precious stones. Every atom of the gold and silver, that lies under the earth, belongs to me, to say nothing of the copper and iron, and of the coal-mines, which supply me with abundance of fuel. Do you see this splendid crown upon my head? You may have it for a plaything! Oh, we shall be very good friends, and you will find me more agreeable than you expect, when once we get out of this troublesome sunshine!"

"Let me go home!" cried Proserpina. "Let me go home!"

"My home is better than your mother's," answered King Pluto. "It is a palace, all made of gold, with crystal windows; and because there is little or no sunshine thereabouts, the apartments are illuminated with diamond lamps. You never saw anything half so magnificent as my throne. If you like, you may sit down on it, and be my little queen, and I will sit on the footstool."

"I don't care for golden palaces and thrones," sobbed Proserpina. "Oh, my mother, my mother! Carry me back to my mother!"

But King Pluto, as he called himself, only shouted to his steeds to go faster.

"Pray do not be foolish, Proserpina," said he, in rather a sullen tone. "I offer you my palace, and my crown, and all the riches that are under the earth; and you treat me as if I were doing you an injury! The one thing which my palace needs is a merry little maid, to run up stairs and down, and cheer up the rooms with her smile. And this is what you must do for King Pluto!"

"Never!" answered Proserpina, looking as miserable as she could. "I shall never smile again, till you set me down at my mother's door."

But she might just as well have talked to the wind that whistled past them; for Pluto urged on his horses, and went faster than ever. Proserpina continued to cry out, and screamed so long and so loudly, that her poor little voice was almost screamed away; and when it was nothing but a whisper, she happened to cast her eyes over a great, broad field of waving grain—and whom do you think she saw? Who, but Mother Ceres, making the corn grow, and too busy to notice the golden chariot as it went rattling along! The child mustered all her strength, and gave one more scream, but was out of sight before Ceres had time to turn her head.

King Pluto had taken a road which now began to grow excessively gloomy. It was bordered on each side with rocks and precipices, between which the rumbling of the chariot-wheels was reverberated, with a noise like rolling thunder. The trees and bushes, that grew in the crevices of the rocks, had very dismal foliage; and, by-and-by, although it was hardly noon, the air became obscured with a gray twilight. The black horses had rushed along so swiftly, that they were already beyond the limits of the sunshine. But the duskier it grew, the more did Pluto's visage assume an air of satisfaction. After all, he was not an ill-looking person, especially when he left off twisting his features into a smile that did not belong to them. Proserpina peeped at his face, through the gathering dusk, and hoped that he might not be so very wicked as she at first thought him.

"Ah, this twilight is truly refreshing," said King Pluto, "after being so tormented with that ugly and impertinent glare of the sun! How much more agreeable is lamplight or torchlight, more particularly when reflected from diamonds! It will be a magnificent sight, when we get to my palace."

"Is it much farther?" asked Proserpina. "And will you carry me back, when I have seen it?"

"We will talk of that, by-and-by," answered Pluto. "We are just entering my dominions. Do you see that tall gateway before us? When we pass those gates, we are at home. And there lies my faithful mastiff at the threshold. Cerberus! Cerberus! Come hither, my good dog!"

So saying, Pluto pulled at the reins, and stopt the chariot right between the tall, massive pillars of the gateway. The mastiff, of which he had spoken, got up from the threshold, and stood on his hinder legs, so as to put his fore-paws on the chariot-wheel. But, my stars, what a strange dog it was! Why, he was a big, rough, ugly-looking monster, with three separate heads, and each of them fiercer than the two others; but, fierce as they were, King Pluto patted them all. He seemed as fond of his three-headed dog, as if it had been a sweet little spaniel, with silken ears and curly hair. Cerberus, on the other hand, was evidently rejoiced to see his master, and expressed his attachment, as other dogs do, by wagging his tail at a great rate. Proserpina's eyes being drawn to it by its brisk motion, she saw that this tail was neither more nor less than a live dragon, with fiery eyes, and fangs that had a very poisonous aspect. And, while the three-headed Cerberus was fawning so lovingly on King Pluto, there was the dragon-tail wagging against its will, and looking as cross and ill-natured as you can imagine, on its own separate account!

"Will the dog bite me?" asked Proserpina, shrinking closer to Pluto. "What an ugly creature he is!"

"Oh, never fear!" answered her companion. "He never harms people, unless they try to enter my dominions without being sent for, or to get away when I wish to keep them here. Down, Cerberus! Now, my pretty Proserpina, we will drive on."

On went the chariot; and King Pluto seemed greatly pleased to find himself once more in his own kingdom. He drew Proserpina's attention to the rich veins of gold that were to be seen among the rocks, and pointed to several places, where one stroke of a pickaxe would loosen a bushel of diamonds. All along the road, indeed, there were sparkling gems, which would have been of inestimable value, above ground, but which here were reckoned of the meaner sort, and hardly worth a beggar's stooping for.

Not far from the gateway, they came to a bridge, which seemed to be built of iron. Pluto stopt the chariot, and bade Proserpina look at the stream which was gliding so lazily beneath it. Never in her life had she beheld so torpid, so black, so muddy-looking a stream; its waters reflected no images of anything that was on the banks; and it moved as sluggishly as if it had quite forgotten which way it ought to flow, and had rather stagnate than flow either one way or the other.

"This is the river Lethe," observed King Pluto. "Is it not a very pleasant stream?"

"I think it a very dismal one," said Proserpina.

"It suits my taste, however," answered Pluto, who was apt to be sullen when anybody disagreed with him. "At all events, its water has one very excellent quality; for a single draught of it makes people forget every care and sorrow that has hitherto tormented them. Only sip a little of it, my dear Proserpina; and you will instantly cease to grieve for your mother, and will have nothing in your memory that can prevent your being perfectly happy in my palace. I will send for some, in a golden goblet, the moment we arrive."

"Oh, no, no, no!" cried Proserpina, weeping afresh. "I had a thousand times rather be miserable with remembering my mother, than be happy in forgetting her. That dear, dear mother! I never, never will forget her!"

"We shall see," said King Pluto. "You do not know what fine times we will have in my palace. Here we are just at the portal. These pillars are solid gold, I assure you!"

He alighted from the chariot, and taking Proserpina in his arms, carried her up a lofty flight of steps into the great hall of the palace. It was splendidly illuminated by means of large precious stones, of various hues, which seemed to burn like so many lamps, and glowed with a hundred-fold radiance all through the vast apartment. And yet there was a kind of gloom in the midst of this enchanted light; nor was there a single object in the hall that was really agreeable to behold, except the little Proserpina herself, a lovely child, with one earthly flower which she had not let fall from her hand. It is my opinion that even King Pluto had never been happy in his palace, and that this was the true reason why he had stolen away Proserpina, in order that he might have something to love, instead of cheating his heart any longer with this tiresome magnificence. And, though he pretended to dislike the sunshine of the upper world, yet the effect of the child's presence, bedimmed as she was by her tears, was as if a faint and watery sunbeam had somehow or other found its way into the enchanted hall.

Pluto now summoned his domestics, and bade them lose no time in preparing a most sumptuous banquet, and, above all things, not to fail of setting a golden beaker of the water of Lethe by Proserpina's plate.

"I will neither drink that, nor anything else," said Proserpina. "Nor will I taste a morsel of food, even if you keep me forever in your palace!"

"I should be sorry for that," replied King Pluto, patting her cheek; for he really wished to be kind, if he had only known how. "You are a spoilt child, I perceive, my little Proserpina; but when you see the nice things which my cook will make for you, your appetite will quickly come again!"

Then, sending for the head-cook, he gave strict orders that all sorts of delicacies, such as young people are usually fond of, should be set before Proserpina. He had a secret motive in this; for, you are to understand, it is a fixed law, that, when persons are carried off to the land of magic, if they once taste any food there, they can never get back to their friends. Now, if King Pluto had been cunning enough to offer Proserpina some fruit, or bread and milk, (which was the simple fare to which the child had always been accustomed,) it is very probable that she would soon have been tempted to eat it. But he left the matter entirely to his cook, who, like all other cooks, considered nothing fit to eat unless it were rich pastry, or highly seasoned meat, or spiced sweet-cakes—things which Proserpina's mother had never given her, and the smell of which quite took away her appetite, instead of sharpening it.

But my story must now clamber out of King Pluto's dominions, and see what Mother Ceres has been about, since she was bereft of her daughter. We had a glimpse of her, as you remember, half-hidden among the waving grain, while the four black steeds were swiftly whirling along the chariot, in which her beloved Proserpina was so unwillingly borne away. You recollect, too, the loud scream which Proserpina gave, just when the chariot was out of sight.

Of all the child's outcries, this last shriek was the only one that reached the ears of Mother Ceres. She had mistaken the rumbling of the chariot-wheels for a peal of thunder, and imagined that a shower was coming up, and that it would assist her in making the corn grow. But, at the sound of Proserpina's shriek, she started, and looked about in every direction, not knowing whence it came, but feeling almost certain that it was her daughter's voice. It seemed so unaccountable, however, that the girl should have strayed over so many lands and seas, (which she herself could not have traversed without the aid of her winged dragons,) that the good Ceres tried to believe that it must be the child of some other parent, and not her own darling Proserpina, who had uttered this lamentable cry. Nevertheless, it troubled her with a vast many tender fears, such as are ready to bestir themselves in every mother's heart, when she finds it necessary to go away from her dear children without leaving them under the care of some maiden-aunt, or other such faithful guardian. So she quickly left the field in which she had been so busy; and, as her work was not half done, the grain looked, next day, as if it needed both sun and rain, and as if it were blighted in the ear and had something the matter with its roots.

The pair of dragons must have had very nimble wings; for, in less than an hour, Mother Ceres had alighted at the door of her home, and found it empty! Knowing, however, that the child was fond of sporting on the sea-shore, she hastened thither as fast as she could, and there beheld the wet faces of the poor sea-nymphs peeping over a wave. All this while, the good creatures had been waiting on the bank of sponge, and, once every half-minute or so, had popt up their four heads above water, to see if their playmate were yet coming back. When they saw Mother Ceres, they sat down on the crest of the surf-wave, and let it toss them ashore at her feet.

"Where is Proserpina?" cried Ceres. "Where is my child? Tell me, you naughty sea-nymphs, have you enticed her under the sea?"

"Oh no, good Mother Ceres!" said the innocent sea-nymphs, tossing back their green ringlets and looking her in the face. "We never should dream of such a thing. Proserpina has been at play with us, it is true; but she left us a long while ago, meaning only to run a little way upon the dry land, and gather some flowers for a wreath. This was early in the day, and we have seen nothing of her since!"

Ceres scarcely waited to hear what the nymphs had to say, before she hurried off to make inquiries all through the neighborhood. But nobody told her anything that could enable the poor mother to guess what had become of Proserpina. A fisherman, it is true, had noticed her little footprints in the sand, as he went homeward along the beach with a basket of fish; a rustic had seen the child stooping to gather flowers; several persons had heard either the rattling of chariot-wheels, or the rumbling of distant thunder; and one old woman, while plucking vervain and catnip, had heard a scream, but supposed it to be some childish nonsense, and therefore did not take the trouble to look up. The stupid people! It took them such a tedious while to tell the nothing that they knew, that it was dark night before Mother Ceres found out that she must seek her daughter elsewhere. So she lighted a torch and set forth, resolving never to come back until Proserpina was discovered.

In her haste and trouble of mind, she quite forgot her car and the winged dragons; or, it may be, she thought that she could follow up the search more thoroughly, on foot. At all events, this was the way in which she began her sorrowful journey, holding her torch before her, and looking carefully at every object along the path. And, as it happened, she had not gone far, before she found one of the magnificent flowers which grew on the shrub, that Proserpina had pulled up.

"Ha!" thought Mother Ceres, examining it by torchlight. "Here is mischief in this flower! The earth did not produce it by any help of mine, nor of its own accord. It is the work of enchantment, and is therefore poisonous; and perhaps it has poisoned my poor child!"

But she put the poisonous flower in her bosom, not knowing whether she might ever find any other memorial of Proserpina.

All night long, at the door of every cottage and farmhouse, Ceres knocked, and called up the weary laborers to inquire if they had seen her child; and they stood, gaping and half-asleep, at the threshold, and answered her pityingly, and besought her to come in and rest. At the portal of every palace, too, she made so loud a summons that the menials hurried to throw open the gate, thinking that it must be some great king or queen, who would demand a banquet for supper, and a stately chamber to repose in. And when they saw only a sad and anxious woman, with a torch in her hand and a wreath of withered poppies on her head, they spoke rudely, and sometimes threatened to set the dogs upon her. But nobody had seen Proserpina, nor could give Mother Ceres the least hint which way to seek her. Thus passed the night; and still she continued her search, without sitting down to rest, or stopping to take food, or even remembering to put out the torch; although first the rosy dawn, and then the glad light of the morning sun, made its red flame look thin and pale. But I wonder what sort of stuff this torch was made of; for it burned dimly through the day, and, at night, was as bright as ever, and never was extinguished by the rain or wind, in all the weary days and nights while Ceres was seeking for Proserpina.

It was not merely of human beings that she asked tidings of her daughter. In the woods and by the streams, she met creatures of another nature, who used, in those old times, to haunt the pleasant and solitary places, and were very sociable with persons who understood their language and customs, as Mother Ceres did. Sometimes, for instance, she tapped with her finger against the knotted trunk of a majestic oak; and immediately its rude bark would cleave asunder, and forth would step a beautiful maiden who was the hamadryad of the oak, dwelling inside of it, and sharing its long life, and rejoicing when its green leaves sported with the breeze. But not one of these leafy damsels had seen Proserpina. Then, going a little farther, Ceres would perhaps come to a fountain, gushing out of a pebbly hollow in the earth, and would dabble with her hand in the water. Behold, up through its sandy and pebbly bed, along with the fountain's gush, a young woman with dripping hair would arise, and stand gazing at Mother Ceres, half out of the water, and undulating up and down with its ever-restless motion! But when the mother asked whether her poor, lost child had stopt to drink out of the fountain, the naiad, with weeping eyes, (for these water-nymphs had tears to spare for everybody's grief,) would answer 'No!'—in a murmuring voice, which was just like the murmur of the stream.

Often, likewise, she encountered fauns, who looked like sun-burnt country people, except that they had hairy ears, and little horns upon their foreheads, and the hinder legs of goats, on which they gambolled merrily about the woods and fields. They were a frolicsome kind of creature, but grew as sad as their cheerful dispositions would allow, when Ceres inquired for her daughter, and they had no good news to tell. But, sometimes, she came suddenly upon a rude gang of satyrs, who had faces like monkeys, and horses' tails behind them, and who were generally dancing in a very boisterous manner, with shouts of noisy laughter. When she stopt to question them, they would only laugh the louder, and make new merriment out of the lone woman's distress. How unkind of those ugly satyrs! And once, while crossing a solitary sheep-pasture, she saw a personage named Pan, seated at the foot of a tall rock, and making music on a shepherd's flute. He, too, had horns, and hairy ears, and goat's feet; but, being acquainted with Mother Ceres, he answered her question as civilly as he knew how, and invited her to taste some milk and honey out of a wooden bowl. But neither could Pan tell her what had become of Proserpina, any better than the rest of these wild people.

And thus Mother Ceres went wandering about, for nine long days and nights, finding no trace of Proserpina, unless it were now-and-then a withered flower; and these she picked up and put in her bosom, because she fancied that they might have fallen from her poor child's hand. All day, she travelled onward through the hot sun; and at night, again, the flame of the torch would redden and gleam along the pathway, and she continued her search by its light, without ever sitting down to rest.

On the tenth day, she chanced to espy the mouth of a cavern, within which (though it was bright noon, everywhere else) there would have been only a dusky twilight; but it so happened that a torch was burning there. It flickered, and struggled with the duskiness, but could not half light up the gloomy cavern, with all its melancholy glimmer. Ceres was resolved to leave no spot without a search; so she peeped into the entrance of the cave, and lighted it up a little more, by holding her own torch before her. In so doing, she caught a glimpse of what seemed to be a woman, sitting on the brown leaves of the last autumn, a great heap of which had been swept into the cave by the wind. This woman (if woman it were) was by no means so beautiful as many of her sex; for her head, they tell me, was shaped very much like a dog's, and, by way of ornament, she wore a wreath of snakes around it. But Mother Ceres, the moment she saw her, knew that this was an odd kind of a person, who put all her enjoyment in being miserable, and never would have a word to say to other people, unless they were as melancholy and wretched as she herself delighted to be.

"I am wretched enough now," thought poor Ceres, "to talk with this melancholy Hecate, were she ten times sadder than ever she was yet!"

So she stept into the cave, and sat down on the withered leaves by the dog-headed woman's side. In all the world, since her daughter's loss, she had found no other companion.

"Oh, Hecate," said she, "if ever you lose a daughter, you will know what sorrow is! Tell me, for pity's sake, have you seen my poor child Proserpina pass by the mouth of your cavern?"

"No," answered Hecate, in a cracked voice, and sighing betwixt every word or two; "no, Mother Ceres, I have seen nothing of your daughter. But my ears, you must know, are made in such a way that all cries of distress and affright, all over the world, are pretty sure to find their way to them; and nine days ago, as I sat in my cave, making myself very miserable, I heard the voice of a young girl, shrieking as if in great distress. Something terrible has happened to the child, you may rest assured. As well as I could judge, a dragon or some other cruel monster was carrying her away."

"You kill me by saying so!" cried Ceres, almost ready to faint. "Where was the sound, and which way did it seem to go?"

"It passed very swiftly along," said Hecate, "and, at the same time, there was a heavy rumbling of wheels towards the eastward. I can tell you nothing more, except that, in my honest opinion, you will never see your daughter again. The best advice I can give you is, to take up your abode in this cavern, where we will be the two most wretched women in the world."

"Not yet, dark Hecate!" replied Ceres. "But do you first come with your torch, and help me to seek for my lost child. And when there shall be no more hope of finding her, (if that black day is ordained to come,) then, if you will give me room to fling myself down, either on these withered leaves or on the naked rock, I will show you what it is to be miserable! But, until I know that she has perished from the face of the earth, I will not allow myself space even to grieve!"

The dismal Hecate did not much like the idea of going abroad into the sunny world. But then she reflected that the sorrow of the disconsolate Ceres would be like a gloomy twilight roundabout them both, let the sun shine ever so brightly, and that therefore she might enjoy her bad spirits quite as well, as if she were to stay in the cave. So she finally consented to go, and they set out together, both carrying torches, although it was broad daylight and clear sunshine. The torchlight seemed to make a gloom; so that the people whom they met, along the road, could not very distinctly see their figures; and, indeed, if they once caught a glimpse of Hecate, with the wreath of snakes round her forehead, they generally thought it prudent to run away, without waiting for a second glance.

As the pair travelled along, in this woe-begone manner, a thought struck Ceres.

"There is one person," she exclaimed, "who must have seen my poor child, and can doubtless tell what has become of her! Why did not I think of him before? It is Phœbus."

"What," said Hecate, "the young man that always sits in the sunshine? Oh, pray do not think of going near him! He is a gay, light, frivolous young fellow, and will only smile in your face. And besides, there is such a glare of the sun about him that he will quite blind my poor eyes, which I have almost wept away, already."

"You have promised to be my companion," answered Ceres. "Come; let us make haste, or the sunshine will be gone, and Phœbus along with it."

Accordingly, they went along in quest of Phœbus, both of them sighing grievously, and Hecate, to say the truth, making a great deal worse lamentation than Ceres; for all the pleasure she had, you know, lay in being miserable, and therefore she made the most of it. By-and-by, after a pretty long journey, they arrived at the sunniest spot in the whole world. There they beheld a beautiful young man with long, curling ringlets, which seemed to be made of golden sunbeams; his garments were like light summer clouds; and the expression of his face was so exceedingly vivid, that Hecate held her hands before her eyes, muttering that he ought to wear a black veil. Phœbus (for this was the very person whom they were seeking) had a lyre in his hands, and was making its chords tremble with sweet music; at the same time singing a most exquisite song, which he had recently composed. For, besides a great many other accomplishments, this young man was renowned for his admirable poetry.

As Ceres and her dismal companion approached him, Phœbus smiled on them so cheerfully that Hecate's wreath of snakes gave a spiteful hiss, and Hecate heartily wished herself back in her cave. But as for Ceres, she was too earnest in her grief either to know or care whether Phœbus smiled or frowned.

"Phœbus!" exclaimed she, "I am in great trouble, and have come to you for assistance. Can you tell me what has become of my dear child Proserpina?"

"Proserpina! Proserpina, did you call her name?" answered Phœbus, endeavoring to recollect; for there was such a continual flow of pleasant ideas in his mind, that he was apt to forget what had happened no longer ago than yesterday. "Ah, yes, I remember her now! A very lovely child, indeed! I am happy to tell you, my dear madam, that I did see the little Proserpina, not many days ago. You may make yourself perfectly easy about her. She is safe, and in excellent hands!"

"Oh, where is my dear child?" cried Ceres, clasping her hands and flinging herself at his feet.

"Why," said Phœbus—and as he spoke, he kept touching his lyre so as to make a thread of music run in and out among his words—"as the little damsel was gathering flowers, (and she has really a very exquisite taste for flowers,) she was suddenly snatched up by King Pluto, and carried off to his dominions. I have never been in that part of the universe; but the royal palace, I am told, is built in a very noble style of architecture, and of the most splendid and costly materials. Gold, diamonds, pearls, and all manner of precious stones, will be your daughter's ordinary playthings. I recommend to you, my dear lady, to give yourself no uneasiness. Proserpina's sense of beauty will be duly gratified, and, even in spite of the lack of sunshine, she will lead a very enviable life."

"Hush! Say not such a word!" answered Ceres indignantly. "What is there to gratify her heart! What are all the splendors you speak of, without affection! I must have her back again! Will you go with me, Phœbus, to demand my daughter of this wicked Pluto?"

"Pray excuse me," replied Phœbus, with an elegant obeisance. "I certainly wish you success, and regret that my own affairs are so immediately pressing, that I cannot have the pleasure of attending you. Besides, I am not upon the best of terms with King Pluto. To tell you the truth, his three-headed mastiff would never let me pass the gateway; for I should be compelled to take a sheaf of sunbeams along with me, and those, you know, are forbidden things in Pluto's kingdom."

"Ah, Phœbus," said Ceres, with bitter meaning in her words, "you have a harp instead of a heart! Farewell."

"Will not you stay a moment," asked Phœbus, "and hear me turn the pretty and touching story of Proserpina into extemporary verses?"

But Ceres shook her head, and hastened away, along with Hecate. Phœbus (who, as I have told you, was an exquisite poet) forthwith began to make an ode about the poor mother's grief; and, if we were to judge of his sensibility by this beautiful production, he must have been endowed with a very tender heart. But when a poet gets into the habit of using his heart-strings to make chords for his lyre, he may thrum upon them as much as he will, without any great pain to himself. Accordingly, though Phœbus sang a very sad song, he was as merry, all the while, as were the sunbeams amid which he dwelt.

Poor Mother Ceres had now found out what had become of her daughter, but was not a whit happier than before. Her case, on the contrary, looked more desperate than ever. As long as Proserpina was above ground, there might have been hopes of regaining her. But, now that the poor child was shut up within the iron gates of the King of the Mines, at the threshold of which lay the three-headed Cerberus, there seemed no possibility of her ever making her escape. The dismal Hecate, who loved to take the darkest view of things, told Ceres that she had better come with her to the cavern, and spend the rest of her life in being miserable. Ceres answered, that Hecate was welcome to go back thither herself, but that, for her part, she would wander about the earth in quest of the entrance to King Pluto's dominions. And Hecate took her at her word, and hurried back to her beloved cave, frightening a great many little children with a glimpse of her dog's face, as she went.

Poor Mother Ceres! It is melancholy to think of her, pursuing her toilsome way, all alone, and holding up that never-dying torch, the flame of which seemed an emblem of the grief and hope that burned together in her heart. So much did she suffer, that, though her aspect had been quite youthful when her troubles began, she grew to look like an elderly person, in a very brief time. She cared not how she was dressed, nor had she ever thought of flinging away the wreath of withered poppies, which she put on the very morning of Proserpina's disappearance. She roamed about in so wild a way, and with her hair so dishevelled, that people took her for some distracted creature, and never dreamed that this was

Mother Ceres, who had the oversight of every seed which the husbandman planted. Now-a-days, however, she gave herself no trouble about seed-time nor harvest, but left the farmers to take care of their own affairs, and the crops to fade or flourish, as the case might be. There was nothing, now, in which Ceres seemed to feel an interest, unless when she saw children at play, or gathering flowers along the wayside. Then, indeed, she would stand and gaze at them with tears in her eyes. The children, too, appeared to have a sympathy with her grief, and would cluster themselves in a little group about her knees, and look up wistfully in her face; and Ceres, after giving them a kiss all round, would lead them to their homes, and advise their mothers never to let them stray out of sight.

"For, if they do," said she, "it may happen to you, as it has to me, that the iron-hearted King Pluto will take a liking to your darlings, and snatch them up in his chariot, and carry them away!"

One day, during her pilgrimage in quest of the entrance to Pluto's kingdom, she came to the palace of King Celeus, who reigned at Eleusis. Ascending a lofty flight of steps, she entered the portal, and found the royal household in very great alarm about the queen's baby. The infant, it seems, was sickly, (being troubled with its teeth, I suppose,) and would take no food, and was all the time moaning with pain. The queen—her name was Metanira—was desirous of finding a nurse; and when she beheld a woman of matronly aspect coming up the palace-steps, she thought, in her own mind, that here was the very person whom she needed. So Queen Metanira ran to the door, with the poor wailing baby in her arms, and besought Ceres to take charge of it, or, at least, to tell her what would do it good.

"Will you trust the child entirely to me?" asked Ceres.

"Yes; and gladly too," answered the queen, "if you will devote all your time to him. For I can see that you have been a mother."

"You are right," said Ceres. "I once had a child of my own. Well; I will be the nurse of this poor, sickly boy. But beware, I warn you, that you do not interfere with any kind of treatment which I may judge proper for him. If you do so, the poor infant must suffer for his mother's folly."

Then she kissed the child, and it seemed to do him good; for he smiled, and nestled closely into her bosom.

So Mother Ceres set her torch in a corner, (where it kept burning, all the while,) and took up her abode in the palace of King Celeus, as nurse to the little Prince Demophoön. She treated him as if he were her own child, and allowed neither the king nor the queen to say whether he should be bathed in warm or cold water, or what he should eat, or how often he should take the air, or when he should be put to bed. You would hardly believe me, if I were to tell how quickly the baby-prince got rid of his ailments, and grew fat, and rosy, and strong, and how he had two rows of ivory teeth in less time than any other little fellow, before or since. Instead of the palest, and wretchedest, and puniest imp in the world, (as his own mother confessed him to be, when Ceres first took him in charge,) he was now a strapping baby, crowing, laughing, kicking up his heels, and rolling from one end of the room to the other. All the good women of the neighborhood crowded to the palace, and held up their hands, in unutterable amazement, at the beauty and wholesomeness of this darling little prince. Their wonder was the greater, because he was never seen to taste any food; not even so much as a cup of milk.

"Pray, nurse," the queen kept saying, "how is it that you make the child thrive so?"

"I was a mother once," Ceres always replied; "and having nursed my own child, I know what other children need."

But Queen Metanira, as was very natural, had a great curiosity to know precisely what the nurse did to her child. One night, therefore, she hid herself in the chamber where Ceres and the little prince were accustomed to sleep. There was a fire in the chimney, and it had now crumbled into great coals and embers, which lay glowing on the hearth, with a blaze flickering up, now-and-then, and flinging a warm and ruddy light upon the walls. Ceres sat before the hearth, with the child in her lap, and the firelight making her shadow dance upon the ceiling overhead. She undressed the little prince, and bathed him all over with some fragrant liquid out of a vase. The next thing she did was to rake back the red embers, and make a hollow place among them, just where the back-log had been. At last, while the baby was crowing, and clapping its fat little hands, and laughing in the nurse's face, (just as you may have seen your little brother or sister do, before going into its warm bath,) Ceres suddenly laid him, all naked as he was, in the hollow among the red-hot embers. She then raked the ashes over him, and turned quietly away.

You may imagine, if you can, how Queen Metanira shrieked, thinking nothing less than that her dear child would be burnt to a cinder. She burst forth from her hiding-place, and, running to the hearth, raked open the fire, and snatched up poor little Prince Demophoön out of his bed of live coals, one of which he was griping in each of his fists. He immediately set up a grievous cry, as babies are apt to do, when rudely startled out of a sound sleep. To the queen's astonishment and joy, she could perceive no token of the child's being injured by the hot fire in which he had lain. She now turned to Mother Ceres, and asked her to explain the mystery.

"Foolish woman," answered Ceres, "did you not promise to entrust this poor infant entirely to me? You little know the mischief you have done him. Had you left him to my care, he would have grown up like a child of celestial birth, endowed with superhuman strength and intelligence, and would have lived forever. Do you imagine that earthly children are to become immortal, without being tempered to it in the fiercest heat of the fire? But you have ruined your own son! For, (though he will be a strong man and a hero in his day,) yet, on account of your folly, he will grow old, and finally die, like the sons of other women. The weak tenderness of his mother has cost the poor boy an immortality! Farewell!"

Saying these words, she kissed the little Prince Demophoön, and sighed to think what he had lost, and took her departure, without heeding Queen Metanira, who intreated her to remain, and cover up the child among the hot embers as often as she pleased. Poor baby! He never slept so warmly again.

While she dwelt in the king's palace, Mother Ceres had been so continually occupied with taking care of the young prince, that her heart was a little lightened of its grief for Proserpina. But now, having nothing else to busy herself about, she became just as wretched as before. At length, in her despair, she came to the dreadful resolution that not a stalk of grain, nor a blade of grass, not a potatoe nor a turnip, nor any other vegetable that was good for man or beast to eat, should be suffered to grow, until her daughter were restored. She even forbade the flowers to bloom, lest somebody's heart should be cheered by their beauty.

Now, as not so much as a head of asparagus ever presumed to poke itself out of the ground, without the especial permission of Ceres, you may conceive what a terrible calamity had here fallen upon the earth! The husbandmen ploughed and planted, as usual; but there lay the rich, black furrows all as barren as a desert of sand. The pastures looked as brown, in the sweet month of June, as ever they did in chill November. The rich man's broad acres and the cottager's small garden patch were equally blighted. Every little girl's flower-bed showed nothing but dry stalks. The old people shook their white heads, and said that the earth had grown aged, like themselves, and was no longer capable of wearing the warm smile of summer on its face. It was really piteous to see the poor starving cattle and sheep, how they followed behind Ceres, lowing and bleating, as if their instinct taught them to expect help from her; and everybody, that was acquainted with her power, besought her to have mercy on the human race, and, at all events, to let the grass grow. But Mother Ceres, though naturally of an affectionate disposition, was now inexorable.

"Never!" said she. "If the earth is ever again to see any verdure, it must first grow along the path which my daughter will tread, in coming back to me!"

Finally, as there seemed to be no other remedy, our old friend Quicksilver was sent post-haste to King Pluto, in hopes that he might be persuaded to undo the mischief he had done, and to set everything right again, by giving up Proserpina. Quicksilver, accordingly, made the best of his way to the great gate, took a flying leap right over the three-headed mastiff, and stood at the door of the palace in an inconceivably short time. The servants knew him both by his face and garb; for his short cloak, and his winged cap and shoes, and his snaky staff, had often been seen thereabouts, in times gone by. He requested to be shown immediately into the king's presence; and Pluto, who heard his voice from the top of the stairs, and who loved to recreate himself with Quicksilver's merry talk, called out to him to come up. And while they settle their business together, we must inquire what Proserpina has been doing, ever since we saw her last.

The child had declared, as you may remember, that she would not taste a mouthful of food, as long as she should be compelled to remain in King Pluto's palace. How she contrived to maintain her resolution, and, at the same time, to keep herself tolerably plump and rosy, is more than I can explain; but some young ladies, I am given to understand, possess the faculty of living on air, and Proserpina seems to have possessed it, too. At any rate, it was now six months since she left the outside of the earth; and not a morsel, so far as the attendants were able to testify, had yet passed between her teeth. This was the more creditable to Proserpina; inasmuch as King Pluto had caused her to be tempted, day after day, with all manner of sweetmeats, and richly preserved fruits, and delicacies of every sort, such as young people are generally most fond of. But her good mother had often told her of the hurtfulness of these things; and for that reason alone, if there had been no other, she would have resolutely refused to taste them.

All this time, being of a cheerful and active disposition, the little damsel was not quite so unhappy as you may have supposed. The immense palace had a thousand rooms, and was full of beautiful and wonderful objects. There was a never-ceasing gloom, it is true, which half-hid itself among the innumerable pillars, gliding before the child as she wandered among them, and treading stealthily behind her in the echo of her footsteps. Neither was all the dazzle of the precious stones, which flamed with their own light, worth one gleam of natural sunshine; nor could the most brilliant of the many-colored gems, which Proserpina had for playthings, vie with the simple beauty of the flowers she used to gather. But still, wherever the girl went, among those gilded halls and chambers, it seemed as if she carried nature and sunshine along with her, and as if she scattered dewy blossoms on her right hand and on her left. After Proserpina came, the palace was no longer the same abode of stately artifice and dismal magnificence, that it had before been.

The inhabitants all felt this, and King Pluto more than any of them.

"My own little Proserpina," he used to say, "I wish you could like me a little better! We gloomy and cloudy-natured persons have often as warm hearts, at bottom, as those of a more cheerful character. If you would only stay with me of your own accord, it would make me happier than the possession of a hundred such palaces as this."

"Ah," said Proserpina, "you should have tried to make me like you before carrying me off! And the best thing you can now do, is to let me go again. Then I might remember you, sometimes, and think that you were as kind as you knew how to be. Perhaps, too, one day or other, I might come back and pay you a visit."

"No, no," answered Pluto, with his gloomy smile, "I will not trust you for that! You are too fond of living in the broad daylight and gathering flowers. What an idle and childish taste that is! Are not these gems, which I have ordered to be dug for you, and which are richer than any in my crown— are they not prettier than a violet?"

"Not half so pretty!" said Proserpina, snatching the gems from Pluto's hand and flinging them to the other end of the hall. "Oh, my sweet violets, shall I never see you again!"

And then she burst into tears. But young people's tears have very little saltness or acidity in them, and do not inflame the eyes so much as those of grown persons; so that it is not to be wondered at, if, a few moments afterwards, Proserpina was sporting through the hall, almost as merrily as she and the four sea-nymphs had sported along the edge of the surf-wave. King Pluto gazed after her, and wished that he too was a child. And little Proserpina, when she turned about, and beheld this great king standing in his splendid hall, and looking so grand, and so melancholy, and so lonesome, was smitten with a kind of pity. She ran back to him, and, for the first time in all her life, put her small, soft hand in his.

"I love you a little!" whispered she, looking up in his face.

"Do you indeed, my dear child?" cried Pluto, bending his dark face down to kiss her; but Proserpina shrank away from the kiss, for, though his features were noble, they were very dusky and grim. "Well! I have not deserved it of you, after keeping you a prisoner for so many months, and starving you, besides. Are you not terrible hungry? Is there nothing which I can get you to eat?"

In asking this question, the King of the Mines had a very cunning purpose; for, you will recollect, if Proserpina tasted a morsel of food in his dominions, she would never afterwards be at liberty to quit them.

"No, indeed," said Proserpina. "Your head-cook is always baking, and stewing, and roasting, and rolling out paste, and contriving one dish or another, which he imagines may be to my liking. But he might just as well save himself the trouble, poor fat little man that he is! I have no appetite for anything in the world, unless it were a slice of bread, of my mother's own baking, or a little fruit out of her garden."

When Pluto heard this, he began to see that he had mistaken the best method of tempting Proserpina to eat. The cook's made-dishes and artificial dainties were not half so delicious, in the good child's opinion, as the simple fare to which Mother Ceres had accustomed her. Wondering that he had never thought of it before, the king now sent one of his trusty attendants, with a large basket, to get some of the finest and juiciest pears, peaches, and plums, which could anywhere be found in the upper world. Unfortunately, however, this was during the time when Ceres had forbidden any fruits or vegetables to grow; and, after seeking all over the earth, King Pluto's servant found only a single pomegranate, and that so dried up as to be not worth eating. Nevertheless, since there was no better to be had, he brought this dry, old, withered pomegranate home to the palace, put it on a magnificent golden salver, and carried it up to Proserpina. Now it happened, curiously enough, that, just as the servant was bringing the pomegranate into the back-door of the palace, our friend Quicksilver had gone up the front-steps, on his errand to get Proserpina away from King Pluto.

As soon as Proserpina saw the pomegranate, on the golden salver, she told the servant he had better take it away again.

"I shall not touch it, I assure you!" said she. "If I were ever so hungry, I should never think of eating such a miserable dry pomegranate as that!"

"It is the only one in the world!" said the servant.

He set down the golden salver, with the wizened pomegranate upon it, and left the room. When he was gone, Proserpina could not help coming close to the table, and looking at this poor specimen of dried fruit with a great deal of eagerness; for, to say the truth, on seeing something that suited her taste, she felt all the six months' appetite taking possession of her at once. To be sure, it was a very wretched-looking pomegranate, and seemed to have no more juice in it than an oyster-shell. But there was no choice of such things in King Pluto's palace. This was the first fruit she had seen there, and the last she was ever likely to see; and unless she ate it up immediately, it would grow drier than it already was, and be wholly unfit to eat.

"At least, I may smell it," thought Proserpina.

So she took up the pomegranate, and applied it to her nose; and, somehow or other, being in such close neighborhood to her mouth, the fruit found its way into that little red cave. Dear me, what an everlasting pity! Before Proserpina knew what she was about, her teeth had actually bitten it, of their own accord! Just as this fatal deed was done, the door of the apartment opened, and in came King Pluto, followed by

Quicksilver, who had been urging him to let his little prisoner go. At the first noise of their entrance, Proserpina withdrew the pomegranate from her mouth. But Quicksilver (whose eyes were very keen, and his wits the sharpest that ever anybody had) perceived that the child was a little confused; and seeing the empty salver, he suspected that she had been taking a sly nibble of something or other. As for honest Pluto, he never guessed at the secret.

"My little Proserpina," said the king, sitting down, and affectionately drawing her between his knees, "here is Quicksilver, who tells me that a great many misfortunes have befallen innocent people, on account of my detaining you in my dominions. To confess the truth, I myself had already reflected that it was an unjustifiable act, to take you away from your good mother. But, then, you must consider, my dear child, that this vast palace is apt to be gloomy, (although the precious stones certainly shine very bright,) and that I am not of the most cheerful disposition, and that therefore it was a natural thing enough, to seek for the society of some merrier creature than myself. I hoped you would take my crown for a plaything, and me—ah, you laugh, naughty Proserpina!—me, grim as I am, for a playmate. It was a silly expectation."

"Not so extremely silly," whispered Proserpina. "You have really amused me very much, sometimes."

"Thank you!" said King Pluto, rather dryly. "But I can see, plainly enough, that you think my palace a dusky prison, and me the iron-hearted keeper of it. And an iron heart I should surely have, if I could detain you here any longer, my poor child, when it is now six months since you tasted food. I give you your liberty! Go with Quicksilver! Hasten home to your dear mother!"

Now, although you may not have supposed it, Proserpina found it impossible to take leave of poor King Pluto, without some regrets, and a good deal of compunction for not telling him about the pomegranate. She even shed a tear or two, thinking how lonely and cheerless the great palace would seem to him, with all its ugly glare of artificial light, after she herself—his one little ray of natural sunshine, whom he had stolen, to be sure, but only because he valued her so much—after she should have departed. I know not how many kind things she might have said to the disconsolate King of the Mines, had not Quicksilver hurried her away.

"Come along quickly," whispered he in her ear, "or his Majesty may change his royal mind. And take care, above all things, that you say nothing of what was brought you on the golden salver!"

In a very short time, they had passed the great gateway, (leaving the three-headed Cerberus, barking, and yelping, and growling, with threefold din, behind them,) and emerged upon the surface of the earth. It was delightful to behold, as Proserpina hastened along, how the path grew verdant, behind, and on either side of her. Wherever she set her blessed foot, there was at once a dewy flower. The violets gushed up, along the wayside. The grass and the grain began to sprout, with tenfold vigor and luxuriance, to make up for the dreary months that had been wasted in barrenness. The starved cattle immediately set to work grazing, after their long fast, and ate enormously, all day, and got up at midnight to eat more. But, I can assure you, it was a busy time of year with the farmers, when they found the summer coming upon them with such a rush. Nor must I forget to say, that all the birds in the whole world hopt about upon the newly blossoming trees, and sang together, in a prodigious ecstasy of joy.

Mother Ceres had returned to her deserted home, and was sitting disconsolately on the door-step, with her torch burning in her hand. She had been idly watching the flame, for some moments past, when, all at once, it flickered and went out.

"What does this mean?" thought she. "It was an enchanted torch, and should have kept burning till my child came back!"

Lifting her eyes, she was surprised to see a sudden verdure flashing over the brown and barren fields, exactly as you may have observed a golden hue gleaming far and wide across the landscape, from the just-risen sun.

"Does the earth disobey me?" exclaimed Mother Ceres, indignantly. "Does it presume to be green, when I have bidden it be barren, until my daughter shall be restored to my arms?"

"Then open your arms, dear mother," cried a well-known voice, "and take your little daughter into them!"

And Proserpina came running, and flung herself upon her mother's bosom. Their mutual transport is not to be described. The grief of their separation had caused both of them to shed a great many tears; and now they shed a great many more, because their joy could not so well express itself in any other way.

When their hearts had grown a little more quiet, Mother Ceres looked anxiously at Proserpina.

"My child," said she, "did you taste any food, while you were in King Pluto's palace?"

"Dearest mother," answered Proserpina, "I will tell you the whole truth. Until this very morning, not a morsel of food had passed my lips. But, to-day, they brought me a pomegranate, (a very dry one it was, and all shrivelled up, till there was little left of it, but seeds and skin,) and having seen no fruit for so long a time, and being faint with hunger, I was tempted just to bite it. The instant I tasted it, King Pluto and Quicksilver came into the room. I had not swallowed a morsel; but—dear mother, I hope it was no harm—but, six of the pomegranate-seeds, I am afraid, remained in my mouth!"

"Ah, unfortunate child, and miserable me!" exclaimed Ceres. "For each of those six pomegranate-seeds you must spend one month of every year in King Pluto's palace. You are but half restored to your mother. Only six months with me, and six with that good-for-nothing King of Darkness!"

"Do not speak so harshly of poor King Pluto," said Proserpina, kissing her mother. "He has some very good qualities; and I really think I can bear to spend six months in his palace, if he will only let me spend the other six with you. He certainly did very wrong to carry me off; but then, as he says, it was but a dismal sort of life for him, to live in that great, gloomy place, all alone; and it has made a wonderful change in his spirits, to have a little girl to run up stairs and down. There is some comfort in making him so happy; and so, upon the whole, dearest mother, let us be thankful that he is not to keep me the whole year round!"

THE GOLDEN FLEECE

WHEN Jason, the son of the dethroned King of Iolcos, was a little boy, he was sent away from his parents, and placed under the queerest schoolmaster that ever you heard of. This learned person was one of the people, or quadrupeds, called Centaurs. He lived in a cavern, and had the body and legs of a white horse with the head and shoulders of a man. His name was Chiron; and, in spite of his odd appearance, he was a very excellent teacher, and had several scholars who afterwards did him credit, by making a great figure in the world. The famous Hercules was one, and so was Achilles, and Philoctetes, likewise, and Esculapius, who acquired immense repute as a doctor. The good Chiron taught his pupils how to play upon the harp, and how to cure diseases, and how to use the sword and shield, together with various other branches of education, in which the lads of those days used to be instructed, instead of writing and arithmetic.

I have sometimes suspected that Master Chiron was not really very different from other people, but that, being a kind-hearted and merry old fellow, he was in the habit of making-believe that he was a horse, and scrambling about the school-room on all-fours, and letting the little boys ride upon his back. And so, when his scholars had grown up, and grown old, and were trotting their grandchildren on their knees, they told them about the sports of their school-days; and these young folks took the idea that their grandfathers had been taught their letters by a Centaur, half-man and half-horse. Little children, not quite understanding what is said to them, often get such absurd notions into their heads, you know!

Be that as it may, it has always been told for a fact, (and always will be told, as long as the world lasts,) that Chiron, with the head of a schoolmaster, had the body and legs of a horse. Just imagine the grave old gentleman clattering and stamping into the schoolroom on his four hoofs, perhaps treading on some little fellow's toes, flourishing his switch-tail instead of a rod, and, now-and-then, trotting out of doors to eat a mouthful of grass! I wonder what the blacksmith charged him for a set of iron shoes!

So Jason dwelt in the cave, with this four-footed Chiron, from the time that he was an infant, only a few months old, until he had grown to the full height of a man. He became a very good harper, I suppose, and skilful in the use of weapons, and tolerably acquainted with herbs and other doctor's stuff, and, above all, an admirable horseman; for, in teaching young people to ride, the good Chiron must have been without a rival among schoolmasters. At length, being now a tall and athletic youth, Jason resolved to seek his fortune in the world, without asking Chiron's advice, or telling him anything about the matter. This was very unwise, to be sure; and I hope none of you, my little hearers, will ever follow Jason's example. But, you are to understand, he had heard how that he himself was a prince royal, and how his father, King Æson, had been deprived of the kingdom of Iolcos by a certain Pelias, who would also have killed Jason, had he not been hidden in the Centaur's cave. And, being come to the strength of a man, Jason determined to set all this business to rights, and to punish the wicked Pelias for wronging his dear father, and to cast him down from the throne, and seat himself there instead.

With this intention, he took a spear in each hand, and threw a leopard's skin over his shoulders, to keep off the rain, and set forth on his travels, with his long yellow ringlets waving in the wind. The part of his dress, on which he most prided himself, was a pair of sandals that had been his father's. They were handsomely embroidered, and were tied upon his feet with strings of gold. But his whole attire was such as people did not very often see; and as he passed along, the women and children ran to the doors and windows, wondering whither this beautiful youth was journeying, with his leopard's skin and his golden-tied sandals, and what heroic deeds he meant to perform, with a spear in his right hand and another in his left!

I know not how far Jason had travelled, when he came to a turbulent river, which rushed right across his pathway, with specks of white foam among its black eddies, hurrying tumultuously onward, and roaring angrily as it went. Though not a very broad river, in the dry seasons of the year, it was now swollen by heavy rains, and by the melting of the snow on the sides of Mount Olympus; and it thundered so loudly, and looked so wild and dangerous, that Jason, bold as he was, thought it prudent to pause upon the brink. The bed of the stream seemed to be strewn with sharp and rugged rocks, some of which thrust themselves above the water. By-and-by, an uprooted tree, with shattered branches, came drifting along the current, and got entangled among the rocks. Now-and-then, a drowned sheep, and once, the carcass of a cow, floated past.

In short, the swollen river had already done a great deal of mischief. It was evidently too deep for Jason to wade, and too boisterous for him to swim; he could see no bridge; and as for a boat, had there been any, the rocks would have broken it to pieces in an instant.

"See the poor lad!" said a cracked voice close to his side. "He must have had but a poor education, since he does not know how to cross a little stream like this! Or is he afraid of wetting his fine golden-stringed sandals? It is a pity his four-footed schoolmaster is not here, to carry him safely across on his back!"

Jason looked round, greatly surprised, for he did not know that anybody was near. But beside him stood an old woman with a ragged mantle over her head, leaning on a staff, the top of which was carved into the shape of a cuckoo. She looked very aged, and wrinkled, and infirm; and yet her eyes, which were as brown as those of an ox, were so extremely large and beautiful, that, when they were fixed on Jason's eyes, he could see nothing else but them. The old woman had a pomegranate in her hand, although the fruit was then quite out of season.

"Whither are you going, Jason?" she now asked.

She seemed to know his name, you will observe; and, indeed, those great brown eyes looked as if they had a knowledge of everything, whether past or to come. While Jason was gazing at her, a peacock strutted forward, and took his stand at the old woman's side.

"I am going to Iolcos," answered the young man, "to bid the wicked King Pelias come down from my father's throne, and let me reign in his stead."

"Ah, well then," said the old woman, still with the same cracked voice, "if that is all your business, you need not be in a very great hurry! Just take me on your back, there's a good youth, and carry me across the river! I and my peacock have something to do on the other side, as well as yourself."

"Good mother," replied Jason, "your business can hardly be so important as the pulling down a king from his throne! Besides, as you may see for yourself, the river is very boisterous; and if I should chance to stumble, it would sweep both of us away, more easily than it has carried off yonder uprooted tree. I would gladly help you if I could; but I doubt whether I am strong enough to carry you across."

"Then," said she, very scornfully, "neither are you strong enough to pull King Pelias off his throne! And, Jason, unless you will help an old woman at her need, you ought not to be a king. What are kings made for, save to succor the feeble and distressed? But do as you please! Either take me on your back, or, with my poor old limbs, I shall try my best to struggle across the stream."

Saying this, the old woman poked with her staff in the river, as if to find the safest place in its rocky bed, where she might make the first step. But Jason, by this time, had grown ashamed of his reluctance to help her. He felt that he could never forgive himself, if this poor, feeble creature should come to any harm in attempting to wrestle against the headlong current. The good Chiron, whether half-horse or no, had taught him that the noblest use of his strength was, to assist the weak; and also that he must treat every young woman as if she were his sister, and every old one like a mother. Remembering these maxims, the vigorous and beautiful young man knelt down, and requested the good dame to mount upon his back.

"The passage seems to me not very safe," he remarked. "But, as your business is so urgent, I will try to carry you across. If the river sweeps you away, it shall take me too!"

"That, no doubt, will be a great comfort to both of us!" quoth the old woman. "But never fear! We shall get safely across."

So she threw her arms around Jason's neck; and lifting her from the ground, he stepped boldly into the raging and foamy current, and began to stagger away from the shore. As for the peacock, it alighted on the old dame's shoulder.

Jason's two spears, one in each hand, kept him from stumbling, and enabled him to feel his way among the hidden rocks; although, every instant, he expected that his companion and himself would go down the stream, together with the drift-wood of shattered trees, and the carcasses of the sheep and cow. Down came the cold, snowy torrent from the steep side of Olympus, raging and thundering as if it had a real spite against Jason, or, at all events, were determined to snatch off his living burthen from his shoulders. When he was half-way across, the uprooted tree (which I have already told you about) broke loose from among the rocks, and bore down upon him, with all its splintered branches sticking out like the hundred arms of the giant Briareus. It rushed past, however, without touching him. But, the next moment, his foot was caught in a crevice between two rocks, and stuck there so fast, that, in the effort to get free, he lost one of his golden-stringed sandals.

At this accident, Jason could not help uttering a cry of vexation.

"What is the matter, Jason?" asked the old woman.

"Matter enough!" said the young man. "I have lost a sandal here among the rocks. And what sort of a figure shall I cut, at the court of King Pelias, with a golden-stringed sandal on one foot, and the other foot bare?"

"Do not take it to heart," answered his companion, cheerily. "You never met with better fortune than in losing that sandal. It satisfies me that you are the very person whom the Speaking Oak has been talking about!"

There was no time, just then, to inquire what the Speaking Oak had said. But the briskness of her tone encouraged the young man; and, besides, he had never in his life felt so vigorous and mighty, as since taking this old woman on his back. Instead of being exhausted, he gathered strength as he went on; and struggling up against the torrent, he at last gained the opposite shore, clambered up the bank, and set down the old dame and her peacock, safely on the grass. As soon as this was done, however, he could not help looking rather despondently at his bare foot, with only a remnant of the golden string of the sandal, clinging round his ancle.

"You will get a handsomer pair of sandals, by-and-by," said the old woman, with a kindly look out of her beautiful brown eyes. "Only let King Pelias get a glimpse of that bare foot, and you shall see him turn as pale as ashes, I promise you! There is your path. Go along, my good Jason, and my blessing go with you! And when you sit on your throne, remember the old woman whom you helped over the river!"

With these words she hobbled away, giving him a smile over her shoulder, as she departed. Whether the light of her beautiful brown eyes threw a glory roundabout her, or whatever the cause might be, Jason fancied that there was something very noble and majestic in her figure, after all, and that, though her gait seemed to be a rheumatic hobble, yet she moved with as much grace and dignity as any queen on earth. Her peacock, which had now fluttered down from her shoulder, strutted behind her in prodigious pomp, and spread out its magnificent tail on purpose for Jason to admire it.

When the old dame and her peacock were out of sight, Jason set forward on his journey. After travelling a pretty long distance, he came to a town, situated at the foot of a mountain, and not a great way from the shore of the sea. On the outside of the town, there was an immense crowd of people, not only men and women, but children too, all in their best clothes, and evidently enjoying a holiday. The crowd was thickest towards the sea-shore; and in that direction, over the people's heads, Jason saw a wreath of smoke curling upward to the blue sky. He inquired of one of the multitude, what town it was, near by, and why so many persons were here assembled together.

"This is the kingdom of Iolcos," answered the man; "and we are the subjects of King Pelias. Our monarch has summoned us together, that we may see him sacrifice a black bull to Neptune, who, they say, is his majesty's father. Yonder is the king, where you see the smoke going up from the altar."

While the man spoke, he eyed Jason with great curiosity; for his garb was quite unlike that of the Iolchians, and it looked very odd to see a youth with a leopard's skin over his shoulders, and each hand grasping a spear. Jason perceived, too, that the man stared particularly at his feet, one of which, you remember, was bare, while the other was decorated with his father's golden-stringed sandal.

"Look at him!—only look at him!" said the man to his next neighbor. "Do you see? He wears but one sandal!"

Upon this, first one person, and then another, began to stare at Jason, and everybody seemed to be greatly struck with something in his aspect; though they turned their eyes much oftener towards his feet, than to any other part of his figure. Besides, he could hear them whispering to one another.

"One sandal! One sandal!"—they kept saying.—"The man with one sandal! Here he is, at last! Whence has he come? What does he mean to do? What will the king say to the one-sandalled man?"

Poor Jason was greatly abashed, and made up his mind that the people of Iolcos were exceedingly ill-bred, to take such public notice of an accidental deficiency in his dress. Meanwhile, whether it were that they hustled him forward, or that Jason, of his own accord, thrust a passage through the crowd, it so happened that he soon found himself close to the smoking altar, where King Pelias was sacrificing the black bull. The murmur and hum of the multitude, in their surprise at the spectacle of Jason with his one bare foot, grew so loud that it disturbed the ceremonies; and the king, holding the great knife with which he was just going to cut the bull's throat, turned angrily about, and fixed his eyes on Jason. The people had now withdrawn from around him, so that the youth stood in an open space, near the smoking altar, front to front with the angry King Pelias.

"Who are you?" cried the king, with a terrible frown. "And how dare you make this disturbance, while I am sacrificing a black bull to my father Neptune?"

"It is no fault of mine!" answered Jason. "Your majesty must blame the rudeness of your subjects, who have raised all this tumult because one of my feet happens to be bare."

When Jason said this, the king gave a quick, startled glance down at his feet.

"Ha!" muttered he, "Here is the one-sandalled fellow, sure enough! What can I do with him?"

And he clutched more closely the great knife in his hand, as if he were half a mind to slay Jason, instead of the black bull. The people roundabout caught up the king's words, indistinctly as they were uttered; and first there was a murmur among them, and then a loud shout.

"The one-sandalled man has come! The prophecy must be fulfilled!"

For you are to know, that, many years before, King Pelias had been told by the Speaking Oak of Dodona, that a man with one sandal should cast him down from his throne. On this account, he had given strict orders that nobody should ever come into his presence, unless both sandals were securely tied upon his feet; and he kept an officer in his palace, whose sole business it was to examine people's sandals, and to supply them with a new pair, at the expense of the royal treasury, as soon as the old ones began to wear out. In the whole course of the king's reign, he had never been thrown into such a fright and agitation as by the spectacle of poor Jason's bare foot. But, as he was naturally a bold and hard-hearted man, he soon took courage, and began to consider in what way he might rid himself of this terrible one-sandalled stranger.

"My good young man," said King Pelias, taking the softest tone imaginable, in order to throw Jason off his guard, "you are excessively welcome to my kingdom! Judging by your dress, you must have travelled a long distance; for it is not the fashion to wear leopard-skins, in this part of the world. Pray what may I call your name?—and where did you receive your education?"

"My name is Jason," answered the young stranger. "Ever since my infancy, I have dwelt in the cave of Chiron the Centaur. He was my instructor, and taught me music, and horsemanship, and how to cure wounds, and likewise how to inflict wounds with my weapons!"

"I have heard of Chiron the schoolmaster," replied King Pelias, "and how that there is an immense deal of learning and wisdom in his head, although it happens to be set on a horse's body. It gives me great delight to see one of his scholars at my court. But, to test how much you have profited under so excellent a teacher, will you allow me to ask you a single question?"

"I do not pretend to be very wise," said Jason. "But ask me what you please, and I will answer to the best of my ability."

Now King Pelias meant cunningly to entrap the young man, and to make him say something that should be the cause of mischief and destruction to himself. So, with a crafty and evil smile upon his face, he spoke as follows.

"What would you do, brave Jason," asked he, "if there were a man in the world, by whom, as you had reason to believe, you were doomed to be ruined and slain—what would you do, I say, if that man stood before you, and in your power?"

When Jason saw the malice and wickedness, which King Pelias could not prevent from gleaming out of his eyes, he probably guessed that the king had discovered what he came for, and that he intended to turn his own words against himself. Still, he scorned to tell a falsehood. Like an upright and honorable prince, as he was, he determined to speak out the real truth. Since the king had chosen to ask him the question, and since Jason had promised him an answer, there was no right way, save to tell him precisely what would be the most prudent thing to do, if he had his worst enemy in his power.

Therefore, after a moment's consideration, he spoke up, with a firm and manly voice.

"I would send such a man," said he, "in quest of the Golden Fleece!"

This enterprise, you will understand, was, of all others, the most difficult and dangerous in the world. In the first place, it would be necessary to make a long voyage through unknown seas. There was hardly a hope, or a possibility, that any young man, who should undertake this voyage, would either succeed in obtaining the Golden Fleece, or would survive to return home, and tell of the perils he had run. The eyes of King Pelias sparkled with joy, therefore, when he heard Jason's reply.

"Well said, wise Man with the one Sandal!" cried he. "Go, then, and, at the peril of your life, bring me back the Golden Fleece!"

"I go!" answered Jason, composedly. "If I fail, you need not fear that I will ever come back to trouble you again. But, if I return to Iolcos with the prize, then, King Pelias, you must hasten down from your lofty throne, and give me your crown and sceptre!"

"That I will!" said the king, with a sneer. "Meantime, I will keep them very safely for you!"

The first thing that Jason thought of doing, after he left the king's presence, was to go to Dodona, and inquire of the Talking Oak what course it was best to pursue. This wonderful tree stood in the centre of an ancient wood. Its stately trunk rose up a hundred feet into the air, and threw a broad and dense shadow over more than an acre of ground. Standing beneath it, Jason looked up among the knotted branches and green leaves, and into the mysterious heart of the old tree, and spoke aloud, as if he were addressing some person who was hidden in the depths of the foliage.

"What shall I do," said he, "in order to win the Golden Fleece?"

At first, there was a deep silence, not only within the shadow of the Talking Oak, but all through the solitary wood. In a moment or two, however, the leaves of the oak began to stir and rustle, as if a gentle breeze were wandering amongst them, although the other trees of the wood were perfectly still. The sound grew louder, and became like the roar of a high wind. By-and-by, Jason imagined that he could distinguish words, but very confusedly, because each separate leaf of the tree seemed to be a tongue, and the whole myriad of tongues were babbling at once. But the noise waxed broader and deeper, until it resembled a tornado sweeping through the oak, and making one great utterance out of the thousand and thousand of little murmurs, which each leafy tongue had caused by its rustling. And now, though it still had the tone of a mighty wind roaring among the branches, it was also like a deep, bass voice, speaking, as distinctly as a tree could be expected to speak, the following words:—

"Go to Argus, the ship-builder, and bid him build a galley with fifty oars!"

Then the voice melted again into the indistinct murmur of the rustling leaves, and died gradually away. When it was quite gone, Jason felt inclined to doubt whether he had actually heard the words, or whether his fancy had not shaped them out of the ordinary sound made by a breeze, while passing through the thick foliage of the tree.

But, on inquiry among the people of Iolcos, he found that there was really a man in the city, by the name of Argus, who was a very skilful builder of vessels. This showed some intelligence in the oak; else how should it have known that any such person existed? At Jason's request, Argus readily consented to build him a galley, so big that it should require fifty strong men to row it; although no vessel of such a size and burden had heretofore been seen in the world. So the head-carpenter, and all his journeymen and apprentices, began their work; and, for a good while afterwards, there they were, busily employed, hewing out the timbers, and making a great clatter with their hammers; until the new ship, which was called the Argo, seemed to be quite ready for sea. And, as the Talking Oak had already given him such good advice, Jason thought that it would not be amiss to ask for a little more. He visited it again, therefore, and standing beside its huge, rough trunk, inquired what he should do next.

This time, there was no such universal quivering of the leaves, throughout the whole tree, as there had been before. But, after a while, Jason observed that the foliage of a great branch, which stretched above his head, had begun to rustle, as if the wind were stirring that one bough, while all the other boughs of the oak were at rest.

"Cut me off!" said the branch, as soon as it could speak distinctly. "Cut me off! Cut me off! And carve me into a figure-head for your galley!"

Accordingly, Jason took the branch at its word, and lopped it off the tree. A carver in the neighborhood engaged to make the figure-head. He was a tolerably good workman, and had already carved several figure-heads, in what he intended for feminine shapes, and looking pretty much like those which we see now-a-days, stuck up under a vessel's bowsprit, with great staring eyes that never wink at the dash of the spray. But (what was very strange) the carver found that his hand was guided by some unseen power, and by a skill beyond his own, and that his tools shaped out an image which he had never dreamed of. When the work was finished, it turned out to be the figure of a beautiful woman, with a helmet on her head, from beneath which the long ringlets fell down upon her shoulders. On the left arm was a shield, and in its centre appeared a lifelike representation of the head of Medusa with the snaky locks. The right arm was extended, as if pointing onward. The face of this wonderful statue, though not angry or forbidding, was so grave and majestic, that perhaps you might call it severe; and as for the mouth, it seemed just ready to unclose its lips, and utter words of the deepest wisdom.

Jason was delighted with the oaken image, and gave the carver no rest until it was completed, and set up where a figure-head has always stood, from that time to this, in the vessel's prow.

"And now," cried he, as he stood gazing at the calm, majestic face of the statue, "I must go to the Talking Oak, and inquire what next to do?"

"There is no need of that, Jason," said a voice which, though it was far lower, reminded him of the mighty tones of the great oak. "When you desire good advice, you can seek it of me!"

Jason had been looking straight into the face of the image, when these words were spoken. But he could hardly believe either his ears or his eyes. The truth was, however, that the oaken lips had moved, and, to all appearance, the voice had proceeded from the statue's mouth. Recovering a little from his surprise, Jason bethought himself that the image had been carved out of the wood of the Talking Oak, and that therefore it was really no great wonder, but, on the contrary, the most natural thing in the world, that it should possess the faculty of speech. It would have been very odd, indeed, if it had not! But, certainly, it was a great piece of good fortune that he should be able to carry so wise a block of wood along with him, in his perilous voyage.

"Tell me, wondrous image," exclaimed Jason—"(Since you inherit the wisdom of the Speaking Oak of Dodona, whose daughter you are)—tell me, where shall I find fifty bold youths, who will take each of them an oar of my galley? They must have sturdy arms to row, and brave hearts to encounter perils; or we shall never win the Golden Fleece!"

"Go!" replied the oaken image. "Go summon all the heroes of Greece!"

And, in fact, considering what a great deed was to be done, could any advice be wiser than this, which Jason received from the figure-head of his vessel? He lost no time in sending messengers to all the cities, and making known to the whole people of Greece, that Prince Jason, the son of King Æson, was going in quest of the Fleece of Gold, and that he desired the help of forty-nine of the bravest and strongest young men alive, to row his vessel and share his dangers. And Jason himself would be the fiftieth.

At this news, the adventurous youths, all over the country, began to bestir themselves. Some of them had already fought with giants and slain dragons; and the younger ones, who had not yet met with such good fortune, thought it a shame to have lived so long without getting astride of a flying serpent, or sticking their spears into a Chimæra, or, at least, thrusting their right arms down a monstrous lion's throat. There was a fair prospect that they would meet with plenty of such adventures, before finding the Golden Fleece. As soon as they could furbish up their helmets and shields, therefore, and gird on their trusty swords, they came thronging to Iolcos, and clambered on board the new galley. Shaking hands with Jason, they assured him that they did not care a pin for their lives, but would help row the vessel to the remotest edge of the world, and as much farther as he might think it best to go.

Many of these brave fellows had been educated by Chiron, the four-footed pedagogue, and were therefore old schoolmates of Jason, and knew him to be a lad of spirit. The mighty Hercules, whose shoulders afterwards held up the sky, was one of them. And there were Castor and Pollux, the twin-brothers, who were never accused of being chicken-hearted, although they had been hatched out of an egg; and Theseus, who was so renowned for killing the Minotaur; and Lynceus, with his wonderfully sharp eyes, which could see through a mill-stone, or look right down into the depths of the earth, and discover the treasures that were there; and Orpheus, the very best of harpers, who sang and played upon his lyre so sweetly, that the brute-beasts stood upon their hind-legs, and capered merrily to the music. Yes; and, at some of his more moving tunes, the rocks bestirred their moss-grown bulk out of the ground, and a grove of forest-trees uprooted them-selves, and, nodding their tops to one another, performed a country-dance!

One of the rowers was a beautiful young woman, named Atalanta, who had been nursed among the mountains by a bear. So light of foot was this fair damsel, that she could step from one foamy crest of a wave to the foamy crest of another, without wetting more than the sole of her sandal. She had grown up in a very wild way, and talked much about the rights of women, and loved hunting and war far better than her needle. But, in my opinion, the most remarkable of this famous company were two sons of the North Wind, (airy youngsters, and of rather a blustering disposition,) who had wings on their shoulders, and, in case of a calm, could puff out their cheeks and blow almost as fresh a breeze as their father. I ought not to forget the prophets and conjurers, of whom there were several in the crew, and who could foretell what would happen tomorrow, or the next day, or a hundred years hence, but were generally quite unconscious of what was passing at the moment.

Jason appointed Tiphys to be helmsman, because he was a star-gazer and knew the points of the compass. Lynceus, on account of his sharp sight, was stationed as a look-out in the prow, where he saw a whole day's sail ahead, but was rather apt to overlook things that lay directly under his nose. If the sea only happened to be deep enough, however, Lynceus could tell you exactly what kind of rocks or sands were at the bottom of it; and he often cried out to his companions, that they were sailing over heaps of sunken treasure, which yet he was none the richer for beholding. To confess the truth, few people believed him when he said it.

Well! But when the Argonauts, as these fifty brave adventurers were called, had prepared everything for the voyage, an unforeseen difficulty threatened to end it before it was begun. The vessel, you must understand, was so long, and broad, and ponderous, that the united force of all the fifty was insufficient to shove her into the water. Hercules, I suppose, had not grown to his full strength; else he might have set her afloat, as easily as a little boy launches his boat upon a puddle. But here were these fifty heroes, pushing and straining, and growing red in the face, without making the Argo start an inch! At last, quite wearied out, they sat themselves down on the shore, exceedingly disconsolate, and thinking that the vessel must be left to rot and fall in pieces, and that they must either swim across the sea, or lose the Golden Fleece.

All at once, Jason bethought himself of the galley's miraculous figure-head.

"Oh, Daughter of the Talking Oak," cried he, "how shall we set to work to get our vessel into the water?"

"Seat yourselves," answered the image, (for it had known what ought to be done, from the very first, and was only waiting for the question to be put,)—"Seat yourselves, and handle your oars, and let Orpheus play upon his harp!"

Immediately, the fifty heroes got on board, and seizing their oars, held them perpendicularly in the air, while Orpheus (who liked such a task far better than rowing) swept his fingers across the harp. At the first ringing note of the music, they felt the vessel stir. Orpheus thrummed away briskly, and the galley slid at once into the sea, dipping her prow so deeply that the figure-head drank the wave with its marvellous lips, and rising again as buoyant as a swan. The rowers plied their fifty oars; the white foam boiled up before the prow; the water gurgled and bubbled in their wake; while Orpheus continued to play so lively a strain of music, that the vessel seemed to dance over the billows by way of keeping time to it. Thus triumphantly did the Argo sail out of the harbor, amidst the huzzas and good wishes of everybody, except the wicked old Pelias, who stood on a promontory, scowling at her, and wishing that he could blow out of his lungs the tempest of wrath that was in his heart, and so sink the galley with all on board! When they had sailed above fifty miles over the sea, Lynceus happened to cast his sharp eyes behind, and said that there was this bad-hearted king, still perched upon the promontory, and scowling so gloomily that it looked like a black thunder-cloud, in that quarter of the horizon.

In order to make the time pass away more pleasantly, during the voyage, the heroes talked about the Golden Fleece. It originally belonged, it appears, to a Bœotian ram, who had taken on his back two children, when in danger of their lives, and fled with them over land and sea, as far as Colchis. One of the children, whose name was Helle, fell into the sea and was drowned. But the other, (a little boy, named Phrixus) was brought safe ashore by the faithful ram, who, however, was so exhausted that he immediately lay down and died. In memory of this good deed, and as a token of his true heart, the fleece of the poor, dead ram was miraculously changed to gold, and became one of the most beautiful objects ever seen on earth. It was hung upon a tree, in a sacred grove, where it had now been kept I know not how many years, and was the envy of mighty kings, who had nothing so magnificent in any of their palaces.

If I were to tell you all the adventures of the Argonauts, it would take me till nightfall, and perhaps a great deal longer. There was no lack of wonderful events, as you may judge from what you have already heard. At a certain island, they were hospitably received by King Cyzicus, its sovereign, who made a feast for them, and treated them like brothers. But the Argonauts saw that this good king looked downcast and very much troubled, and they therefore inquired of him what was the matter. King Cyzicus hereupon informed them, that he and his subjects were greatly abused and incommoded by the inhabitants of a neighboring mountain, who made war upon them, and killed many people, and ravaged the country. And while they were talking about it, Cyzicus pointed to the mountain, and asked Jason and his companions what they saw there.

"I see some very tall objects," answered Jason; "but they are at such a distance that I cannot distinctly make out what they are. To tell your majesty the truth, they look so very strangely that I am inclined to think them clouds, which have chanced to take something like human shapes."

"I see them very plainly," remarked Lynceus, whose eyes, you know, were as far-sighted as a telescope. "They are a band of enormous giants, all of whom have six arms a-piece, and a club, a sword, or some other weapon, in each of their hands!"

"You have excellent eyes!" said King Cyzicus. "Yes; they are six-armed giants, as you say; and these are the enemies whom I and my subjects have to contend with."

The next day, when the Argonauts were about setting sail, down came these terrible giants, stepping a hundred yards at a stride, brandishing their six arms a-piece, and looking very formidable, so far aloft in the air. Each of these monsters was able to carry on a whole war by himself; for, with one of his arms, he could fling immense stones, and wield a club with another, and a sword with a third, while the fourth was poking a long spear at the enemy, and the fifth and sixth were shooting him with a bow and arrow. But, luckily, though the giants were so huge, and had so many arms, they had each but one heart, and that no bigger nor braver than the heart of an ordinary man. Besides, if they had been like the hundred-armed Briareus, the brave Argonauts would have given them their handsful of fight. Jason and his friends went boldly to meet them, slew a great many, and made the rest take to their heels, so that, if the giants had had six legs a-piece, instead of six arms, it would have served them better to run away with!

Another strange adventure happened when the voyagers came to Thrace, where they found a poor blind king, named Phineus, deserted by his subjects, and living in a very sorrowful way, all by himself. On Jason's inquiring whether they could do him any service, the king answered that he was terribly tormented by three great winged creatures, called Harpies, which had the faces of women, and the wings, bodies, and claws of vultures. These ugly wretches were in the habit of snatching away his dinner, and allowed him no peace of his life. Upon hearing this, the Argonauts spread a plentiful feast on the sea-shore, well knowing, from what the blind king said of their greediness, that the Harpies would snuff up the scent of the victuals, and quickly come to steal them away. And so it turned out; for, hardly was the table set, before the three hideous vulture-women came flapping their wings, seized the food in their talons, and flew off as fast as they could. But the two sons of the North Wind drew their swords, spread their pinions, and set off through the air in pursuit of the thieves, whom they at last overtook among some islands, after a chase of hundreds of miles. The two winged youths blustered terribly at the Harpies, (for they had the rough temper of their father,) and so frightened them with their drawn swords, that they solemnly promised never to trouble King Phineus again.

Then the Argonauts sailed onward, and met with many other marvellous incidents, any one of which would make a story by itself. At one time, they landed on an island, and were reposing on the grass, when they suddenly found themselves assailed by what seemed a shower of steel-headed arrows. Some of them stuck in the ground, while others hit against their shields, and several penetrated their flesh. The fifty heroes started up, and looked about them for the hidden enemy, but could find none, nor see any spot, on the whole island, where even a single archer could lie concealed. Still, however, the steel-headed arrows came whizzing among them; and, at last, happening to look upward, they beheld a large flock of birds, hovering and wheeling aloft, and shooting their feathers down upon the Argonauts. These feathers were the steel-headed arrows that had so tormented them. There was no possibility of making any resistance; and the fifty heoric Argonauts might all have been killed or wounded by a flock of troublesome birds, without ever setting eyes on the Golden Fleece, if Jason had not thought of asking the advice of the oaken image.

So he ran to the galley, as fast as his legs would carry him.

"Oh, Daughter of the Speaking Oak," cried he, all out of breath, "we need your wisdom more than ever before! We are in great peril from a flock of birds, who are shooting us with their steel-pointed feathers! What can we do, to drive them away?"

"Make a clatter on your shields!" said the image.

On receiving this excellent counsel, Jason hurried back to his companions, (who were far more dismayed than when they fought with the six-armed giants,) and bade them strike with their swords upon their brazen shields. Forthwith, the fifty heroes set heartily to work, banging with might and main, and raised such a terrible clatter, that the birds made what haste they could to get away; and, though they had shot half the feathers out of their wings, they were soon seen skimming among the clouds, a long distance off, and looking like a flock of wild geese. Orpheus celebrated this victory by playing a triumphant anthem on his harp, and sang so melodiously that Jason begged him to desist; lest, as the steel-feathered birds had been driven away by an ugly sound, they might be enticed back again by a sweet one.

While the Argonauts remained on this island, they saw a small vessel approaching the shore, in which were two young men of princely demeanor, and exceedingly handsome, as young princes generally were, in those days. Now, who do you imagine these two voyagers turned out to be? Why, if you will believe me, they were the sons of that very Phrixus, who, in his childhood, had been carried to Colchis on the back of the golden-fleeced ram! Since that time, Phrixus had married the king's daughter; and the two young princes had been born and brought up at Colchis, and had spent their play days in the outskirts of the grove, in the centre of which the Golden Fleece was hanging upon a tree. They were now on their way to Greece, in hopes of getting back a kingdom that had been wrongfully taken from their father.

When the princes understood whither the Argonauts were going, they offered to turn back and guide them to Colchis. At the same time, however, they spoke as if it were very doubtful whether Jason would succeed in getting the Golden Fleece. According to their account, the tree, on which it hung, was guarded by a terrible dragon, who never failed to devour, at one mouthful, every person who might venture within his reach.

"There are other difficulties in the way," continued the young princes. "But is not this enough? Ah, brave Jason, turn back before it is too late! It would grieve us to the heart, if you and your nine-and-forty brave companions should be eaten up, at fifty mouthfulls, by this execrable dragon!"

"My young friends," quietly replied Jason, "I do not wonder that you think the dragon very terrible. You have grown up from infancy in the fear of this monster, and therefore still regard him with the awe that children feel for the bugbears and hobgoblins, which their nurses have talked to them about. But, in my view of the matter, the dragon is merely a pretty large serpent, who is not half so likely to snap me up at one mouthful, as I am to cut off his ugly head, and strip the skin from his body. At all events, turn back who may, I will never see Greece again, unless I carry with me the Golden Fleece!"

"We will none of us turn back!" cried his nine-and-forty brave comrades. "Let us get on board the galley, this instant; and if the dragon is to make a breakfast of us, much good may it do him!"

And Orpheus (whose custom it was to set everything to music) began to harp and sing most gloriously, and made every mother's son of them feel as if nothing in this world were so delectable as to fight dragons, and nothing so truly honorable as to be eaten up at one mouthful, in case of the worst.

After this, (being now under the guidance of the two princes, who were well acquainted with the way,) they quickly sailed to Colchis. When the king of the country, whose name was Æetes, heard of their arrival, he instantly summoned Jason to court. The king was a stern and cruel-looking potentate; and though he put on as polite and hospitable an expression as he could, Jason did not like his face a whit better than that of the wicked King Pelias, who dethroned his father.

"You are welcome, brave Jason!" said King Æetes. "Pray are you on a pleasure-voyage?—or do you meditate the discovery of unknown islands?—or what other cause has procured me the happiness of seeing you at my court?"

"Great Sir," replied Jason, with an obeisance—for Chiron had taught him how to behave with propriety, whether to kings or beggars—"I have come hither with a purpose which I now beg your majesty's permission to execute. King Pelias, who sits on my father's throne, (to which he has no more right, than to the one on which your excellent majesty is now seated,) has engaged to come down from it, and to give me his crown and sceptre, provided I bring him the Golden Fleece. This, as your majesty is aware, is now hanging on a tree here at Colchis; and I humbly solicit your gracious leave to take it away!"

In spite of himself, the king's face twisted itself into an angry frown; for, above all things else in the world, he prized the Golden Fleece, and was even suspected of having done a very wicked act, in order to get it into his own possession. It put him into the worst possible humor, therefore, to hear that the gallant Prince Jason, and forty-nine of the bravest young warriors of Greece, had come to Colchis with the sole purpose of taking away his chief treasure.

"Do you know," asked King Æetes, eyeing Jason very sternly, "what are the conditions which you must fulfil, before getting possession of the Golden Fleece?"

"I have heard," rejoined the youth, "that a dragon lies beneath the tree on which the prize hangs, and that whoever approaches him runs the risk of being devoured at a mouthful."

"True!" said the king, with a smile that did not look particularly good-natured. "Very true, young man! But there are other things as hard, or perhaps a little harder, to be done, before you can even have the privilege of being devoured by the dragon. For example, you must first tame my two brazen-footed and brazen-lunged bulls, which Vulcan, the wonderful blacksmith, made for me. There is a furnace in each of their stomachs; and they breathe such hot fire out of their mouths and nostrils, that nobody has hitherto gone nigh them without being instantly burnt to a small, black cinder! What do you think of this, my brave Jason?"

"I must encounter the peril," answered Jason composedly, "since it stands in the way of my purpose."

"After taming the fiery bulls," continued King Æetes, who was determined to scare Jason if possible, "you must yoke them to a plough, and must plough the sacred earth in the grove of Mars, and sow some of the same dragon's teeth from which Cadmus raised a crop of armed men. They are an unruly set of reprobates, those sons of the dragon's teeth; and unless you treat them suitably, they will fall upon you, sword in hand! You and your nine-and-forty Argonauts, my bold Jason, are hardly numerous or strong enough to fight with such a host as will spring up!"

"My master Chiron," replied Jason, "taught me, long ago, the story of Cadmus. Perhaps I can manage the quarrelsome sons of the dragon's teeth, as well as Cadmus did!"

"I wish the dragon had him," muttered King Æetes to himself, "and the four-footed pedant, his schoolmaster, into the bargain! Why, what a fool-hardy, self-conceited coxcomb he is! We'll see what my fire-breathing bulls will do for him! Well, Prince Jason," he continued, aloud, and as complaisantly as he could, "make yourself comfortable for to-day; and tomorrow morning, since you insist upon it, you shall try your skill at the plough."

While the king talked with Jason, a beautiful young woman was standing behind the throne. She fixed her eyes earnestly upon the youthful stranger, and listened attentively to every word that was spoken; and when Jason withdrew from the king's presence, this young woman followed him out of the room.

"I am the king's daughter," she said to him; "and my name is Medea. I know a great deal, of which other young princesses are ignorant, and can do many things, which they would be afraid so much as to dream of! If you will trust to me, I can instruct you how to tame the fiery bulls, and sow the dragon's teeth, and get the Golden Fleece!"

"Indeed, beautiful princess," answered Jason, "if you will do me this service, I promise to be grateful to you, my whole life long!"

Gazing at Medea, he beheld a wonderful intelligence in her face. She was one of those persons whose eyes are full of mystery; so that, while looking into them, you seem to see a very great way, as into a deep well, yet can never be certain whether you see into the farthest depths, or whether there be not something else hidden at the bottom. If Jason had been capable of fearing anything, he would have been afraid of making this young princess his enemy; for, beautiful as she now looked, she might, the very next instant, become as terrible as the dragon that kept watch over the Golden Fleece.

"Princess," he exclaimed, "you seem indeed very wise, and very powerful! But, how can you help me to do the things of which you speak? Are you an enchantress?"

"Yes, Prince Jason," answered Medea, with a smile, "you have hit upon the truth. I am an enchantress! Circe, my father's sister, taught me to be one. And I could tell you, if I pleased, who was the old woman, with the peacock, the pomegranate, and the cuckoo-staff, whom you carried over the river; and, likewise, who it is that speaks through the lips of the oaken image, that stands in the prow of your galley.

I am acquainted with some of your secrets, you perceive! It is well for you, that I am favorably inclined; for, otherwise, you would hardly escape being snapt up by the dragon."

"I should not so much care for the dragon," replied Jason, "if I only knew to manage the brazen-footed and fiery-lunged bulls."

"If you are as brave as I think you, and as you have need to be," said Medea, "your own bold heart will teach you that there is but one way of dealing with a mad bull. What it is, I leave you to find out in the moment of peril. As for the fiery breath of these animals, I have a charmed ointment here, which will prevent you from being burned up, and cure you if you chance to be a little scorched."

So she put a golden box into his hand, and directed him how to apply the perfumed unguent which it contained, and where to meet her, at midnight.

"Only be brave," added she; "and, before daybreak, the brazen bulls shall be tamed!"

The young man assured her that his heart would not fail him. He then rejoined his comrades, and told them what had passed between the princess and himself, and warned them to be in readiness, in case there might be need of their help.

At the appointed hour, he met the beautiful Medea on the marble steps of the king's palace. She gave him a basket, in which were the dragon's teeth, just as they had been pulled out of the monster's jaws by Cadmus, long ago. Medea then led Jason down the palace-steps, and through the silent streets of the city, and into the royal pasture-ground, where the two brazen-footed bulls were kept. It was a starry night, with a bright gleam along the eastern edge of the sky, where the moon was soon going to show herself. After entering the pasture, the princess paused, and looked around.

"There they are," said she, "reposing themselves and chewing their fiery cuds, in that farthest corner of the field.

It will be excellent sport, I assure you, when they catch a glimpse of your figure! My father and all his court delight in nothing so much as to see a stranger trying to yoke them, in order to come at the Golden Fleece. It makes a holiday in Colchis, whenever such a thing happens. For my part, I enjoy it immensely. You cannot imagine in what a mere twinkling of an eye, their hot breath shrivels a young man into a black cinder!"

"Are you sure, beautiful Medea," asked Jason, "quite sure, that the unguent in the gold box will prove a remedy against those terrible burns?"

"If you doubt—if you are in the least afraid—" said the princess, looking him in the face, by the dim starlight— "you had better never have been born, than go a step nigher to the bulls!"

But Jason had set his heart steadfastly on getting the Golden Fleece; and I positively doubt whether he would have gone back without it, even had he been certain of finding himself turned into a red-hot cinder, or a handful of white ashes, the instant he made a step farther. He therefore let go Medea's hand, and walked boldly forward in the direction whither she had pointed. At some distance before him, he perceived four streams of fiery vapor, regularly appearing, and again vanishing, after dimly lighting up the surrounding obscurity. These, you will understand, were caused by the breath of the brazen bulls, which was quietly stealing out of their four nostrils, as they lay chewing their cuds.

At the first two or three steps, which Jason made, the four fiery streams appeared to gush out somewhat more plentifully; for the two brazen bulls had heard his foot-tramp, and were lifting up their hot noses to snuff the air. He went a little farther; and by the way in which the red vapor now spouted forth, he judged that the creatures had got upon their feet. Now, he could see glowing sparks, and vivid jets of flame.

At the next step, each of the bulls made the pasture echo with a terrible roar, while the burning breath, which they thus belched forth, lit up the whole field with a momentary flash. One other stride did bold Jason make; and, suddenly as a streak of lightning, on came these fiery animals, roaring like thunder, and sending out sheets of white flame, which so kindled up the scene that the young man could discern every object more distinctly than by daylight. Most distinctly of all, he saw the two horrible creatures, galloping right down upon him, their brazen hoofs rattling and ringing over the ground, and their tails sticking up stiffly into the air, as has always been the fashion with angry bulls. Their breath scorched the herbage before them. So intensely hot it was, indeed, that it caught a dry tree, under which Jason was now standing, and set it all in a light blaze. But as for Jason himself, (thanks to Medea's enchanted ointment,) the white flame curled around his body, without injuring him a jot more than if he had been made of asbestos!

Greatly encouraged at finding himself not yet turned into a cinder, the young man awaited the attack of the bulls. Just as the brazen brutes fancied themselves sure of tossing him into the air, he caught one of them by the horn, and the other by his screwed-up tail, and held them in a gripe like that of an iron vice, one with his right hand, the other with his left. Well; he must have been wonderfully strong in his arms, to be sure! But the secret of the matter was, that the brazen bulls were enchanted creatures, and that Jason had broken the spell of their fiery fierceness by his bold way of handling them. And, ever since that time, it has been the favorite method of brave men, when danger assails them, to do what they call 'taking the bull by the horns'—and to gripe him by the tail is pretty much the same thing—that is, to throw aside fear, and overcome the peril by despising it.

It was now easy to yoke the bulls, and to harness them to the plough, which had lain rusting on the ground for a great many years gone by; so long was it, before anybody could be found capable of ploughing that piece of land! Jason, I suppose, had been taught how to draw a furrow by the good old Chiron, who, perhaps, used to allow himself to be harnessed to the plough. At any rate, our hero succeeded perfectly well in breaking up the green sward; and, by the time that the moon was a quarter of her journey up the sky, the ploughed field lay before him, a large tract of black earth, ready to be sown with the dragon's teeth. So Jason scattered them broadcast, and harrowed them into the soil with a brush-harrow, and took his stand on the edge of the field, anxious to see what would happen next.

"Must we wait long for harvest-time?" he inquired of Medea, who was now standing by his side.

"Whether sooner or later, it will be sure to come," answered the princess. "A crop of armed men never fails to spring up, when the dragon's teeth have been sown."

The moon was now high aloft in the heavens, and threw its bright beams over the ploughed field, where as yet there was nothing to be seen. Any farmer, on viewing it, would have said that Jason must wait weeks before the green blades would peep from among the clods, and whole months, before the yellow grain would be ripened for the sickle. But, by-and-by, all over the field, there was something that glistened in the moonbeams, like sparkling drops of dew. These bright objects sprouted higher, and proved to be the steel-heads of spears. Then there was a dazzling gleam from a vast number of polished brass helmets, beneath which, as they grew farther out of the soil, appeared the dark and bearded visages of warriors, struggling to free themselves from the imprisoning earth. The first look that they gave at the upper world, was a glare of wrath and defiance. Next were seen their bright breastplates; in every right hand there was a sword or a spear, and on each left arm a shield; and when this strange crop of warriors had but half grown out of the earth, they struggled, such was their impatience of restraint, and, as it were, tore themselves up by the roots. Wherever a dragon's tooth had fallen, there stood a man armed for battle. They made a clangor with their swords against their shields, and eyed one another fiercely; for they had come into this beautiful world, and into the peaceful moonlight, full of rage and stormy passions, and ready to take the life of every human brother, in recompense of the boon of their own existence.

There have been many other armies in the world, that seemed to possess the same fierce nature with the one which had now sprouted from the dragon's teeth; but these, in the moonlit field, were the more excusable, because they never had women for their mothers. And how it would have rejoiced any great captain, who was bent on conquering the world, like Alexander or Napoleon, to raise a crop of armed soldiers as easily as Jason did!

For a while, the warriors stood flourishing their weapons, clashing their swords against their shields, and boiling over with the red-hot thirst for battle. Then they began to shout— 'Show us the enemy!'—'Lead us to the charge!'—'Death or victory!'—'Come on, brave comrades!'—'Conquer or die!'— and a hundred other outcries, such as men always bellow forth, on a battle-field, and which these dragon-people seemed to have at their tongues-ends. At last, the front-rank caught sight of Jason, who, beholding the flash of so many weapons in the moonlight, had thought it best to draw his sword. In a moment, all the sons of the dragon's teeth appeared to take Jason for an enemy; and crying with one voice—'Guard the Golden Fleece!'—they ran at him with uplifted swords and protruded spears. Jason knew that it would be impossible to withstand this blood-thirsty battalion with his single arm, but determined, since there was nothing better to be done, to die as valiantly as if he himself had sprung from a dragon's tooth.

Medea, however, bade him snatch up a stone from the ground.

"Throw it among them quickly!" cried she. "It is the only way to save yourself!"

The armed men were now so nigh that Jason could discern the fire flashing out of their enraged eyes; when he let fly the stone, and saw it strike the helmet of a tall warrior, who was rushing upon him with his blade aloft. The stone glanced from this man's helmet to the shield of his nearest comrade, and thence flew right into the angry face of another, hitting him smartly between the eyes. Each of the three, who had been struck by the stone, took it for granted that his next neighbor had given him a blow; and, instead of running any farther towards Jason, they began a fight among themselves. The confusion spread through the host; so that it seemed scarcely a moment before they were all hacking, hewing, and stabbing at one another, lopping off arms, heads, and legs, and doing such memorable deeds that Jason was filled with immense admiration; although, at the same time, he could not help laughing to behold these mighty men punishing each other for an offence which he himself had committed. In an incredibly short space of time, (almost as short, indeed, as it had taken them to grow up,) all but one of the heroes of the dragon's teeth were stretched lifeless on the field. The last survivor, the bravest and strongest of the whole, had just force enough to wave his crimson sword over his head, and give a shout of exultation, crying—'Victory! Victory! Immortal fame!'—when he himself fell down, and lay quietly among his slain brethren.

And there was the end of the army that had sprouted from the dragon's teeth! That fierce and feverish fight was the only enjoyment which they had tasted, on this beautiful earth!

"Let them sleep in the bed of honor!" said the Princess Medea, with a sly smile at Jason. "The world will always have simpletons enough, just like them, fighting and dying for they know not what, and fancying that Posterity will take the trouble to put laurel wreaths on their rusty and battered helmets! Could you help smiling, Prince Jason, to see the self-conceit of that last fellow, just as he tumbled down?"

"It made me very sad," answered Jason, gravely. "And, to tell you the truth, Princess, the Golden Fleece does not appear so well worth the winning, after what I have here beheld."

"You will think differently, in the morning," said Medea. "True; the Golden Fleece may not be so valuable as you have thought it; but then there is nothing better in the world—and one must needs have an object, you know! Come! Your night's work has been well performed; and, tomorrow, you can inform King Æetes that the first part of your allotted task is fulfilled."

Agreeably to Medea's advice, Jason went, betimes in the morning, to the palace of King Æetes. Entering the presence-chamber, he stood at the foot of the throne, and made a low obeisance.

"Your eyes look heavy, Prince Jason!" observed the king. "You appear to have spent a sleepless night. I hope you have been considering the matter a little more wisely, and have concluded not to get yourself scorched to a cinder, in attempting to tame my brazen-lunged bulls!"

"That is already accomplished, may it please your majesty," replied Jason. "The bulls have been tamed and yoked; the field has been ploughed; the dragon's teeth have been sown broadcast, and harrowed into the soil; the crop of armed warriors have sprung up—and they have slain one another, to the last man! And, now, I solicit your majesty's permission to encounter the dragon, that I may take down the Golden Fleece from the tree, and depart, with my nine-and-forty comrades!"

King Æetes scowled, and looked very angry and excessively disturbed; for he knew that, in accordance with his kingly promise, he ought now to permit Jason to win the fleece, if his courage and skill should enable him to do so. But, since the young man had met with such good luck in the matter of the brazen bulls and the dragon's teeth, the king feared that he would be equally successful in slaying the dragon. And, therefore, though he would gladly have seen Jason snapt up at a mouthful, he was resolved (and it was a very wrong thing of this wicked potentate) not to run any further risk of losing his beloved fleece.

"You never would have succeeded in this business, young man," said he, "if my undutiful daughter Medea had not helped you with her enchantments. Had you acted fairly, you would have been, at this instant, a black cinder, or a handful of white ashes! I forbid you, on pain of death, to make any more attempts to get the Golden Fleece! To speak my mind plainly, you shall never set eyes on so much as one of its glistening locks!"

Jason left the king's presence in great sorrow and anger. He could think of nothing better to be done, than to summon together his forty-nine brave Argonauts, march at once to the Grove of Mars, slay the dragon, take possession of the Golden Fleece, get on board the Argo, and spread all sail for Iolcos. The success of this scheme depended, it is true, on the doubtful point whether all the fifty heroes might not be snapt up, at so many mouthfuls, by the dragon. But, as Jason was hastening down the palace-steps, the Princess Medea called after him, and beckoned him to return. Her black eyes shone upon him with such a keen intelligence, that he felt as if there were a serpent peeping out of them; and, although she had done him so much service, only the night before, he was by no means very certain that she would not do him an equally great mischief, before sunset. These enchantresses, you must know, are never to be depended upon.

"What says King Æetes, my royal and upright father?" inquired Medea, slightly smiling. "Will he give you the Golden Fleece, without any further risk or trouble?"

"On the contrary," answered Jason, "he is very angry with me for taming the brazen bulls, and sowing the dragon's teeth. And he forbids me to make any more attempts, and positively refuses to give up the Golden Fleece, whether I slay the dragon or no!"

"Yes, Jason," said the princess; "and I can tell you more. Unless you set sail from Colchis before tomorrow's sunrise, the king means to burn your fifty-oared galley, and put yourself and your forty-nine brave comrades to the sword! But be of good courage! The Golden Fleece you shall have, if it lies within the power of my enchantments to get it for you. Wait for me here, an hour before midnight!"

At the appointed hour, you might again have seen Prince Jason and the Princess Medea, side by side, stealing through the streets of Colchis, on their way to the sacred grove, in the centre of which the Golden Fleece was suspended to a tree. While they were crossing the pasture-ground, the brazen bulls came towards Jason, lowing, nodding their heads, and thrusting forth their snouts, which, as other cattle do, they loved to have rubbed and caressed by a friendly hand. Their fierce nature was thoroughly tamed; and, with their fierceness, the two furnaces in their stomachs had likewise been extinguished, insomuch that they probably enjoyed far more comfort, in grazing and chewing their cuds, than ever before. Indeed, it had heretofore been a great inconvenience to these poor animals, that, whenever they wished to eat a mouthful of grass, the fire out of their nostrils had shrivelled it up, before they could manage to crop it. How they contrived to keep themselves alive, is more than I can imagine. But, now, instead of emitting jets of flame and streams of sulphurous vapor, they breathed the very sweetest of cow-breath!

After kindly patting the bulls, Jason followed Medea's guidance into the Grove of Mars, where the great oak-trees, that had been growing for centuries, threw so thick a shade that the moonbeams struggled vainly to find their way through it. Only, here and there, a glimmer fell upon the leaf-strewn earth; or, now-and-then, a breeze stirred the boughs aside, and gave Jason a glimpse of the sky, lest, in that deep obscurity, he might forget that there was one, overhead. At length, when they had gone farther and farther into the heart of the duskiness, Medea squeezed Jason's hand.

"Look yonder!" she whispered. "Do you see it?"

Gleaming among the venerable oaks, there was a radiance, not like the moonbeams, but rather resembling the golden glory of the setting sun. It proceeded from an object, which appeared to be suspended at about a man's height from the ground, a little farther within the wood.

"What is it?" asked Jason.

"Have you come so far to seek it," exclaimed Medea, "and do you not recognize the meed of all your toils and perils, when it glitters before your eyes? It is the Golden Fleece!"

Jason went onward a few steps farther, and then stopt to gaze. Oh, how beautiful it looked, shining with a marvellous light of its own, that inestimable prize, which so many heroes had longed to behold, but had perished in the quest of it, either by the perils of their voyage, or by the fiery breath of the brazen-lunged bulls!

"How gloriously it shines!" cried Jason, in a rapture. "It has surely been dipt in the richest gold of sunset! Let me hasten onward, and take it to my bosom!"

"Stay!" said Medea, holding him back. "Have you forgotten what guards it?"

To say the truth, in the joy of beholding the object of his desires, the terrible dragon had quite slipt out of Jason's memory. Soon, however, something came to pass, that reminded him what perils were still to be encountered. An antelope, that probably mistook the yellow radiance for sunrise, came bounding fleetly through the grove. He was rushing straight towards the Golden Fleece, when suddenly there was a frightful hiss, and the immense head and half the scaly body of the dragon was thrust forth, (for he was twisted round the trunk of the tree, on which the fleece hung,) and seizing the poor antelope, swallowed him with one snap of his jaws!

After this feat, the dragon seemed sensible that some other living creature was within reach, on which he felt inclined to finish his meal. In various directions, he kept poking his ugly snout among the trees, stretching out his neck a terrible long way, now here, now there, and now close to the spot where Jason and the princess were hiding behind an oak. Upon my word, as the head came waving and undulating through the air, and reaching almost within arm's length of Prince Jason, it was a very hideous and uncomfortable sight! The gape of his enormous jaws was nearly as wide as the gateway of the king's palace.

"Well, Jason," whispered Medea, (for she was ill-natured, as all enchantresses are, and wanted to make the bold youth tremble,) "what do you think now of your prospect of winning the Golden Fleece?"

Jason answered only by drawing his sword, and making a step forward.

"Stay, foolish youth!" said Medea, grasping his arm. "Do not you see you are lost, without me as your good angel? In this gold box I have a magic potion, which will do the dragon's business far more effectually than your sword!"

The dragon had probably heard the voices; for swift as lightning, his black head and forked tongue came hissing among the trees again, darting full forty feet at a stretch. As it approached, Medea tossed the contents of the gold box right down the monster's wide-open throat. Immediately, with an outrageous hiss and a tremendous wriggle—flinging his tail up to the tip-top of the tallest tree, and shattering all its branches as it crashed heavily down again—the dragon fell at full length upon the ground, and lay quite motionless.

"It is only a sleeping-potion," said the enchantress to Prince Jason. "One always finds a use for these mischievous creatures, sooner or later; so I did not wish to kill him outright. Quick! Snatch the prize, and let us begone! You have won the Golden Fleece!"

Jason caught the fleece from the tree, and hurried through the grove, the deep shadows of which were illuminated, as he passed, by the golden glory of the precious object that he bore along. A little way before him, he beheld the old woman whom he had helped over the stream, with her peacock beside her. She clapped her hands for joy, and beckoning him to make haste, disappeared among the duskiness of the trees. Espying the two winged sons of the North Wind, (who were disporting themselves in the moonlight, a few hundred feet aloft), Jason bade them tell the rest of the Argonauts to embark as speedily as possible. But Lynceus, with his sharp eyes, had already caught a glimpse of him, bringing the Golden Fleece, although several stone-walls, a hill, and the black shadows of the Grove of Mars, intervened between. By his advice, the heroes had seated themselves on the benches of the galley, with their oars held perpendicularly, ready to let fall into the water.

As Jason drew near, he heard the Talking Image, calling to him with more than ordinary eagerness in its grave, sweet voice:—

"Make haste, Prince Jason! For your life, make haste!"

With one bound, he leaped aboard. At sight of the glorious radiance of the Golden Fleece, the nine-and-forty heroes gave a mighty shout; and Orpheus, striking his harp, sang a song of triumph, to the cadence of which the galley flew over the water, homeward bound, as if careering along with wings!

EDITORIAL APPENDICES

TEXTUAL INTRODUCTION

A WONDER BOOK

AS INDICATED in Professor Pearce's Introduction to Hawthorne's children's books (*True Stories*, Centenary Edition, Volume VI), *A Wonder Book* had been long in contemplation, but not until May 23, 1851, did Hawthorne express to Fields his plan to write "within six weeks or two months next ensuing, a book of stories, made up of classical myths."[1] Fields was as usual enthusiastic, and to Hawthorne's suggestion that Billings be employed as illustrator, remarked that the artist "prefers to see the Mss. before he attempts the designs."[2] Writing started on June 1,[3] and on June 5, Hawthorne wrote Fields, "I hope to send you some of the Wonder Book in a fortnight or thereabouts."[4] The final section of the manuscript was mailed to Fields on July 15, the date subscribed to the Preface.[5] However, Mrs. Fields had died on July 13, and as a consequence nothing was done to put the book into production. But on August 14, Fields wrote Hawthorne: "It is now in Billings's hands who is making the drawings. During my absence all things in the Publishing way stopped and now that I am back to my

[1] MS, Huntington Library.

[2] Fields to Hawthorne, May 24, 1851, MS, Berg Collection, New York Public Library.

[3] Hawthorne to Louisa Hawthorne, July 10, 1851, quoted in Julian Hawthorne, *Nathaniel Hawthorne and His Wife* (Boston, 1885), I, 408; Hawthorne to Horatio Bridge, July 22, 1851, MS, Bowdoin College.

[4] MS, Buffalo Public Library.

[5] Hawthorne to Fields, July 15, 1851, MS transcription, Houghton Library, Harvard University.

desk I trust all will be well & in progress." [6] A week later Fields again wrote to Hawthorne: "Billings is so uncertain that up to this hour I have not yet been able to get from him the Mss. of the Wonder Book to put into the Printer's hands. I have given him the Porch drawing which he promises with the rest tomorrow. Just as soon as he is done with the Mss. we begin to print." [7]

Composition of the book must have started in late August, if Billings completed his drawings as Fields hoped. In his July 15 letter Hawthorne had remarked: "I must see the proof sheets of this book. It is a cursed bore, for I want to be done with it from this moment. Can't you arrange it so that two or three, or more sheets may be sent at once, on stated days; and so my journeys to the village be fewer?" [8] Whether or not the mailings of the sheets followed this request, by September 13 Hawthorne had read proof at Lenox at least through sheet 10 (pages 145–60), for he complains: "The proof-sheets struggle hither ward very irregularly, and seem to be often delayed on the road. One of them (from page 122 to 143 inclusive) has not come at all." [9] These pages conclude "The Paradise of Children" and go well into "The Three Golden Apples." No indication is preserved whether the sheet was later sent or whether Fields followed Hawthorne's suggestion: "Perhaps you will take the trouble to look over that proof carefully yourself. Generally they are very correct." [10] The final proofs were mailed

6 MS, Berg Collection, New York Public Library.

7 August 21, 1851, MS, Berg Collection, New York Public Library.

8 The custom seems to have been to send a sheet a day, or at any rate any single sheet when it was set and imposed.

9 Hawthorne to Fields, MS transcription, Hawthorne-Fields Letter Book, Houghton Library, Harvard University.

10 In this sheet Hawthorne's manuscript slip "maiden's" for "maidens" (93.9) was repaired, but what seem to be two unauthoritative departures from copy were not changed: the omission of MS "and" at 88.21 and the reading "spy" for MS "espy" at 89.31.

on Monday, September 22, to Salem, where Hawthorne had made a trip, on the evidence of a newly redated letter from Fields: "As the printers are now all ready for the author and the Bk. as you will perceive is in type complete I take the liberty of sending it to Salem & beg that you will read proofs & send back by Tuesday night." [11] By October 2, the *Cost Books* record the completion of the stereotyping, and bill the paper and printing as well as binding, the cost being 38¢ per copy against a retail price of 75¢.[12] On October 22, Hawthorne wrote to Ticknor & Co., "I suppose the Wonder Book will soon be out," and gave directions for a number of complimentary copies; on October 24, Ticknor replied, "The Wonder Book is in the Binders hands & will be ready very soon", and on November 5 again wrote to Hawthorne, announcing publication for November 8.[13] The book was advertised November 15 in the *Literary World;* deposit was on December 22 (*BAL* 7606). As was customary for books published so late in the year, the title page was dated ahead, in 1852.

The first edition may be described as follows:

A | WONDER-BOOK | FOR | GIRLS AND BOYS. | BY | NATHANIEL HAWTHORNE. | WITH EN-GRAVINGS BY BAKER FROM DESIGNS BY BILLINGS. | BOSTON: | TICKNOR, REED, AND FIELDS. | MDCCCLII.

[1]⁸ 2–16⁸, 128 leaves, pp. [i–iii] iv [v] vi [7] 8–256; pages 15, 54, 57, 62, 89, 93, 98, 125, 128, 136, 169, 173, 177, 208, 210, 214, and 251, unnumbered; inserted

11 MS, Berg Collection, New York Public Library.

12 Warren S. Tryon and William Charvat, eds., *The Cost Books of Ticknor and Fields* (New York, 1949), A228a.

13 MS, University of Virginia; MSS, Ticknor Domestic Letter Books, vol. 3, nos. 320 and 348, Houghton Library, Harvard University.

frontispiece and six plates,[14] facing pp. 15, 62, 98, 136, 177, and 214.

p. i: title; p. ii: 'Entered according to Act of Congress, in the year 1851, | by NATHANIEL HAWTHORNE, | In the Clerk's Office of the District Court for the District of Massachusetts. | Stereotyped by | HOBART & ROB-BINS, | BOSTON.'; p. iii: 'PREFACE.', subscribed on p. iv 'LENOX, *July 15th*, 1851.'; p. v: 'CONTENTS.'; pp. 7–256: text; on p. 256: 'THE END.'

The *Cost Books* give a total of $1,126.16 for the 3,067 copies, including binding, but excluding a charge of $150.82 for the stereotype plates. These plates produced a number of printings including the uniform edition of 1865, and were continued in use as late as 1886. In the second printing the plate for page 21, line 3, was altered to correct the misprint "lifed" for "lifted". Collation of first and last known printings (New Fireside, *c.* 1886)[15] on the Hinman Collating Machine discloses no further substantive variants; all re-settings were substantively faithful to the original.

The second printing of 1,600 copies was dated December 4, 1851, the *Cost Books* noting that in February, 1852, of the total of 4,667 copies in the two printings, 1,013 remained on hand. The third printing, of 500 copies, was not called for until September, 1853; printings of 1,000 followed in December, 1853, 672 in August, 1855, 500 in March–April, 1857, and 1,000 in August–September, 1858. The unpublished Cost Books record other printings in Hawthorne's lifetime:

[14] The plate illustrating "The Golden Touch" by a misunderstanding represented Midas conversing with Mercury, not Bacchus. In a letter to Robert Carter, March 19, 1853, Hawthorne explained: "I did not convert Bacchus into Mercury, in the story of Midas. The erudite Mr. Billings is solely responsible for that transformation. But I did not see any method of strongly identifying Bacchus—unless on the supposition that King Midas merely fancied himself possessed of the golden faculty, while under the influence of the grape." (MS, University of Virginia.)

[15] OSU first printing, uncatalogued, flyleaf inscription Dec. 25, 1851, and OSU New Fireside, uncatalogued, copy 1.

in February, September, and December of 1859, and in September, 1863, each consisting of 500 copies.[16]

On November 18, 1851, Ticknor addressed the Henry G. Bohn Co. in London: "We sent you by the Steamer of the 12th from this Port, a complete copy of 'The Wonder Book By Hawthorne,' in sheets per mail. We also send you by the Steamer from New York, on the 19th inst. a Copy of the 'Snow Image' by Hawthorne' as far as page 208.—and in a small case, care of Baring Bros. & Co. by the same conveyance, we send a duplicate of The Snow Image—also, a complete copy of The Wonder Bk,—& The Electrotypes from the 7 Wood Cuts of the latter book,—all which have been sent in accordance with your instructions to our Mr. Fields.— And for which you are charged £40.–0,0.–".[17]

Bohn published the first English edition in December, 1851, priced at 2/6. The *Publishers' Circular* lists the *Wonder Book* among books published between December 13 and December 29; in the Ohio State University Libraries is a copy (Turner, uncatalogued) inscribed by the owner on December 25, 1851. Every effort would have been made, of course, to put the book on sale before Christmas.

A | WONDER-BOOK | FOR | GIRLS AND BOYS. | BY NATHANIEL HAWTHORNE. | WITH ILLUS- TRATIVE ENGRAVINGS. | LONDON: | HENRY G. BOHN, YORK STREET, COVENT GARDEN. | 1852.

[A]⁴ B–I⁸ K–O⁸ P⁴, 112 leaves, pp. [a–b] [i–iii] iv [v] vi [1] 2–213 [214–216]; inserted frontispiece and seven engravings.

p. a: half-title, 'A | WONDER-BOOK | FOR | GIRLS AND BOYS.'; p. b: blank; p. i: title; p. ii: 'PRINTED

16 *Cost Books*, A234c, B36c, B49c, B122b, B204c, and B259c; unpublished Ticknor Cost Books, MS, Houghton Library, Harvard University.
17 Ticknor Foreign Letter Books, vol. 2, no. 242, MS, Houghton Library, Harvard University.

BY HARRISON AND SON, | LONDON GAZETTE OFFICE, ST. MARTIN'S LANE; | AND | OR-CHARD STREET, WESTMINSTER.'; p. iii: 'PREF-ACE.', subscribed on p. iv, '*July 15th*, 1851.'; p. v: 'CONTENTS.'; pp. 1–213: text; on p. 214: colophon, as on p. ii; pp. 215–216: blank.

The illustrative engravings are those of the American edition, but Bohn added a new illustration facing page 141, entitled 'HILL-SIDE WOOD', signed 'H. THOMPSON DEL'.

A piracy by Knight and Son appeared in 1855, confusingly entitled *Tanglewood Tales: A Wonder-Book for Girls and Boys*, with copies of the American illustrations but a new frontispiece. The British Museum copy carries a front binding title *A Wonder Book for Girls and Boys*, but *Tanglewood Tales* on the spine. This edition was reissued in 1860 with the Knight piracy *Tanglewood Tales for Girls and Boys, Being a Second Wonder Book*, first published in 1856, a resetting of the Chapman and Hall first English edition, and again copying the Baker illustrations. Another English edition was published by Routledge in 1867, using the Bohn plates, which had been sold on the dissolution of the company in 1864. These editions have not been collated since they could have no authority.

Preserved in the Barrett Collection at the University of Virginia Library is the printer's copy holograph manuscript of *A Wonder Book* consisting of 71 leaves written on both sides of the paper in a black ink now faded brown. What might have been a 72nd leaf, a blank after "Pandora's Box" (retitled "A Paradise of Children" before printing), is wanting. The manuscript is now bound in marbled boards with red-leather spine and corners. On the flyleaf in pencil is written "from Francis Lathrop | brother of Hawthorne's son-in-law" and to the right, "W A White | 14 July, 1900—". On the first page of the manuscript is the title, "A WONDER BOOK | for Girls and Boys. | by | Nathaniel Hawthorne." The verso is laid out for the contents except for the blank page numbers. There follow 16 leaves, or 32 pages, of the links, numbered consecutively, with a notation to the printer after each introductory piece, typified by the first: "(Here insert the Gorgon's Head, beginning it on a separate page.)". At the head of each of the afterpieces the notation "Here begin on a separate page)" or "(Begin . . . " appears. At the foot of the final afterpiece is written "The End." Following page 32 of this material, "The Gorgon's Head" starts. Each story is separately numbered, and there is no continuous numbering anywhere in the manuscript. Each story, moreover, begins on the recto of a leaf, even if the preceding verso was blank. Together, these facts suggest that Hawthorne wished to keep the final order of the stories fluid until the last moment. Within each story, as within each link, he wrote as a running head the appropriate title, within parentheses. The original title of "The Paradise of Children" was "Pandora's Box" both in head-title and in running heads, but Fields in pencil changed it to conform to the altered title as found in the contents and in Hawthorne's note at the end of the introduction "Tanglewood Play-room" where he wrote, "(Here begin a page with 'Pandora's Box, changing the title to 'The Paradise of Children.'". One recalls Hawthorne's letter to Fields of July 15 beginning, "Here you have the rest of the Wonder Book"; hence it is clear that "Pandora's Box" had been sent in an earlier batch, and Hawthorne could not himself change the title in that part of the manuscript. The same situation holds with "The Miraculous Pitcher," which had been "Baucis and Philemon" in head-title and running heads, the head-title changed in pencil in accord with the instruction at the end of the introduction "The Hill-side"—"(Here begin a page with 'Baucis and Philemon—changing the title to 'The Miraculous Pitcher.'" Thus the material sent to Fields on July 15 could at the most have comprised no more than "The Chimæra" and the linking and introductory material, and probably it was no more than the first 32 pages—all the stories having been dispatched earlier.

The evidence of the paper agrees with this general hypothesis. Two papers are involved, identified by their size and by their differing embossed seals. Both papers are blue, with the recto of the leaf a darker shade than the verso. The sheet is folded once to make gatherings of two leaves, or four pages, thus forming a pattern of dark-light-light-dark.[18] The first story, "The Gorgon's Head," begins with a light-blue paper with a greenish tinge and an embossed seal of plumes with the initials B&G beneath. A page of this unwatermarked wove paper measures 247 × 199 mm. This paper continues through to the end of the text. However, the title and preface, followed by all the introductory and afterpiece links, are written on a paper of different manufacture, also blue, wove, and unwatermarked, but slightly darker in shade and measuring 247 × 191 mm., its embossed seal reading SOUTHWORTH CO. above a dove carrying an envelope in its beak. This difference in paper suggests that the stories were written at one time and the preliminaries and the links at another, and thus the odds are favorable that the July 15 mailing consisted only of the latest material, which would be written on this different paper.

In order to keep each story as a unit, and thus movable in its order (in fact we have no evidence as to the order

18 Two exceptions may be observed, both without significance. The first gathering containing the title, contents, and preface was reversed in the folding so that the pattern is light-dark-dark-light. The mistake in folding also occurs in pages 13–16 of "The Chimæra," the next-to-the-last gathering.

of composition), Hawthorne allowed a blank leaf to stand at the end of "The Golden Touch" and also of "The Three Golden Apples," a fact that suggests that the missing blank following "Pandora's Box" was removed at some later time. In the links part of the manuscript, the leaf containing the afterpiece of "Shadow Brook" is detached from its conjugate in the introductory part, probably for the convenience of the compositor, Nichols, who had a stint beginning in the text of "The Golden Touch" and going through the afterpiece of "Shadow Brook." Just above this stint assigned to Nichols, the leaf containing pages 7–8 of "The Golden Touch" has been cut horizontally, but both halves are still conjunct with the previous leaf; possibly this was an effort to allow two compositors to use the leaf simultaneously. The leaf of pages 29–30, the end of the introductory "Bald-summit" and the start of the afterpiece, is detached from its conjugate pages 31–32 for the lower half only.

Two compositors, their stints marked by their signatures, set the book, Nichols composing 3,557 lines and Stevenson 2,094. A third compositor, Ware, intervenes with 240 lines. The breakdown of the typesetting is provided in an appendix "Compositorial Stints", where it will be noted that the takes were considerably longer than was usual. Despite the fact that Nichols set almost 1,500 more lines than Stevenson, the editor's judgment about the extent of Hawthorne's proof-reading in relation to the number of substantive variants assigns nine substantive departures from copy that are not simple modernizations to Nichols but fifteen to Stevenson, whereas Ware in his two short stints has one.[19] Word changes in Stevenson's share, therefore, are to be viewed with con-

[19] See "Rejected First-Edition Substantive Variants," pp. 403–4. The compositors' departures are: Nichols: 14.6, 20.3, 32.13, 52.8, 53.2, 56.21, 149.23, 152.7, and 154.7; Stevenson; 39.13, 39.19, 39.23, 41.29, 42.18, 44.6, 48.10, 69.32, 71.6, 88.21, 89.31, 95.15, 126.27, 131.5, and 131.13; Ware: 123.8.

siderable suspicion when they seem to be paraphrases or misreadings, whereas Nichols's errors seem to be confined almost exclusively to misreadings.

As in the other books of stories for children, Hawthorne seems to have been bent less on literary improvement in his proofreading than on removing positive errors. As usual, although we do not know how many mistakes he altered back to the manuscript readings, his revision was casual. The addition in proof at 169.9–10 is a clear indication of his hand. Otherwise, it seems fairly certain that he changed manuscript "glassy" to "perfect" at 36.1, "living" to "tender" at 53.22, "(whose eyesight, you know, was none of the best)" to "(whose eyes, you know, were getting rather dim)" at 123.25, and "half-a-dozen" to "a few" at 169.8. Whether manuscript "glistening" but book "glittering" at 13.15 is a proof change or a Nichols misreading or paraphrase is doubtful, and at 50.8 the change from manuscript "astounded" to "astonished", although reasons may be adduced in its favor, is even more suspicious since it occurs in Stevenson's stint.

Although a few readings in the Bohn English edition could be argued for as resulting from early American proof as copy, the known facts of the sale discourage any such hypothesis, and it is clear that the English is a completely derived edition from the printed American sheets and thus that none of its readings can have any authority. Also, since substantive plate changes were not made in later American printings, only two textual documents contribute to the establishment of the text, the manuscript and the first Boston printing. The manuscript, of course, is selected as the copy-text because of its absolute authority in respect to the accidentals. Certain corrections of its errors are admitted from the first Boston edition,[20] and also admitted are a handful of sub-

[20] See "Editorial Emendations in the Copy-Text", pp. 395–98, at 20.9, 70.27, 76.27, 79.27, 82.8, 130.2, and 142.11.

stantives taken to represent Hawthorne's identifiable proof alterations. In general, however, the present text is a faithful copy of the manuscript, corrected and revised to a limited extent from the book.

In Hawthorne's letter to Fields describing the project, he had suggested as titles "A Wonder-Book for Girls and Boys" and "The Wonder Book of Old Stories"; Fields replied that he liked "A Wonder Book for Girls and Boys." From then on, "Wonder Book" is without a hyphen in all known correspondence of Hawthorne before publication, including twice in the letter dispatching the manuscript with its inscribed unhyphenated title.[21] In the introductory chapter of *Tanglewood Tales*, the inscriptions are "Wonder Book". It would seem that the Boston printed title (which is the only occurrence of the title in the book) is the printer's form, not Hawthorne's, and that the speck of a hyphen in "A Second Wonder-Book" for his title of *Tanglewood Tales* (the Pierpont Morgan Library holograph manuscript) was influenced by the established usage of the printed edition of *A Wonder-Book*. In the present edition, therefore, is restored what appears to be the more authoritative form of the title as evidenced from the manuscript and from Hawthorne's letters.

TANGLEWOOD TALES

THE MANUSCRIPT of *Tanglewood Tales* was mailed to Ticknor from Concord on March 15, 1853, with a plea that

[21] Hawthorne to Fields: June 5, 1851, MS, Buffalo Public Library; July 15, 1851, MS transcription, Houghton Library, Harvard University; August 18, 1851, MS, St. Lawrence University. Fields to Hawthorne, May 24, August 14, and August 21, 1851, MSS, Berg Collection, New York Public Library. Hawthorne to Horatio Bridge, July 22 and October 11, 1851, MSS, Bowdoin College. Hawthorne to Ticknor & Co., October 22, 1851, MS, University of Virginia.

it be sent to press immediately and should not be delayed by the illustrations, which would be made after printing was completed. The *Cost Books*[1] date for 3,000 copies of the first printing by T. R. Marvin was April 28, an entry that also included the cost of seven illustrations by Hammat Billings, the engraving by Baker, Smith & Andrew, and their separate printing. The cost per copy was 48¢; the price is given as 87 1/2¢, which becomes 88¢ in later printings. The entry gives September 20 for publication; but advance copies were in existence for a month before as evidenced by the *BAL* note of a copy in the New York Public Library presumably presented to Duyckinck and inscribed by him August 24, 1853. On August 24, an excerpt printed from sheets or an advance copy was published in the *New York Evening Post*. It consisted of the first ten pages of the chapter "The Pygmies," presented as: "Antaeus and the Pygmies. By Nathaniel Hawthorne. [From the Tanglewood Papers, in the press of Ticknor, Reed & Fields of Boston.]"[2] *BAL* notes that the book was advertised for September 3 in *Literary World* of August 27, and reviewed in the issue of September 10. Copies of this first printing may contain catalogues dated July, August, September, or October.

TANGLEWOOD TALES, | FOR | GIRLS AND BOYS; | BEING | A SECOND WONDER-BOOK. | BY | NATHANIEL HAWTHORNE. | WITH FINE ILLUSTRATIONS. | BOSTON: | TICKNOR, REED, AND FIELDS. | M DCCC LIII.

[1]⁸ 2–21⁸, pp. [1–4] 5 [6] 7–336; engraved title tipped in before printed title; six illustrations tipped in facing pp. 64, 84, 114, 190, 220, 272.

[1] Warren S. Tryon and William Charvat, eds., *The Cost Books of Ticknor and Fields* (New York, 1949), B23a.

[2] The passage was reprinted, with the *Evening Post* given as the source, and still referring to the "Tanglewood Papers," in the *Lowell Weekly Journal and Courier*, Lowell, Massachusetts, on September 16.

pp. 1–2: blank; p. 3: printed title; p. 4: copyright notice with imprint, 'STEREOTYPED AT THE | BOSTON STEREOTYPE FOUNDRY.'; p. 5: 'CONTENTS.'; p. 6: blank; pp. 7–336: text.

The engraved title page, facing p. 2, reads with decorative lettering, 'TANGLEWOOD | TALES, | ANOTHER | WONDER-BOOK | [picture of the storyteller lying on the ground surrounded by six children] | BY | NATHANIEL HAWTHORNE'. The six illustrations have the following captions: (facing p. 64) '"And made his bull head skip six yards from his human body, which fell | down flat upon the ground."'; (facing p. 85) '"By this time the whole nation of Pygmies had seen the new wonder," &c.'; (facing p. 114) 'Europa all the while looked down upon her brothers, &c.'; (facing p. 191) '"Assume your proper shapes, gormandizers, and begone to the sty."'; (facing p. 220) '"Come! Will you not like to ride a little way with me in my beautiful chariot."'; (facing p. 272) '"This learned person was one of the people or quadrupeds, called Centaurs."'

The *Cost Books* record for September 16 a second printing of 800 copies and give the printer as Rand. In the first printing the printer listed in the *Cost Books* as Marvin had not appeared in the imprint, but the second printing may be distinguished by the notation below the copyright notice, "PRESS OF GEO. C. RAND, | WOOD CUT AND BOOK PRINTER, | CORNHILL, BOSTON." Beneath this is the regular imprint of the first printing, "STEREOTYPED AT THE | BOSTON STEREOTYPE FOUNDRY."

A third printing of 1,000 copies, at 88¢, is listed in the *Cost Books* on January 5, 1854, a fourth on March 7–22, 1856, of 500, and a fifth on June 10, 1857, of 500. Further printings in Hawthorne's lifetime appear in the unpublished Cost Books,[3] the sixth of 500 copies on September 21, 1859, the seventh of 280 copies on February 10, 1862, and the eighth of 350 copies on August 21, 1863.

On May 16, 1853, Ticknor & Co. wrote as follows to the London publishers Chapman and Hall, to whom Fields had triumphantly sold *The Blithedale Romance* for £200 in 1852: "We have a new Juvenile Book by Nathaniel Hawthorne called 'Tanglewood Tales' in press. It is similar in its style to 'The Wonder Book' which Bohn published. We offer it to you, as we shall all Hawthornes new works, first. The price for copyright & early sheets is 50 £. The Book will contain 7 engravings from original designs, casts of which we will supply for £14. Let us hear from you by return steamer." A postscript reads "—about 300 pages."[4] The rest of the correspondence is missing, but on June 20 Fields was able to write to the London publisher S. O. Beeton, apparently in response to an enquiry, "Hawthorne's Tanglewood Tales is sold to C & Hall as they have the refusal of all of Hawthorne's Books, having paid liberally heretofore for his other works."[5] The book was noted as in press by *Publisher's Circular* on August 1, advertised in the *Athenæum* of August 13 as to be published on the 18th, and on August 20 advertised as "this day" and listed with new books, and again advertised as "now ready" on September 10. It was reviewed on September 24 in the *Literary Gazette*. It would seem that the American edition was delayed to allow for the slower production of the English and to protect Chapman and Hall from piracy.

TANGLEWOOD TALES, | FOR | GIRLS AND BOYS: | [The following line is set in black-letter

[3] MS, Houghton Library, Harvard University.

[4] Ticknor and Fields Foreign Letter Books, vol. 3, no. 138; MS, Houghton Library, Harvard University.

[5] Ticknor and Fields Foreign Letter Books, vol. 3, no. 151; MS, Houghton Library, Harvard University.

type.] Being a Second Wonder-Book. | BY | NA-
THANIEL HAWTHORNE. | WITH ILLUSTRA-
TIONS. | LONDON: | CHAPMAN AND HALL,
193, PICCADILLY. | 1853

[A]² (A1+1) B–I⁸ K–Q⁸ R⁶, pp. [i–vi] [1] 2–251
[252]; A1+1 is the printed title page on plate paper,
tipped in; before it is bound in after A1 a two-leaf fold
on plate paper containing an illustration ('EUROPA
AND THE BULL. Page 81.') on the verso of the first
leaf and the engraved title page on the recto of the
second leaf, each obverse being blank; engraved illustrations are tipped in facing pp. 44, 72, 141, 162,
and 202.

p. i: half-title; p. ii: blank; p. iii: printed title; p. iv:
blank; p. v: contents; p. vi: blank; pp. 1–251: text, end-
ing with colophon, 'LONDON: | BRADBURY AND
EVANS, PRINTERS, WHITEFRIARS.'; p. 252:
blank.

(NOTE: The engraved title page is the same as in the
American edition, as are the plates for the engraved
illustrations except that these have been given story
captions and page references instead of the quotations
used in the American edition.)

The use of plate paper for the disjunct leaf of the
printed title A1+1 is unusual but explicable. A² would
be printed with R⁶ in 8's, but the six illustrations plus
the engraved title left a leaf of plate paper unused, and
it would be most economical to fit the printed title on
it and then insert it in the preliminaries.

As noted above, the Ticknor & Co. letter to Chapman and
Hall offered "early sheets" as copy as well as casts for the
seven engravings, including the special title. The reply could
scarcely have come before June 1, so no question can exist
that actual printed sheets of the book, not proofs, were avail-

able and would have been sent. The substantive variants of the first English edition show no sign of authorial intervention and can all be lumped as unauthoritative.

Preserved in The Pierpont Morgan Library is the printer's-copy holograph manuscript, with the presentation note from Fields, "To Henry C. Baird from his friend James T. Fields. Boston. 1853." This is accompanied by a letter dated from Boston on June 7, 1853: "My dear Harry, I send you with this the Mss. of Hawthorne's Tanglewood Tales a book we shall not publish till September, so you will please keep it from the public gaze till after the book has appeared. . . . " The manuscript is written in black ink, now faded to brown, on the rectos of 146 leaves of glazed light-blue wove paper, folded once to make gatherings of two leaves, the leaf measurement being 251 × 196 mm. Each sheet of paper is blindstamped with a mark consisting of a shield coat of arms surmounted by a coronet, the whole within a laurel wreath. Two leaves are written on the verso, about one-third of a page on fol. 30^v containing the end of "The Minotaur," and about one-half of a page of the end of "The Pygmies" on fol. 46^v. The first two leaves are preliminary. As a title, Hawthorne wrote on the first, "Tanglewood Tales | for | Girls and Boys. | Being a second Wonder-Book. | By Nathaniel Hawthorne." He had first started to write "Boys and G" but then stopped, wiped out the letters, and wrote the final form over them. The second leaf contains the contents. The introduction and each chapter are numbered independently, the first page being left unnumbered though counted. The sequence is as follows: "The Wayside. Introductory" fols. [1] 2–6; "The Minotaur" fols. [1] 2–23 (23 being paged on the verso of fol. 22); "The Pygmies" fols. [1] 2–17 (17 being paged on the verso of fol. 16); "The Dragon's Teeth" fols. [1] 2–24; "Circe's Palace" fols. [1] 2–24; "The Pomegranate-Seeds" fols. [1] 2–22; and "The Golden Fleece" fols. [1]

2–30. Each story is headed with the full title triple under-lined, and the succeeding pages carry a short form in one or two words centered at the top before the foliation. The short title "Wayside" is omitted inadvertently on fol. 6 of the introduction.

Two main compositors set the book, the proprietor Marvin and a workman named Manning, each of whom marked his stints by writing his name in pencil at the start of a paragraph indention. The compositor of "The Wayside" is unknown (207 lines of the first edition), but otherwise Marvin set 3,821 lines of text and Manning 3,201 lines. Two other workmen intervened only rarely, Martin setting 551 lines and Squire setting 367. The stints of these compositors are provided in an appendix to the present edition; but they furnish little or no evidence to assist an editor in the choice of variants between the manuscript and the first edition since the setting was on the whole very faithful, and the extent of Hawthorne's proofreading is much in doubt. According to the conjectured revisions by Hawthorne in proof (the corrections he made that returned the readings to those of the manuscript cannot, of course, be determined), Marvin made ten substantive departures from copy and three that might be called moderni-zations, whereas Manning made eight departures and five modernizations. It is fortunate that Squire had so little to do with the book, for in his short stint he made two departures and one modernization; Ignoto and Martin, so far as can be told, were impeccable in their shares.[6] Sixteen actual sub-stantive differences occur between the manuscript and the print that are accepted by the present editor as necessary emendations to the copy-text, whether as corrections or as

[6] Taken together these variants comprise the appendix "Rejected First-Edition Substantive Variants," pp. 404–5. Broken down by compositor, this list reads: Marvin: 184.31, 199.8, 206.26, 237.19, 239.6, 259.11, 263.28, 274.3, 290.19, 308.22, 348.33, 349.14, and 356.5; Manning: 185.33, 200.32, 225.6, 242.23, 244.16, 244.30, 268.15, 279.3–4, 283.21, 297.24, 313.8, 346.35, and 360.28; and Squire: 215.20, 216.29, and 217.32.

proof-revisions exclusive of mechanical manuscript errors like dittography. Of these, one is found in the work of Ignoto (177.21), nine in Marvin's (196.2, 202.28, 208.30, 220.28, 265.18, 287.32, 306.11, 310.33, and 342.19), and six in Manning's (222.28, 223.3, 313.14, 315.12–13, 317.3, and 325.2).[7] Given the limited number, the percentage disparity between Marvin and Manning is probably of no significance, especially since a cluster of four of the most clearly assignable authorial revisions occurs in Manning's share.

Hawthorne's concern that the manuscript should be put into type so that he could see the proofs before he left the United States for his consulship in Liverpool was manifested by his letter of March 15, 1853, accompanying the copy. He wrote to Ticknor on April 6 about a prospective jaunt to Washington, "I think we had better be off as soon as the book is in type—which I suppose it will be in the course of the next week."[8] It is true that he added, "In fact, I should not object to going early in the week, whether or no"; but he and Ticknor did not leave until April 14, and by that date composition must have been completed, or nearly so. If not, proofs could readily have been sent him in Washington, although no record is preserved of such a necessity. It is likely that all or most of the proofs, then, were read in Concord, sent him in the usual fashion sheet by sheet as composition was completed. At least, the first probably identifiable substantive authorial alteration (as distinct from necessary changes conjectured to have been compositorial) occurs on page 87 of the Boston edition, with another on page 88, a more definite one on page 231, another on page 243, possibles on page 247 and on page 250, with the last identifiable one on page 263.[9] If the latter is correct, no more than

[7] For the readings see the appendix "Editorial Emendations in the Copy-Text," pp. 399–402.

[8] MS, Berg Collection, New York Public Library.

[9] For the readings see the appendix "Editorial Emendations in the Copy-Text," at 222.28, 223.3, 306.11, 313.14, 315.12–13, 317.3, and 325.2.

the last four sheets could have gone without proofreading, but there is no reason to suppose that they were not looked over like the others.

As with the other children's books, Hawthorne's proof revision was not at all extensive. Here and there a word was changed, but in general he must have gone through the proofs concerned chiefly for their substantive agreement with the manuscript. No reason exists to suppose that he would ordinarily object to the printer's styling of the accidentals. That not all of the substantive variants between manuscript and book can necessarily be imputed to Hawthorne is not surprising in view of the evidence of his more "literary" works—where perhaps more attention would be devoted to stylistic revision—that he did not collate his manuscript against the proof and in relatively indifferent readings would ordinarily be unaware that a change from his copy had been made.

The copy-text for the present edition is, of course, the manuscript, which alone has authority for the accidentals. A few necessary corrections found in the first Boston edition and a handful of conjectured Hawthorne proof-corrections from its variants have been used to emend the copy-text. Collation on the Hinman Machine reveals no variation at all between the first two Boston printings, nor any substantive variation in any printing of the plates in Hawthorne's life-time.[10] Hence the establishment of the text rests on the evidence of only two documents, of which the manuscript has prime authority.

F. B.

[10] Collation was of first printing OSU PS 1869 A1, Copy 1, against second printing OSU 1869 A1, Copy 5, and of first printing against last known printing of the plates, c. 1886, New Fireside edition, OSU uncatalogued, copy 1, with spot-checking in all intermediate printings.

TEXTUAL NOTES

A WONDER BOOK

9.5 great, old grandmother] The comma after "great" is clearly present in MS, although wanting in I. Ordinarily, "old" would join with the following noun to form a single unit so that no comma would precede. An illustration comes to hand at 22.22, "My dear, good, admirable old ladies", and again at 36.21, "a good old dog". However, one may speculate that at 9.5 the comma was intended to avoid the possible misconstruction associating "great" with "grandmother" to mean "old great grandmother". Thus the two adjectives are strictly equal, applying with separate force to the noun, and the comma is justified, as in *Tanglewood Tales* 177.31, "my small, old cottage".

20.3 discerned] Although the word is by no means written in such a manner as to encourage a misreading, MS "discerned" has been partly mended at the beginning, perhaps to repair a false start as "de", and apparently the compositor of I was thrown off the track and set the word as "discovered". The sense does not encourage the theory that "discovered" is a Hawthorne proof-correction. It is true that a number of sight-words have been employed in the two sentences beginning this paragraph: "looked" . . . "descried" . . . "discerned" . . . "saw". But to substitute "discovered" for "discerned" is scarcely to relieve the pattern. In the faint light, Perseus is able to see only the important identification of the gray hair although not "what sort of figures they were". Then as he comes closer, he sees the empty sockets in their foreheads. The continuation of the sight-pattern in "discerned" is almost essential to the continuity.

32.13 in the island] The correctness of this phrase in MS, and the lack of authority of the I variant "on", is indicated by the phrase "in this unfortunate island" at 12.21, and "in an island" at 97.2.

37.5 chestnuts] The MS here uses a common but not invariable Hawthorne spelling "chesnuts" that is acceptable. However, at 112.4–5 MS has the more conventional spelling "chestnut", and hence the present variant is brought into conformity with it. In both places, I prints the usual spelling "chestnuts" but without authority, of course.

42.16 wonderful] Some connection seems to be present— although its nature is obscure—between the omission in I of MS "very" before "wonderful" and the substitution in I of "only" for MS "very" at 42.18 below. The latter is a manifest error in context since the comparison is between (a) things that in our day we should consider wonderful, and that (although this statement is missing) the old times would not have considered out of the ordinary, and (b) on the other hand things happening now that seem commonplace to us but that would have aroused astonishment in former days. It may be that Hawthorne himself was responsible for the excision of the first "very" in order to avoid a weak repetition with the second at 42.18; if so—or even if it was an editor or compositor who made the change—some misunderstanding seems to have developed at 42.18 that led to the substitution of "only" for "very" there, with a consequential corruption of the sense. One may speculate that the difficulty developed as a result of a marking in the proof.

45.33 ceiling] Hawthorne's characteristic spelling "cieling" found in MS here and elsewhere, he altered only late in life. Although it is not strictly speaking an error since it is occasionally found in the eighteenth century as a presumably acceptable form, it would seem that Hawthorne did not actually derive it from the previous century and that it was, instead, a simple misspelling for him. On this ground it has been emended here, as elsewhere in the Centenary texts.

50.8 astonished] Although Hawthorne's proof-revision of this text was so very light that any change needs to be scrutinized suspiciously, this alteration in I from the "astounded" of MS makes sense. If at 50.11 Midas was only "rather aghast", he should be only "astonished" here at 50.8; "astounded" is far too strong a word for his reactions at this point.

131.5 clambered] The reading "climbed" in I for MS "clambered" is probably a sophistication in view of Hawthorne's use at 153.8 of "clambered" once more for a grapevine. The idiom at 131.5 may well have seemed strained to a compositor, more so than with the use of "up" at 153.8.

158.25 than the moon] The reading of I "than—the moon" perhaps came about because the compositor mistook the extra-long crossbar of the "t" of "the" in MS for a dash. It does not seem to be an authorial proof-correction.

170.7 whispers me] Hawthorne's idiom, as against the sophistication in I, "whispers to me", is evident throughout his writing. Examples are in "P.'s Correspondence", Wiley & Putnam *Mosses from an Old Manse*, 1846 edition, II, 117.26, "To whisper you"; in "The Great Stone Face", Ticknor, Reed & Fields *The Snow-Image*, 1852 edition, 49.21, "whispering him", and in *The American Notebooks*, Centenary Edition, 1972, 123.9–10, "whispered one another".

TANGLEWOOD TALES

192.31–32 our dear son] The reading of MS, as of I and E1, is clearly "our", and of course the reading can be defended—although with some strain—as the royal "we" or else the plural of heart and king. Under these circumstances, the tempting impulse to emend to "his" must be rejected. It would be idle speculation to guess that MS is a fair copy and that Hawthorne, in transcribing his draft, misread "his own dear son".

213.2 giant] Throughout this story, MS reads "giant" and I reads "Giant". It seems more probable to take it that the compositor(s) styled MS in this way in the analogy of the capitalization of "Pygmy" than that Hawthorne went to the trouble of correcting each lower-case letter in proof. In fact, the capitalization of "Pygmy" comes about because they were a little people "who were called Pygmies" (213.4), a quite different matter from "giant", which is not a nomenclature except when used with a name like a title, as "Grandmother Earth".

215.20 theirs] The reading of I is "this", but E1 agrees here for the first and only time with MS against I. It is probable that the English compositor automatically corrected the obvious error, which, given the inscription of the word in MS, is likely to have been a misreading in I. To derive E1 "theirs" from an early state of the I proof later miscorrected to "this" is too complicated to contemplate.

222.28 and] The addition of this word in I would ordinarily be taken as a compositor's sophistication, given (a) the lack of Hawthorne's substantive proof-correction up to this point, and (b) the fact that the preceding semicolon in MS has been mended or that it could be mistaken for an ampersand. However, the semicolon is present in I; and presumably if the addition of "just" at 223.3 is authorial (as it would be an odd compositorial sophistication), the addition of "and" at 222.28 is also likely to be Hawthorne's.

279.6 were,] This addition of a comma from I does not emend a MS error, for precisely the same construction—and again without a comma—is found at 342.8. However, the added commas in these two places serve to clarify what could otherwise be a distinct ambiguity in which "were" could be an auxiliary.

363.12 further] The word may just possibly be "farther" in MS, but the reading of I, here followed, seems to be the one intended.

EDITORIAL EMENDATIONS IN THE COPY-TEXT

A Wonder Book

Note: Except for such silent typographical alterations as are remarked in "The Centenary Texts: Editorial Procedures" prefixed to Volume I and suffixed to Volumes II–IV of this edition, every editorial change from the manuscript copy-text is listed here. The two sources of emendation are the 1852 first edition, I, and Centenary. Asterisked readings are discussed in the Textual Notes. The wavy dash ⁓ represents the same word that appears before the bracket and is used in recording punctuation variants. A caret ∧ indicates the absence of a punctuation mark.

3.4–5;8.26	half-a-dozen] Centenary; ⁓∧⁓∧⁓ MS, I
4.15	15th,] I; ⁓. MS
5.0	"the gorgon's head"] I; '⁓ ⁓ ⁓' MS
5.7	Summer] Centenary; summer MS, I
6.24–25;7.6–7	Squash Blossom] Centenary; ⁓ - ⁓ MS, I
8.1	-cup] I; -Cup MS
8.32	story-teller] I; ⁓∧⁓ MS
*9.5	great,] *stet* MS
9.11	what,] I; ⁓∧ MS
12.7	king.] I; ⁓, MS
12.11	Princess Hippodamia."] I; princess ⁓.∧ MS
13.15	glittering] I; glistening MS
13.28	King] I; king MS
14.10	deeds,] I; ⁓∧ MS

14.14	shield,] I; ~∧ MS
15.21	Princess] I; princess MS
*20.3	discerned] *stet* MS
20.9	not] I; *omit* MS
20.25	Sister] I; sister MS
21.5	∧For] I; "~ MS
21.15	auditors,)] CENTENARY; ~), MS, I
23.13	Nightmare] I; Nigtmare MS
27.29	tumultuously] I; tumultously MS
28.28	snakes.] I; ~∧ MS
30.28	done,] I; ~. MS
31.3	brazen-fingers] MS *hyphen doubtful*
32.11	Danaë] I; Danae MS
*32.13	in] *stet* MS
32.28	Princess] CENTENARY; princess MS, I
33.30;34.17	King] I; king MS
34.26–27	evil-counsellors] CENTENARY; ~∧~ MS, I
36.1	perfect] I; glassy MS
36.12	hill-sides] I; hillsides MS
37.0	"THE GOLDEN TOUCH"] I; '~ ~ ~' MS
*37.5	chestnuts] I; chesnuts MS
37.20	to-and-fro] CENTENARY; ~∧~∧~ MS, I
*42.15–16	consider wonderful] I; consider very wonderful MS
*45.33	ceiling] I; cieling MS
46.21	although] I; althought MS
47.21	-latch,] CENTENARY; ~∧ MS, I
48.22	twelvemonth] CENTENARY; twelve-month MS, I
50.4	cupboard] CENTENARY; cup-board MS, I
*50.8	astonished] I; astounded MS
51.1	wheat—] CENTENARY; ~, MS, I
51.27	"pray] I; ∧~ MS
52.6	undoubtedly] I; undoubtedy MS
53.22	tender] I; living MS
54.17	he.] I; ~∧ MS
58.1	∧who] I; "~ MS
58.4	Touch'?] I; ~?' MS
59.34–60.1	hill-sides] I; hillsides MS
61.0	"The . . . Children"] I; '~ . . . ~' MS

62.5	gray] I; grey MS
65.6	playfellow] CENTENARY; play-fellow MS, I
68.1	Epimetheus.] I; ~$_\wedge$ MS
70.27	to be] I; *omit* to MS
74.6	whispered,] I; ~. MS
74.32	sorts.] I; ~$_\wedge$ MS
76.27	bats'] I; bat's MS
78.1	by-and-by] CENTENARY; ~$_\wedge$~$_\wedge$~ MS, I
79.27	Trouble] I; trouble MS
81.9	ceiling] I; cieling MS
81.27	venomous] I; venemous MS
82.8	Trouble!"] I; trouble!$_\wedge$ MS
82.17	$_\wedge$I] I; "~ MS
83.11–12	half-a-dozen] CENTENARY; ~$_\wedge$~$_\wedge$~ MS, I
85.0	"The . . . Apples"] I; '~ . . . ~' MS
86.17	down-hill] CENTENARY; ~$_\wedge$~ MS, I
93.9	maidens] I; maiden's MS
95.12	believe.] I; ~$_\wedge$ MS
96.21	river?"] I; ~?$_\wedge$ MS
97.13	him.] I; ~$_\wedge$ MS
99.23	By-and-by] CENTENARY; ~$_\wedge$~$_\wedge$~ MS, I
101.22;101.30;103.29	Antæus] I; Antaeus MS
104.32	Hesperides] I; Hesperdes MS
104.33	Ho! Ho! Ho!] CENTENARY; Ho! ho! ho! MS, I
105.9–10	now-and-then] CENTENARY; ~$_\wedge$~$_\wedge$~ MS, I
105.24	anew.] I; ~$_\wedge$ MS
106.2	you."] I; ~.$_\wedge$ MS
106.4	mountain?] I; ~. MS
106.25	ache.] I; ~$_\wedge$ MS
107.19	half-hidden] CENTENARY; ~$_\wedge$~ MS, I
107.27	by-the-by] I; ~$_\wedge$~$_\wedge$~ MS
109.16	Giant] I; giant MS
109.23	"At] I; $_\wedge$~ MS
115.0	"THE MIRACULOUS PITCHER"] I; '~ ~ ~' MS
115.15	farther] CENTENARY; further MS, I
116.17–18	Houstonia] CENTENARY; Housatonia MS, I
117.2	proceeded.] I; ~$_\wedge$ MS
119.12	milk,] I; ~$_\wedge$ MS
120.7	fellow-creatures] I; ~$_\wedge$~ MS

122.21	Ah,] CENTENARY; ~ᴧ MS; ~! I
123.25	(whose . . . dim)] I; (whose eyesight, you know, was none of the best) MS
125.9	everywhere] I; everwhere MS
127.7	coarsest] I; coarest MS
127.11;128.15;129.25;135.14	Mother] I; mother MS
130.2	Its] I; It MS
130.12	ceiling] I; cieling MS
*131.5	clambered] stet MS
133.20	long.] I; ~ᴧ MS
135.1	women,] I; ~. MS
136.28	length,] I; ~; MS
137.22	-tree.] I; ~.— MS
138.0	HILL-SIDE] I; ~ᴧ~ MS
138.8;141.1	hill-side] I; ~ᴧ~ MS
141.0	BALD SUMMIT] CENTENARY; ~ - ~ MS, I
141.0	"THE CHIMÆRA"] I; '~ ~' MS (Chimaera)
142.11	all] I; all all MS
142.25	by-and-by] CENTENARY; ~ᴧ~ᴧ~ MS, I
143.3–4	"The . . . Head," and "The . . . Apples,"] I; '~ . . . ~,' ~ '~ . . . ~,' MS
143.14	anything!] CENTENARY; ~? MS; ~. I
144.0	CHIMÆRA] I; CHIMAERA MS
145.9	country fellow] I; ~ - ~ MS
145.10	springᴧ)] I; ~,) MS
145.13	he,] I; ~ᴧ MS
150.3 et seq.	Chimæra] I; Chimaera MS
156.21	fore-legs] CENTENARY; forelegs MS; ~ᴧ~ I
156.33	latterᴧ] I; ~, (doubtful) MS
*158.25	than the moon] stet MS
161.24	soᴧ)] I; ~,) MS
165.29	eyes.] I; ~ᴧ MS
165.31	Fountain] I; fountain MS
167.3	Bellerophon's] I; Bellerophons MS
169.8	a few] I; half-a-dozen MS
169.9–10	Dr. Dewey . . . Taconic.] I; omit MS
170.2	Butter-cupᴧ—] CENTENARY; ~, — MS, I
170.3	Pringle,] I; ~ᴧ MS
*170.7	whispers me] stet MS
170.11	Bruin?] I; ~. MS

TANGLEWOOD TALES

NOTE: The sources of emendation are the 1853 first American edition, I, and CENTENARY. The first English edition, E1, listed because it was published before the American edition, was derived from I.

176.6	Graylock] I; Greylock MS
176.7–8	hill-side] CENTENARY; hillside MS, I–E1
177.21	Are] I; Are as MS
178.11	TALES."] I; ∼.' MS
180.2	Meanwhile] I; Mean while MS
180.19	∧The] I; '∼ MS
180.28	Clover,)] I; ∼∧) MS
181.6;182.1	Butter-cup] CENTENARY; Buttercup MS, I–E1
181.31	beginnings.] I; ∼∧ MS
182.8	WAYSIDE,] I; ∼. MS
189.7	"Behold your son!"] I; '∼ ∼ ∼!' MS
*192.31	our] *stet* MS
195.7	opals,] I; ∼∧ MS
195.13	them,] I; ∼∧ MS
196.2	have] I; *omit* MS
199.1	everybody] CENTENARY; every body MS, I–E1
201.23	maidens,] I; ∼∧ MS
202.28	art] I; are MS
203.6	throne∧] I; ∼, MS
205.9,10;206.8	Dædalus] I; Daedalus MS
208.30	of] I; *omit* MS
212.13	longer;] I; ∼, MS
*213.2	giant] *stet* MS
213.3 *et seq.*	Antæus] I; Antaeus MS
213.5	mother,] I; ∼∧ MS
214.3	Pygmy] I; pigmy MS
214.7	Pygmy] I; Pigmy MS
214.13	chestnut-trees] CENTENARY; ∼∧∼ MS, I–E1
215.11–12	"Halloo . . . fellow?"] I; '∼ . . . ∼?' MS
215.14–15	"Pretty . . . you!"] I; '∼ . . . ∼!' MS
*215.20	theirs] *stet* MS

216.19	catastrophe,)] I; ~ₐ) MS
216.24	forever] I; for ever MS
220.28	should it] I; *omit* it MS
221.16	breastplate] I; breast-plate MS
221.24	you!"] I; ~!ₐ MS
*222.28	and] I; *omit* MS
223.3	just] I; *omit* MS
226.27	ceiling] I; cieling MS
227.2	life,] I; ~ₐ MS
228.17	has] I; has has MS
228.24	thews] I; thewes MS
232.16	toad-stool] CENTENARY; toadstool MS, I–E1
232.31	merriment.] I; ~ₐ MS
233.27	whatever] I; whatₐ|ever MS
234.1 *et seq.*	Phœnix] I; Phoenix MS
234.4	Phœnicia] I; Phoenicia MS
234.21	"Hush!"] I; '~!' MS
239.28	you,] I; ~ₐ MS
241.13	worn out] I; wornout (*doubtful*) MS
245.24	one foot] I; onefoot MS
246.32	bower.] I; ~ₐ MS
247.2	freestone] I; free stone MS
249.9	next."] I; ~.ₐ MS
252.20	wits.] I; ~ₐ MS
255.27	he,] I; ~ₐ MS
259.19	sword-blades] CENTENARY; ~ₐ~ MS, I–E1
260.10	breastplate] I; breast-plate MS
261.31	battle-field] E1; ~ₐ~ MS, I
265.18	be] I; *omit* MS
266.4	Læstrygonia] I; Laestrigonia MS
268.16	weep!] I; ~, MS
269.1	shoulders,] I; ~ₐ MS
269.28	chimneys] I; chimnies MS
270.6 *et seq.*	Læstrygons] I; Laestrigons MS
270.32	twenty-two] I; ~ₐ~ MS
276.2	ceiling] I; cieling MS
278.15	tiger,] I; ~ₐ MS
*279.6	were,] I; ~ₐ MS
282.3	one.] I; ~ₐ MS

282.11	serving-men] Centenary; ~‿~ MS, I–E1
285.25	pe-weep!"] I; ~ - ~!' MS
286.16	Ulysses?] I; ~, MS
287.32	further] I; farther MS
290.24	asked.] I; ~‿ MS
296.12	off.] I; ~‿ MS
301.4	‿What] I; "~ MS
305.12	hundred-fold] Centenary; ~‿~ MS, I; hundredfold E1
306.11	any food] I; anything MS
309.23	burned] I; buned MS
310.13	naiad] I; Naiad MS
310.17	fauns] I; Fauns MS
310.25,30	satyrs] I; Satyrs MS
310.25	monkeys] I; monkies MS
310.33	goat's] I; goats' MS
312.7	cavern?"] I; ~?‿ MS
313.14	wreath of snakes] I; snake-wreath MS
313.21 *et seq.*	Phœbus] I; Phoebus MS
315.12–13	splendors you] I; splendors which you MS
316.10	King . . . Mines] Centenary; king . . . mines MS, I–E1
317.3	nor] I; or MS
319.10	ceiling] I; cieling MS
323.20	violet?"] I; ~?‿ MS
325.2	withered] I; wizened MS
326.9	king,] I; ~‿ MS
327.16	them,] I; ~‿ MS
328.9	until] I; un-| until MS
332.29	branches] I; brances MS
335.9	burthen] Centenary; burden MS, I–E1
335.29	the Speaking] I; the the Speaking MS
336.8	eyes.] I; ~‿ MS
338.21	fulfilled!"] I; ~!‿ MS
340.30	left] I; lelft MS
342.8	were,] I; ~‿ MS
342.19	which] I; that MS
342.23	distinctly.] Centenary; ~‿ MS; ~; I–E1
344.26	Chimæra] I; Chimaera MS

347.28	Bœotian] I; Boeotian MS
350.35	image.] I; ~∧ MS
353.13	seated,)] I; ~∧) MS
359.28	steel-heads] CENTENARY; ~∧~ MS, I–E1
360.24	enemy!'] CENTENARY; ~!∧ MS, I-E1
363.12	potentate∧] I; ~,) MS
*363.12	further] I; farther MS
367.4	gold box] I; ~ - ~ MS
367.8	branches] I; brances MS
368.4	Orpheus,] I; ~∧ MS

REJECTED FIRST-EDITION SUBSTANTIVE VARIANTS

NOTE: Although the readings below are listed in the Historical Collation, they are given separately here since the information is of critical importance. Asterisked readings are discussed in the Textual Notes.

A WONDER BOOK

5.20;7.13;19.3;36.3	farther] MS; further I
14.6	lifted] MS; lifed I (*first printing*)
*20.3	discerned] MS; discovered I
28.12	round] MS; around I
*32.13	in] MS; on I
39.13	had] MS; *omit* I
39.19	How (*no¶*)] MS; ¶ How I
39.23	zest] MS; rest I
41.29	obscurer] MS; obscure I
42.18	very] MS; only I
44.6	thither] MS; hither I
48.10	no] MS; not I
52.8	could] MS; would I
53.2	had] MS; *omit* I
56.21	would] MS; could I
69.32	graver] MS; grave I
71.6	so] MS; *omit* I
88.21	and] MS; *omit* I
89.31	espy] MS; spy I

95.15	Or] MS; On I
101.27;121.15,25	farther] CENTENARY; further MS, I
116.17–18	Houstonia] CENTENARY; Housatonia MS, I
123.8	of] MS; *omit* I
126.27	flush] MS; flash I
*131.5	clambered] MS; climbed I
131.13	have] MS; *omit* I
149.23	ornamented] MS; ornamental I
152.7	came] MS; come I
154.7	on] MS; in I
155.31	farthest] MS; furthest I
161.2	sank] MS; sunk I
161.33	sprang] MS; sprung I
*170.7	whispers me] whispers to me I

TANGLEWOOD TALES

184.31	would] MS; could I
185.33	could] MS; would I
199.8	contrive] MS; continue I
200.32	trode] MS; trod I
206.26	pressed] MS; passed I
*215.20	theirs] MS; this I
216.29	was] MS; were I
217.32	sideways] MS; sidewise I
225.6	million] MS; millions I
237.19	active] MS; as active I
239.6	swum] MS; swam I
242.23	replied] MS; said I
244.16	and brother] MS; *omit* and I
244.30	closely] MS; *omit* I
259.11	aslantwise] MS; slantwise I
263.28	-break] MS; -breakings I
268.15	¶ And] MS; *no* ¶ I
274.3	drunk] MS; drank I
279.3–4	further] MS; farther I
283.21	sticking] MS; was sticking I

290.19	his] MS; my I
297.24	apronful] MS; apron full I
308.22	forgot] MS; forget I
313.8	as if she] MS; as she if she I
346.35	what ought] MS; what had ought I
348.33	six-armed] MS; six armed I
349.14	handsful] MS; hands full I
356.5	knew to] MS; knew how to I
360.28	tongues-ends] MS; tongues' ends I

WORD-DIVISION

1. *End-of-the-Line Hyphenation in the Centenary Edition*

NOTE: No hyphenation of a possible compound at the end of a line in the Centenary text is present in the manuscript except for the following readings, which are hyphenated within the line in the manuscript. Hyphenated compounds in which both elements are capitalized are not included.

A WONDER BOOK

14.35	school-|boy	103.10	to-and-|fro
33.17	good-for-|nothing	109.25	back-|ache
36.10	golden-||leaved	119.27	water-|weeds
38.19	Butter-|cup	120.10	hard-|hearted
48.6	brook-|trout	121.15	village-|street
54.8	treasure-|room	122.5	heavy-|hearted
60.15	Christmas-|time	134.12	green-|margined
61.6;82.11	snow-|storm	137.2	over-|shadowing
66.17	crying-|fits	146.11	rain-|storm
67.7	good-|tempered	149.10	able-|bodied
73.4	flower-|wreathed	150.10	boa-|constrictor
75.9;97.20	flower-|wreaths	156.14	thunder-|bolt
85.6	frost-|work	158.4	mountain-|top
88.23	fire-|place	161.18	three-|headed
88.34	rough-|and-tumble	162.17	mountain-|peak

TANGLEWOOD TALES

181.8	hooping-|cough	273.24	pot-|herbs
199.3	north-|west	276.34	home-|like
201.15	church-|bell	280.3	two-|and-twenty
203.9	iron-|breasted	280.28	kitchen-|fire
203.22	state-|policy	290.5;293.19	two-and-|twenty
209.7	bull-|mouth	292.30	back-|entrance
210.5	iron-|hearted	302.20	chariot-|wheels
214.17	over-|burthened	306.18	sweet-|cakes
217.10	merry-|hearted	307.33	sea-|nymphs
222.4	lazy-|bones	309.4	farm-|house
222.16	pine-|tree	310.30	sheep-|pasture
228.1	twenty-|seven	319.23	hiding-|place
228.33	to-and-|fro	323.29	surf-|wave
240.4	palace-|steps	325.20	wretched-|looking
241.31	harvest-|field	332.28	By-|and-by
249.34	sea-|water	333.6	four-|footed
263.22	long-|lost	345.7	twin-|brothers
267.19	palace-|gate	352.33	cruel-|looking
269.34	one-|eyed	356.5	fiery-|lunged
269.35	milk-|diet	359.25	by-and-|by
270.30	chief-|officers	362.21	presence-|chamber
271.23	roast-|meat	365.9	leaf-|strewn
272.30	palace-|cook		

2. *End-of-the-Line Hyphenation in the Manuscript*

NOTE: The following compounds, or possible compounds, are hyphenated at the end of the line in the manuscript copy-text. The form in which they have been transcribed in the Centenary Edition, as listed below, represents the practice of the manuscript as ascertained by other appearances or by parallels within the manuscript. Other Hawthorne manuscripts of the period have been consulted when evidence was not available in the *Wonder Book* or *Tanglewood Tales* manuscripts.

A Wonder Book

5.17	sunshine	94.25	stable-door
6.25	Milkweed	94.31	warlike
6.30	grandparents	98.28	overgrown
8.2	playmates	100.17	re-appear
11.6	undertake	105.24	sea-shore
16.8	awhile	106.1	half-a-dozen
24.7	half-a-dozen	118.3	sunset
30.14	uplifted	119.18	spoonfull
37.15	sunlight	123.32	cottage-door
38.5	wonder-smitten	129.16	overflowed
40.20	strong-box	136.20	good-humored
40.21	butter-cups	142.30	nine-pins
51.9	story-book	147.27	now-a-days
62.27	snow-storm	159.31	overtook
73.33	playfellow	162.3	headlong
75.15	cottage-door		

Tanglewood Tales

175.18	half-a-dozen	220.4	chief-ruler
176.8	locust-trees	221.19	pine-tree
178.22	worm-eaten	225.18	knock-down
183.10	moss-grown	232.10	roundabout
188.22	roundabout	232.28	warlike
196.13	gold-hilted	236.20	clover-blossom
201.10	clockwork	238.31	white-capt
201.32	never-ceasing	242.6	snow-white
207.34	bull-heads	242.30	overhead

242.34	home-like	308.12	chariot-wheels
253.34	hill-side	327.22	tenfold
259.16	steel-heads	330.22	all-fours
275.3	moonshine	331.5	half-man
279.23	overjoyed	331.15	now-and-then
279.34	two-and-twenty	337.12	golden-stringed
280.16	kick-shaws	342.30	now-a-days
289.35	two-and-twenty	345.12	mill-stone
290.2,23	snow-white	345.34	foretell
291.28	kinglike	348.33	six-armed
292.20	dew-drops	352.12	hobgoblins
293.10	two-and-twenty	358.23	screwed-up
293.22	twelvemonth	359.12	broadcast
297.6	sea-green	360.30	moonlight
300.8	earthquake	363.24	forty-nine
300.29	apronful	364.23	pasture-ground

3. *Special Cases*

(a)

NOTE: In the following list the compound, or possible compound, is hyphenated at the end of the line in the manuscript and in the Centenary Edition.

A WONDER BOOK

62.8	snow-|storm (i.e. snow-storm)
103.23	fifty-|thousand (i.e. fifty-thousand)
112.13	dis-|proportioned (i.e. disproportioned)
142.24	land-|scape (i.e. landscape)
156.19	straight-|forward (i.e. straightforward)
156.21	hind-|legs (i.e. hind-legs)

TANGLEWOOD TALES

176.10	head-	long (i.e. headlong)
177.32	sun-	shine (i.e. sunshine)
248.2	snow-	white (i.e. snow-white)
283.30	back-	yard (i.e. back-yard)

(b)

NOTE: In the following cases the hyphenated compound appears at the end of the line in the Centenary Edition, but the hyphen is an editorial emendation not present in the manuscript.

A WONDER BOOK

3.4,83.11	half-a-	dozen (i.e. half-a-dozen *for* MS half a dozen)
34.26	evil-	counsellors (i.e. evil-counsellors *for* MS evil counsellors)
59.34	hill-	sides (i.e. hill-sides *for* MS hillsides)
105.9	now-and-	then (i.e. now-and-then *for* MS now and then)
112.4	chestnut-	tree (i.e. chestnut-tree *for* MS chestnut tree)

TANGLEWOOD TALES

| 176.7 | hill-side (i.e. hill-side *for* MS hillside) |

HISTORICAL COLLATION

NOTE: Substantive variants from the Centenary text are listed here. The Centenary reading appears to the left of the bracket, and the variant in collated texts follows; texts not noted for a reading are to be taken as agreeing with Centenary.

A WONDER BOOK

NOTE: Collation is recorded through the first edition, 1852, plates of which continued in use without substantive change, following the sole exception recorded at 21.3 (first printing), through the New Fireside edition, c. 1886.

5.20;7.13;19.3;36.3	farther] further I
13.15	glittering] glistening MS
14.6	lifted] lifed I (*first printing*)
20.3	discerned] discovered I
20.9	not] *omit* MS
28.12	round] around I
32.13	in] on I
36.1	perfect] glassy MS
39.13	had] *omit* I
39.19	How] ¶ How I
39.23	zest] rest I
41.29	obscurer] obscure I
42.15–16	consider wonderful] consider very wonderful MS
42.18	very] only I
44.6	thither] hither I

48.10	no] not I
50.8	astonished] astounded MS
52.8	could] would I
53.2	had] *omit* I
53.22	tender] living MS
56.21	would] could I
69.32	graver] grave I
70.27	to be] *omit* to MS
71.6	so] *omit* I
76.27	bats'] bat's MS
79.27;82.8	Trouble] trouble MS
88.21	and] *omit* I
89.31	espy] spy I
93.9	maidens] maiden's MS
95.15	Or] On I
101.27;121.15,25	farther] further I
115.15	farther] further MS, I
116.17–18	Houstonia] Housatonia MS, I
123.8	of] *omit* I
123.25	(whose . . . dim)] (whose eyesight, you know, was none of the best) MS
126.27	flush] flash I
130.2	Its] It MS
131.5	clambered] climbed I
131.13	have] *omit* I
142.11	all] all all MS
149.23	ornamented] ornamental I
152.7	came] come I
154.7	on] in I
155.31	farthest] furthest I
161.2	sank] sunk I
161.33	sprang] sprung I
169.8	a few] half-a-dozen MS
169.9–10	Dr. Dewey . . . Taconic.] *omit* MS
170.7	whispers] whispers to I

TANGLEWOOD TALES

NOTE: Collation is recorded through the first American edition (I), plates of which continued in use without substantive change through the New Fireside edition, *c.* 1886, and the first English edition (E1), which was published before the American but was derived from it.

177.21	Are] Are as MS
181.24	baby-stories] baby's stories E1
184.31	would] could I–E1
185.33	could] would I–E1
196.2	have] *omit* MS
199.8	contrive] continue I–E1
200.32	trode] trod I–E1
202.28	art] are MS
206.26	pressed] passed I–E1
208.30	of] *omit* MS
215.20	million] millions E1
215.20	theirs] this I
216.29	was] were I–E1
217.32	sideways] sidewise I–E1
220.28	should it] should MS
222.28	and] *omit* MS
223.3	just] *omit* MS
224.30	with] with such E1
225.6	million] millions I–E1
226.25	downward] downwards E1
228.17	has] has has MS
232.32	cried] said E1
233.12	exceedingly] exceeding E1
237.19	active] as active I–E1
239.6	swum] swam I–E1
242.23	replied] said I–E1
243.4	here] there E1
244.16	and brother] *omit* and I–E1
244.30	closely] *omit* I–E1
245.31	on] upon E1
254.27	him be] him to be E1
259.11	aslantwise] slantwise I–E1
262.28	get] to get E1
263.28	-break] -breakings I–E1
265.18	be] *omit* MS

267.34	its neck] his neck E1
268.15	¶ And] *no* ¶ I–E1
274.3	drunk] drank I–E1
279.3–4	further] farther I–E1
283.21	sticking] was sticking I–E1
287.32	further] farther MS
289.3	courtesy] curtsey E1
289.23	I before] I have before E1
290.19	his] my I–E1
294.24	on] upon E1
297.24	apronful] apron full I–E1
306.11	any food] anything MS
308.22	forgot] forget I
310.33	goat's] goats' MS
311.29	a person] *omit* a E1
312.33	these] those E1
313.8	as if] as she if I
313.14	wreath of snakes] snake-wreath MS
315.12–13	splendors you] splendors which you MS
315.26	not you] you not E1
317.3	nor] or MS
323.18	is] this E1
325.2	withered] wizened MS
333.3	to] by E1
335.29	the] the the MS
340.17	tell of] *omit* of E1
342.19	which] that MS
344.34	help row] help to row E1
346.35	what ought] what had ought I–E1
348.33	six-armed] six armed I
349.14	handsful] hands full I–E1
356.5	knew to] knew how to I–E1
360.2–3	a spear] *omit* a E1
360.28	tongues-ends] tongues' ends I–E1
361.2	sprung] sprang E1

ALTERATIONS IN THE MANUSCRIPT

Note: With the exceptions listed below, all alterations made in the manuscript during its inscription or review before submission (the two classes are ordinarily not distinguishable with certainty) are described here. The exceptions are as follows: (1) letters or words that have been mended or traced over for clarity without alteration of the original; (2) interlineations that repeat in a more clearly written form the identical original; and (3) deletions, mendings, or readings under alterations that could not be read. In the description, "above" means "interlined" and "over" means "in the same space." The presence of a caret is always noticed. Square brackets signify one or more illegible letters: letters within square brackets are conjectural on some evidence but not wholly certain.

A Wonder Book

4.5	fit] *interlined with a caret*
5.5	the mists] 'the' *precedes deleted* 'the'
6.21	accidentally] *interlined with a caret*
6.34	let] *interlined above deleted* 'tell'
7.1	know] *interlined with a caret*
7.5	he] *interlined with a caret*
7.21	assumed] *interlined above deleted* 'put on'
7.25	crept] *interlined above deleted* 'cept'
8.17	very] *interlined with a caret*
8.20	me] *interlined with a caret*

9.1	if] *precedes deleted* 'I'
10.20–21	strangers— . . . child—] *dashes delete commas*
12.4	go] *interlined with a caret after* 'you', *a previous* 'go' *interlined with a caret after* 'sooner' *having been wiped out*
12.7	And] 'A' *altered from* 'a'
12.30	days] *interlined with a caret above wiped-out and deleted* 'days'
13.4	on] *interlined above deleted* 'out of'
13.8	were] *interlined above deleted* 'was'
13.19	tusks—] *dash deletes comma*
14.34	ashamed] *precedes deleted* 'him'
15.26	statue] *interlined above deleted* 'image'
16.27	Nymphs."] *period and quotes over wiped-out exclamation and quotes*
18.21	syllable] *interlined with a caret above deleted* 'word'
18.27	scarcely] *interlined above deleted* 'hardly'
19.17	one of] *over wiped-out* 'her sister', *then interlined above for clarity*
19.29	joking with] *interlined above deleted* 'making game of'
20.30–31	as you] *interlined with a caret*
21.10	alike] *over wiped-out* 'equally'
22.13	of they] 'they' *over wiped-out* 'of'
22.20	slippers] *interlined above deleted* 'shoes'
22.28	are] *interlined with a caret*
23.1	away] *interlined above deleted* 'from us'
23.20	good stranger] *over wiped-out* 'my good'
23.23	blind] *interlined above deleted* 'poor'
23.26	the Gray] 'the' *over wiped-out* 'they'
23.27	so] *interlined above deleted* 'such'
23.28	restoring] *precedes deleted* 'them'
25.7	bade] *precedes deleted* 'bade'
25.11	find] *interlined with a caret*
25.14	the slippers] 'the' *over wiped-out* 'their' *and* 'slippers' *over* 'sandals'
25.16	fluttered up off] 'fluttered up o' *over wiped-out* 'flew from the g'

26.9	its] *over wiped-out* 'his'
28.11	perceived] *interlined above deleted* 'beheld'
29.12	possibly] *precedes deleted* 'have'
30.5	now!] *exclamation altered from a comma*
30.28	done,"] *quotes over wiped-out exclamation and double quotes, and a period mistakenly inscribed where comma required*
30.29	other] *precedes deleted* 'two'
31.18	horribly] 'rri' *over wiped-out* 'lly'
31.23	knew not in what direction] *interlined with a caret above deleted* 'could not see which way'
32.7	Danaë] *interlined with a caret above deleted* 'her'
32.9	priests—] *dash deletes comma*
32.12	afloat] *interlined with a caret*
33.4	in the right] 'i' *of* 'in' *over wiped-out* 't'
33.23	minding] 'min' *over wiped-out* 'of [ ]'
34.10	yelled] *over wiped-out* 'shouted'
34.28	people.] *precedes deleted* 'At the first glimpse of the terrible head of Medusa,'
35.7	tooth!] *precedes wiped-out closing double quotes*
36.10	woodland] 'w' *over wiped-out* 'f'
36.19	antics] *interlined with a caret above deleted* 'antics'
37.0	INTRODUCTORY] *over wiped-out* 'At noon, our'
37.10	place] *interlined with a caret*
37.13	keep] *interlined above deleted doubtful* 'hav'
37.16	Summer] 'S' *mended from* 's'
37.20	and then] 'a' *over wiped-out* 'was'
38.27	a monkey] 'a m' *over wiped-out* 'monk'
39.19	is this] 'is t' *over wiped-out* 'was'
39.28	Autumn] 'A' *mended from* 'a'
39.32	Midas] 'a' *over wiped-out* 's'
41.3	was] *over wiped-out* 'bec'
41.5	shown] 'sho' *over wiped-out* 'had'
42.9	yet] *interlined with a caret*
42.28	imagination] *first* 'i' *over wiped-out* 'f'

42.29	yellow] *interlined above deleted* 'golden'
43.15	good-humored] 'good-hum' *over wiped-out* 'satisfact'
44.34	regret the] 'regret' *over wiped-out* 'of it'; 't' *of* 'the' *over wiped-out double quotes*
45.32	earliest] 'e' *over wiped-out* 'f'
46.14	assumed] *interlined above deleted* 'took'
46.31	Midas] *over wiped-out* 'He was'
47.20	his] *interlined with a caret*
49.3	child] *over wiped-out* 'li'
49.18	will] *interlined above* 'last'
49.19	years)] 'years' *over wiped-out* 'eons'; *parenthesis deletes comma*
49.34	it] *interlined with a caret*
50.3	be puzzled] 'be puzz' *over wiped-out* 'puzzled'
50.18	admirably] *follows wiped-out* 'd'
50.24	fins] *precedes deleted* 'fins'
51.2	had] *interlined with a caret*
51.23	jumping] *interlined above deleted* 'starting'
51.29	groaned] 'gr' *over wiped-out* 'sa'
52.6	must] 'm' *over wiped-out* 'u'
53.4	assumed] *interlined above deleted* 'became'
53.5	color] *interlined with a caret*
53.22	warm and] 'warm a' *over wiped-out* 'living and'; 'warm' *then interlined above for clarity*
53.29	his] *altered from* 'he'
53.29	eyes were fixed on the] *interlined with a caret above deleted* 'was looking at her'
53.29	image,] *interlined with a caret before* 'he'
54.23	So] *over wiped-out* 'You'
56.9	human] 'huma' *over wiped-out* 'fleshly'
57.14	Marygold's] *interlined with a caret above deleted* 'her'
57.16	trot] *interlined above deleted* 'hold'
57.16	knee] *a final* 's' *wiped out*
57.17	them] *interlined with a caret*
58.17–18	and deepened] *interlined with a caret*
59.8	on the trees,] *interlined with a caret*

59.21	precise] *interlined with a caret*
61.6	came a] 'came' *over wiped-out* 'fell a' *and* 'a' *over wiped-out* 'm'
63.8	Primrose,] *comma deletes period*
63.9	we will] *over wiped-out* 'you shall'
63.15	cousinhood] 'cou' *over wiped-out* 'Cou', *then the entire word deleted and interlined for clarity*
63.23	know] *interlined with a caret above deleted* 'see'
63.24	snow-storms] *precedes deleted possible* 'times'
65.6	playfellow] '-fellow' *interlined with a caret above deleted* 'mate' *of* 'playmate'
65.21	"Oh, come, don't think] *over wiped-out* 'It is thousands of yea'
66.31	and] *over wiped-out* ' "And'
67.15	know!"] *exclamation and quotes over wiped-out comma and quotes*
68.35	far bigger] *over wiped-out* 'much bigger'
69.17	combine] 'c' *over wiped-out* 'f'
69.19	forth] *interlined above deleted* 'out'
69.35	carved] *interlined above deleted* 'caved'
70.28	Troubles] 'T' *altered from* 't'
70.33	Mother Earth] 'Mother' *interlined above deleted* 'the' *and* 'E' *altered from* 'e'
70.33	her] *interlined with a caret above deleted* 'its'
71.8	of ideas] 'of' *interlined with a caret*
71.28	toys in] *over wiped-out* 'play thi'
73.4–5	flower-wreathed] 'flower' *over wiped-out possible* 'carved'
73.11–12	The gold] *over wiped-out* 'It untwi'
75.25	naughty child] *interlined with a caret*
76.2	sage] *interlined above deleted* 'wise'
76.14	creatures] *interlined with a caret*
76.33	stung] *over wiped-out* 'bitten'
77.1	wish] *over wiped-out* 'of'
77.3	Troubles.] *period altered from comma*
77.34	soon] *over wiped-out* 'to be'

78.10	both] *interlined with a caret*
78.10–11	another. In] *period altered from comma;* 'In' *over wiped-out* 'and'
78.13	her head] *interlined with a caret above deleted* 'the lid'
78.22	"You] *follows deleted* 'Again the tap! It sounded like the tiny knuckles'
79.5	was] *interlined with a caret*
79.33	am] *over wiped-out* 'know'
80.28	Troubles] 'Tr' *over wiped-out* 'tr'
80.31	colored] *interlined with a caret*
81.21	glad—] *dash deletes comma*
82.7	lifted] *interlined above deleted* 'opened'
82.14–15	two feet wide] *interlined with a caret*
83.11	him] *interlined with a caret*
86.8	behold!] *exclamation altered from comma*
86.12	And while] *over wiped-out undecipherable word, then deleted and interlined with a caret for clarity*
86.15	scarlet] *interlined with a caret*
86.22	heads] *over wiped-out undecipherable word, then interlined above for clarity*
86.23	and the] 't' *written over wiped-out* 'E'
88.5	understand] *interlined with a caret*
88.23	Child] 'C' *altered from* 'c'
89.1	been] *interlined with a caret*
89.18	exactly] *over wiped-out* 'quite', *then interlined for clarity*
89.18	the auditor] 'the' *over wiped-out* 'au'
89.27	addressing] 'dr' *over wiped-out* 'ess'
90.21	on the watch] *interlined above deleted* 'awake'
91.33	on hearing] 'on hear' *over wiped-out* 'when they'
92.29	and devote] 'n' *of* 'and' *over wiped-out* 'f'
93.6	lay] *interlined above deleted* 'was'
93.6	half-buried] *interlined above deleted* 'rooted'
94.8	him] *interlined with a caret*
94.22	not] *interlined with a caret*
94.33	had given] 'had' *over wiped-out* 'ga'

95.14   three] *interlined above deleted doubtful* 'this'
            or 'these'
95.33   covered] 'cov-'| *over wiped-out* 'h[idden]'
96.18   soon?] *query altered from comma*
97.12   maidens] 'm' *over wiped-out* 'da'
97.26   swung] *follows wiped-out* 'g'
97.30   or a monster] *interlined with a caret*
98.17   sweet-] *over* 'clover', *then interlined above for*
            clarity
98.25–26   had more] 'had' *over wiped-out* 'looked'
99.14   sea-bird] 'sea' *over wiped-out* 'g[ ]'
99.27   as if to] 'if' *over wiped-out* 'to'
100.9   I suppose] *over wiped-out* 'would'
101.26   the giant] *interlined with a caret above deleted*
            'him'
102.3   the deserts of] *over wiped-out* 'African deserts',
            then interlined above for clarity
102.11   beheld] *interlined above deleted* 'seen'
102.29   a-down] 'a' *over wiped-out* 'd'
103.3   Hercules] *interlined above deleted* 'him'
103.30   was ever beheld] *over wiped-out* 'has been t'
104.4   appeared] *interlined above deleted* 'seemed'
104.11   nose] *precedes deleted* 'half'
104.20   long] *over wiped-out* 'good'
105.18   weary] 'y' *over wiped-out* 'ing'
105.19   beaming] *over wiped-out* 'falling', *then inter-*
            lined above for clarity
105.25   world!] *precedes wiped-out double quotes*
107.7   floundering] *interlined above deleted* 'coming'
107.21   view] *over wiped-out* 'sight'
108.19   At his nearer] 'At his' *over wiped-out* 'At At
            las'; 'nearer' *over wiped-out* 'approach', *then*
            interlined above for clarity
108.21   one] *precedes deleted* 'bough'
108.30   for] *interlined with a caret above deleted* 'after'
108.32   Hercules.] *period altered from comma*
108.35   haste—] *dash deletes comma*
110.2   he] *precedes deleted* 'he'
110.11   three] *interlined with a caret*

110.17	waxed] *written as* 'wax', *then deleted and interlined above as* 'waxed'
110.19	stands] *interlined with a caret above deleted* 'is'
111.2	story-teller's] 'y' *altered from doubtful* 'i'
111.17	is] *over wiped-out* 'I'
112.5	stands] *interlined above deleted* 'grows'
113.15	babble] *interlined with a caret*
115.9	so high] *interlined with a caret*
115.18	gazed] *interlined above deleted* 'looked'
115.18	upper] *over wiped-out* 'lip'
116.6	and] *follows deleted* 'and' *and undeleted comma*
116.20	and relatives] *interlined with a caret*
116.27	seclude] *interlined above deleted* 'hide'
116.27	anxiously] *interlined above deleted* 'carefully'
116.30	flowers] *over wiped-out doubtful* 'bloom'
117.5	already] *interlined with a caret*
119.3	affords] *interlined above deleted* 'gives'
119.34	The] *over wiped-out* 'It'
119.34	valley had been] *over wiped-out* 'It had been dry land', *then interlined above for clarity*
120.4	plenty around] *over wiped-out* 'it should have', *then interlined above for clarity*
120.27	object] *over wiped-out possible* 'sight', *then interlined above for clarity*
120.35	riding] *interlined above deleted* 'mounted'
121.9	much] *follows deleted* 'very'
121.10–11	whatever] *interlined above deleted* 'at all'
121.16	There was] *over wiped-out* 'I never', *then interlined above for clarity*
122.18	another] *precedes deleted* 'a'
122.33	the traveller's] *interlined above deleted* 'his'
123.6	Philemon] *over wiped-out* 'He had on'
123.8	sharpest] *interlined above deleted* 'best'
124.7	hopt] *mended from original* 'hopped'
124.18	were] *interlined above deleted* 'was'
124.25	was] *interlined with a caret*
125.16	loquacious] *interlined above deleted* 'talkative'
125.27	there?] *query altered from exclamation*
126.5	moved] *interlined above deleted* 'impelled'
126.5	which] *over wiped-out* 'that he'

126.6	that] *over wiped-out* 'which'
127.5	hearty] *interlined above deleted* 'kindly'
127.9	happen to] *interlined with a caret*
127.26	door-steps] 'door' *over wiped-out* 'steps'
128.26	Baucis] *precedes deleted* 'and Philemon'
129.18	stretched out their] *over wiped-out* 'put out their heads', *then interlined above for clarity*
129.29	it was now] *interlined above deleted* 'she now found it'
129.30	if] *precedes deleted* 'it had been'
129.33	a loaf] *interlined above deleted* 'bread'
130.5	and,] 'and' *over wiped-out* 'but'; *comma altered from semicolon*
130.26	in the pitcher] *interlined with a caret*
130.31	are.] *period over wiped-out exclamation*
131.25	drop] *follows deleted* 'of milk'; *period added after* 'drop'
131.27	speedily filled] *over wiped-out* 'g[ ]ly fi'
132.7	felt,] *precedes deleted* 'and have expressed the wonder which they felt'
132.11	when Philemon] 'when Phi' *over wiped-out* 'Quicksi'
132.20	the stick] *interlined with a caret above deleted* 'it'
132.23	quitted] *interlined above deleted* 'left'
133.22	their door] 'their' *over wiped-out undecipherable word*; 'door' *over wiped-out* 'cottage'
134.13	in] *interlined with a caret*
134.24	and] *over wiped-out* 'with'
135.11	transformed] *interlined above deleted* 'changed'
135.15	he] *interlined with a caret above deleted* 'you'
136.12	him:] *colon altered from comma or semicolon*
136.20	took] *over wiped-out* 'r[ ]'
136.28–29	Philemon] *over wiped-out doubtful* 'Baucis'
138.6	be] *over wiped-out* 'eve'
139.1	respectfully] *interlined with a caret*
139.5	up] *interlined with a caret*
139.9–10	and were] 'and' *over wiped-out* 'among'
141.9	were] *interlined with a caret*
142.18	all these] *over wiped-out* 'so many'

142.24   the dark] *over wiped-out* 'their shadows', *then* 'dark' *deleted and interlined above for clarity*

142.29   was a] 'was' *altered from* 'were'; 'a' *over unde-cipherable letter*

144.14   and begged] 'and' *interlined with a caret above deleted* 'a'

144.16–17   as he rinsed] 'as' *over wiped-out* 'af'

145.15   carry the] 'the' *over wiped-out* 'a br'

146.3   Pegasus] *interlined with a caret above deleted* 'he'

146.11–12   rain-storm,] *precedes deleted* 'it would some-times happen'

146.21   Pegasus] *precedes deleted* 'would'

148.12   Bellerophon.] *period altered from comma which precedes wiped-out* 'an'

148.14   as children] 'as' *over wiped-out* 'with'

149.17   they] *interlined with a caret*

149.27   look] *interlined with a caret*

149.34   I] *interlined with a caret*

150.30   the king.] 'k' *altered from* 'K'

150.30   Lycia] *over wiped-out* 'the coun'

151.19   earth!] *exclamation mended from query*

151.30   horse] *precedes wiped-out comma*

152.20   up hopefully] 'up ho' *over wiped-out* 'hopefu'

153.12   two] *over wiped-out* 'a few'

153.18   an image] 'an' *altered from* 'a'; 'image' *inter-lined above deleted* 'picture'

154.4   so that] 'so th' *over wiped-out doubtful* 'among'

154.19   stooping] *interlined above deleted* 'bending'

155.9   the shrubbery] 'the' *interlined with a caret*

155.10   sight] 's' *over* 'o' *of wiped-out* 'so'

155.14   ears] 'ea' *over wiped-out* 'he'

155.24–25   a great] 'a' *over wiped-out* 'for'; 'g' *of* 'great' *over wiped-out* 'a'

155.34   about, and] *over wiped-out* ', and indole'

156.5   But what] 'what' *over undecipherable word and comma deleted after* 'But'

156.22   out] 'o' *over wiped-out* 'b'

156.30   was shaken] 'was s' *over wiped-out* 'fell out'

156.33   latter (] *parenthesis deletes comma*

157.12	found] *interlined with a caret*
157.19	they] *interlined with a caret*
157.27	affected] *over wiped-out possible* 'struck'
158.6	overtook] 'overt' *over wiped-out* 'caught'
158.12	drew] *over wiped-out* 'came'
158.24	ascended] *interlined above deleted* 'flew'
159.30	flight] *interlined above deleted* 'course'
159.31	came] *over wiped-out* 'got' *which was interlined above deleted* 'flew'
160.1	vallies.] *period mended from comma which precedes wiped-out* 'in'
160.3	Chimæra] 'C' *altered from* 'c'
160.5	gradually] 'grad' *over wiped-out* '[slo]'
160.5	they] *interlined with a caret*
160.10	shadowy] *interlined above deleted* 'rocky'
160.24	mountain-top,] 'top,' *interlined with a caret above* 'mountain-,' *of which the added hyphen deletes an original final* 's' *and a comma is inadvertently undeleted*
162.16	insufferable] 'in' *over wiped-out* 'ab'
162.18	peak] *interlined above deleted* 'top'
163.14	towards] *interlined with a caret above deleted* 'at'
163.20	the left wing] *interlined above deleted* 'one of the wings'
163.27	ear-] *over wiped-out* 'high'
163.30	Well-a-day!] *exclamation altered from comma*
164.20	down] *precedes wiped-out exclamation*
165.6	Over] *over wiped-out* 'But'
165.13	creature] *interlined above deleted* 'monster'
165.23	saw, to their] *over wiped-out* 'beheld the', *then* 'saw to their' *interlined above for clarity, the original comma retained*
166.6	in those] 'in' *over wiped-out* 'then'
166.19	Bellerophon] *interlined above deleted* 'him'
166.24	said he, joyfully,] *interlined with a caret*
166.29	above] *interlined above deleted* 'among'
169.2	now] *precedes deleted* 'now'
169.5	sober] *interlined with a caret*
169.14	our] *precedes deleted* 'own'

169.15	most truthful] *interlined above deleted* 'truthful and gentle'
169.16	sits] *interlined above deleted* 'is'
169.22	the poet] 'the' *interlined above deleted* 'a'
169.26	with two children at his side,] *interlined with a caret*
169.28	or a school-history,] *interlined with a caret*
169.30	hush!] *exclamation altered from comma*
169.31	lip.] *period altered from comma*
170.10	Periwinkle] *interlined above deleted* 'Sweet Fern'
170.19	chat] *interlined above deleted* 'talk'
171.17	went down] *interlined above deleted* 'descended'

Tanglewood Tales

175.7	application] 'app' *over wiped-out* 'appl'
175.8	conclude] *interlined with a caret above deleted* 'observe'
175.8–9	in which] *interlined with a caret*
175.9	saw] 's' *over wiped-out* 'f'
176.6	primeval] 'prime-' *interlined with a caret above deleted* 'prime-'
176.7	could] 'c' *over wiped-out* 'sh'
176.13	familiar] 'ili' *over wiped-out* 'il'
176.13	is] *interlined above deleted* 'was'
176.14	these broad] 'these' *over wiped-out possible* 'the s[ ]'
176.24	rustic] *interlined with a caret*
176.30	become] *interlined with a caret*
176.31	ethereal] 'et' *over wiped-out possible* 'ea'
176.33	had] *over wiped-out* 'has'
176.33	the] *interlined above deleted* 'Alcott's'
177.3	seems] *initial* 's' *over wiped-out possible* 'h'
177.5	Ah, it would] *comma over wiped-out exclamation;* 'it would' *over wiped-out undecipherable*

177.10	branches] 'ches' *altered from* 'ces'
177.17	have] 'h' *over wiped-out* 'ra'
177.32	shut ourselves up] 'shut' *interlined above deleted* 'es-/'; 'tablished' *deleted before* 'ourselves'; 'up' *interlined with a caret*
177.32	south-eastern] '-eastern' *over wiped-out* 'ern room'
178.9	respect] *follows deleted* 'the'
178.10–11	"Tanglewood Tales"] MS *initial single quote over wiped-out double quotes*
178.12	my services] 'my ser' *over wiped-out* 'his [using]' *then* 'my' *interlined above for clarity*
178.12	inasmuch] *over wiped-out* 'since his', *then interlined above for clarity*
178.13	established] 'b' *over wiped-out* 't'
178.15	kind enough] *interlined with a caret above deleted* 'pleased'
178.20	my] *over wiped-out* 'his'
178.22–23	the rustic] *interlined with a caret above deleted* 'Orphic Alcott's'
178.26	rich] *precedes deleted* 'in capabilities,'
179.5	material] *over wiped-out* 'the'
179.24	for] *over wiped-out* 'it'
179.26	to which] 'to' *over wiped-out* 'in'
179.27	waking] 'king' *over wiped-out* 'king'
180.11	situations] *over wiped-out possible* 'attitudes'
180.28	(unless we except Clover,)] *interlined with a caret*
180.31	idle] *interlined with a caret*
180.32	to] *interlined with a caret*
181.2	shut up her baby-house] *over wiped-out* 'throw aside her doll' *then interlined above for clarity*
181.8	Milkweed] *follows deleted* 'Cowslip' *and undeleted comma*
181.12	Poor] *interlined with a caret*
181.16	the] *interlined with a caret above deleted* 'a'
181.21–22	Commencement] 'C' *altered from* 'c'
181.23	Classical] 'C' *altered from* 'c'
181.30	shall] *altered from* 'should'
182.4	ask] *an* 'e' *wiped off the end of the word*

182.9	March 13, 1853.] *double lines below are deleted; 'th.' deleted after '13' and comma added*
183.4	sovereign] *second 'e' over wiped-out 'i'*
183.12–13	he was called] *over wiped-out 'his name was', then interlined above for clarity*
185.30	Theseus] *interlined with a caret above deleted 'him'*
185.31	him] *over wiped-out possible 'to'*
185.31	courtiers] *interlined above deleted 'courtiers'*
186.12	He] *over wiped-out 'h'*
187.3	footsteps] *'te' over wiped-out possible 'ep'*
187.14	very] *'v' over wiped-out possible 'b'*
187.17	perilous] *'per' over wiped-out 'd[a]'*
188.21	all] *over wiped-out 'the'*
188.30	valiant] *'v' over wiped-out 'f'*
189.4	took] *over wiped-out possible 'str'*
189.25	instead] *'in' over wiped-out 'i[n]t'*
190.8	admission] *over wiped-out possible 'your'*
190.15	was in] *over wiped-out 'had been'*
190.21	more important] *over wiped-out 'other ma'*
190.22	fiery] *interlined with a caret*
190.25	nothing] *'n' over wiped-out possible 'b'*
191.6	for] *interlined with a caret*
191.6	shall] *interlined with a caret above deleted 'will'*
191.13	and, as soon] *'as soon' over wiped-out 'gave'; comma probably added*
191.14	poisonous] *'ous' over wiped-out 'wine'*
191.16	set on] *over wiped-out 'placed'*
191.16	meaning] *over wiped-out 'wh[ ]', then interlined above for clarity*
192.4	he attempted] *over wiped-out 'he attempted to', then interlined above for clarity*
192.15	with which Theseus] *over wiped-out 'which Theseus fel', then interlined above for clarity*
192.23	fine] *interlined above deleted 'gentle'*
192.27	him] *interlined with a caret*
193.1	drink] *'n' over wiped-out possible 'k'*

193.4	youth] *over wiped-out* 'youth', *then interlined above for clarity*
193.7	worthy] 'w' *over wiped-out possible* 'th'
193.29	a treacherous enemy] 'a' *altered from* 'an'; 'treach-/' *over wiped-out* 'enemy'; 'erous enemy' *over wiped-out* 'with a de'; *then* 'treacherous enemy' *interlined above for clarity*
193.30	face] *over wiped-out and deleted* 'face', *then interlined above for clarity*
193.31	said he,] *interlined with a caret*
193.33	this!] *exclamation follows wiped-out period*
194.4	sword!] *exclamation deletes comma*
194.9	seek my] *over wiped-out* 'claim my', *then* 'seek' *interlined above for clarity*
194.13	son!] *over wiped-out* 'own dear son', *then interlined above for clarity*
194.22	an aerial] 'an' *over wiped-out* 'the'
194.29	bawled] *interlined above deleted* 'called'
194.29–30	the abominable] *over wiped-out* 'her never to'
194.34	snakes] *interlined above deleted* 'serpents'
195.6	emeralds,] *interlined with a caret*
195.7	opals] *interlined with a caret mistakenly placed before comma following* 'sapphires'
195.9	hail-stones,] 'stones,' *interlined with a caret*
195.14	wicked] *over wiped-out* 'M'
195.16	flew] 'ew' *over wiped-out* 'ew' *or* 'ed'
195.33	foregone] 'f' *over wiped-out possible* 'p'
196.12	as quickly] *over wiped-out* 'not for'
196.17	year] *over wiped-out* 'year'
196.31	exist] *over wiped-out* 'live'
196.32	the duskiness] 'the d' *over wiped-out possible* 'some d'
197.1	took great] *over wiped-out* 'be[ ]ed great'
197.12	fourteen] *over wiped-out* 'vi'
197.32	welfare] 'l' *over wiped-out* 'f'
198.7	and] *interlined above deleted* 'but'
198.12	tender] 'ten' *over wiped-out possible* 'be'
198.30	welcome] *over wiped-out* 'greet' *then interlined above for clarity*

199.10	undulating] *interlined with a caret above deleted* 'sloping'
199.17	although] *interlined above deleted* 'which'
199.17	it] *interlined with a caret*
199.20	long] 'l' *over wiped-out* 'gr'
199.27	while] *interlined with a caret above deleted* 'as'
200.16	master] 'm' *over wiped-out* 'cap'
200.33	into the foamy waves,] *interlined with a caret*
201.16	hammer] *over wiped-out* 'clapper', *then interlined above for clarity*
201.27	a booming] 'a' *over wiped-out* 'b'
202.12	happy] 'h' *over wiped-out possible* 's'
202.18	each] *interlined with a caret*
202.21	the king] *over wiped-out* 'whose fa', *then interlined above for clarity*
202.25	Minotaur] 'Mi' *altered from* 'mi'
202.33	thee] *precedes wiped-out comma*
203.1	me] *over wiped-out* 'me'
203.1	the king] 'the' *over wiped-out* 'Kin'
203.9	from] 'f' *over wiped-out* 't[h]'
203.12	first] 'rs' *over wiped-out possible* 'st'
203.14	even] *interlined with a caret*
203.19	herself] 'r' *over wiped-out* 's'
203.20	especially] 'c' *over wiped-out* 'i'
204.6	across] *interlined with a caret above deleted* 'along'
204.8	softly unbarred] *over wiped-out* 'gently unbarred', *then interlined above for clarity*
204.16	him] *interlined with a caret*
204.23	this] *over wiped-out* 'you'
205.19	disagreeable] 'd' *over wiped-out possible* 'l'
205.22–23	that uttered] *over wiped-out* 'that [made] it,' *then* 'uttered' *interlined above for clarity*
206.5	mizmaze] *interlined above deleted* 'thing'
206.10	before] *over wiped-out* 'before'
206.12	went] *precedes wiped-out comma*
207.7	in an open space,] *interlined with a caret;* 'in' *over wiped-out undecipherable word*
207.29	an] 'a' *altered from* 'e'
207.32	By no] *over wiped-out* 'What!'

208.2   twitch] 'it' *over wiped-out possible* 'ch'
208.3   was] *interlined with a caret above deleted* 'made
             him feel'
208.4   him] *interlined with a caret*
208.24   language.] *precedes wiped-out* 'Without more
             wor'
208.28   the monster] 'the' *over wiped-out possible* 'h'
208.33   noise] 'n' *altered from* 'cr'
209.4   made] *over wiped-out* 'grazed', *then interlined
             above for clarity*
209.12   six] *interlined with a caret above deleted* 'three'
209.13   down] *interlined [with a caret?]*
209.27   we must quickly] *over wiped-out* 'it only
             remains,' *then interlined for clarity*
210.8   King Ægeus,] *interlined with a caret*
210.15   flee] *interlined above deleted* 'sail'
210.17   Prince] *over wiped-out* 'Theseus', *then inter-
             lined with a caret for clarity*
211.8   with] *over wiped-out* 'whis'
211.12   figure] *over wiped-out* 'figure'
211.13–14   enormous strides] *interlined with a caret above
             deleted* 'footsteps'
211.15   Nevertheless] 'N' *over wiped-out* 'S'
211.25   time] *over wiped-out* 'voyage', *then interlined
             above for clarity*
212.7   infirm] *over wiped-out* 'had clam', *then inter-
             lined above for clarity*
212.20   fortune] *over wiped-out* 'affairs'
213.4   who] 'h' *over* 'e'
213.5   Pygmies,] 'P' *altered from* 'p'
213.6   Grandmother] 'G' *altered from* 'g'
213.12   for] *over wiped-out possible* 'to'
213.14   if one] *over wiped-out* 'when'
213.15   six or eight] *interlined above deleted* 'ten or
             twelve'
213.17   paved] *over wiped-out* 'bor'
214.3   plastered] 'pl' *altered from* 'pa'
214.3   Pygmy-workmen] 'pigmy-workmen' *over wiped-
             out* 'little pig'
214.8   conveniently] 'con' *over wiped-out* 'laid'

214.10	Sweet] 'S' *possibly altered from* 's'
214.16	grain] *follows deleted* 'stalks of'
214.17–18	over-burthened] 'over-burth-/' *over wiped-out* '[ ]ding'
214.18	come] 'c' *over wiped-out* 's'
214.25	its] *over wiped-out possible* 't'
214.27–28	a giant] *over wiped-out* 'one huge'
214.30	carried] *interlined with a caret above deleted* 'had'
214.30	which was eight feet through the but,] *interlined with a caret; comma added after* 'tree'
215.1	at] 'a' *possibly altered from* 'i'
215.2	over] *over wiped-out possible* 'all'
215.5	little] 'l' *over wiped-out* 'b'
215.9	Antæus] 'n' *over wiped-out* 't'
215.15	thunderous] 'e' *over wiped-out possible* 'r'
215.26	multitude] *over wiped-out* 'countless'
215.31	so] *over possible* 'a'
215.33	do] *interlined above deleted* 'offer'
216.1	the giant] *over wiped-out* 'Antaeus'
216.2	a-going] 'g' *over wiped-out* 'b'
216.4	kingdom, from] *over wiped-out* 'whole kingdom', *then* 'kingdom' *interlined above for clarity*
216.9	Antæus] 'A' *over wiped-out possible* 't'
216.10	The giant's] 'The' *altered from* 'Their'
216.12	been] 'b' *over wiped-out* 'g'
216.12–13	innumerable] *over wiped-out* 'gener'
216.16	of grandfather's] 'of' *over partial* 'g'
216.18	an obelisk] 'an' *over* 'a'
216.24	acre] *over wiped-out* 'squ'
216.24	where] *altered from* 'whi[c]'
217.7	fancied] *interlined above deleted* 'thought'
217.8	instead of] 'of' *over wiped-out* 'b'
217.9	fought him till one] *over wiped-out* 'fought him till one', *then interlined above for clarity*
217.11	his] *interlined with a caret*
217.16	"He has] 'h' *of* 'has' *over wiped-out possible* 'i'
217.28	lay down his great] *over wiped-out* 'stretch out his great' *then interlined above for clarity*

218.4	of the funny] 'of the' *over wiped-out* 'the f'
218.7	races] 'ra' *altered from* 'ru'
218.16	he] *over wiped-out possible* 'they', *then inter-lined above for clarity*
218.20	huge] *over wiped-out* 'great', *then interlined above for clarity*
218.21	roar] *over wiped-out* 'burst'
218.23	ears—] *dash possibly deletes* 'or'
219.1	must] *interlined above deleted* 'would'
219.5	terrible] *over wiped-out* 'terrible', *then inter-lined above for clarity*
219.6	that] *interlined with a caret*
219.12	middle] 'e' *over wiped-out* 'ie'
219.15	necks] *over wiped-out* 'long'
219.28	triumph] 'ing' *deleted from original* 'triumph-ing'
219.29	to the] 'to' *interlined with a caret*
219.34	life] 'li' *over wiped-out* 'a'
220.1	above-] 'a' *over wiped-out* '[d]'
220.7–8	forefathers] *altered from* 'forefather'
220.11	that] *interlined with a caret above deleted* 'which'
220.15	across] *interlined above deleted* 'out'
220.24	rub] *over wiped-out possible* 'rib'
220.30	vast] 'v' *over wiped-out* 'g'
221.13	soon so nigh] *over wiped-out* 'soon so nigh th', *then interlined above for clarity*
221.15	flaming] *over wiped-out* 'gleaming'
221.17	and a] 'and' *interlined with a caret*
221.17	on his right] *over wiped-out* 'in his right ha', *then interlined above for clarity*
221.27	drew] *over wiped-out* 'came'
221.32	great] *interlined with a caret*
221.33	giant's slow] 'giant's' *over wiped-out* 'slow mo-tions'; 'slow' *over wiped-out* 'of the'; *then entire phrase interlined above for clarity*
222.5	strange] *over wiped-out* '[ ] gia', *then in-terlined above for clarity*
222.14	sooner] *precedes wiped-out comma*
222.14–15	leaping on his feet and] *interlined with a caret*

222.21	hearing] *over wiped-out* 'by hearing'
222.26	remember] *over wiped-out possible* 'know'
222.29	persons] *over wiped-out* 'people'
223.2	got up] *interlined with a caret above deleted* 'rose'
223.5	ease] *altered from* 'easier'
223.6	like] *over wiped-out* 'like'
223.11	Any other] *over wiped-out* 'Any other', *then interlined above for clarity*
223.15	hand,] *over wiped-out* 'hand, at'
223.23	hither?] 'hit' *over wiped-out possible* 'her' *and query altered from exclamation*
223.23	Speak] *follows wiped-out quotes*
223.24	skull] 'ull' *over wiped-out* 'ill'
223.27	civility] 'v' *over wiped-out* 'l'
224.3	"By hitting] *over wiped-out* 'With this', *then interlined with a caret for clarity*
224.3	here!"] *over wiped-out* 'in my ha'
224.7	dwarf] 'w' *altered from* 'a'
224.14	grinning] *over wiped-out* 'all [ ]'
224.24	such] *over wiped-out* 'a' *or* 'as'
224.26	wrath] *interlined with a caret above deleted* 'rage'
224.26	hit] *altered from* 'his'
224.28	His pine-tree went] *over wiped-out* 'The pine-tree w', *then interlined above for clarity*
225.6	out] *over wiped-out* 'of'
225.10	more] 'm' *over wiped-out* 'he'
225.15	most] *interlined above deleted* 'some'
226.1	For] 'F' *altered from possible* 'T'
226.3	Hercules] 'cu' *over wiped-out* 'cl'
226.14	wherewith to wreak] *over wiped-out* 'to [st] his e', *then interlined above for clarity*
226.30	Hercules] 'H' *possibly altered from* 'A'
227.6	easily] 'ea-/' *over wiped-out* 'be'
227.15	if] *altered from* 'o[ ]'
227.25	with] *interlined with a caret above deleted* 'by'
228.11	has here] *over wiped-out* 'have b'

228.17   contumely] *interlined with a caret above de-leted* 'insult'

228.18   now] *over wiped-out* 'ha'

228.18   asleep] 'p' *altered from* 'ep'

228.18   if] *interlined with a caret*

228.22   go] 'g' *over wiped-out* 'f'

228.30   remember] *second* 'em' *over wiped-out* 'ber'

229.1   virtuous] *over wiped-out* 'good and vir-'

229.8   treacherous] 'treach-/' *over wiped-out* 'vic'

229.10   so] 's' *over wiped-out possible* 'g'

229.10   that] *interlined with a caret*

229.11   skeleton] *interlined with a caret*

229.11   as] *interlined with a caret*

229.11   the everlasting] 'the' *over wiped-out* 'ev'

229.12   exhibiting] *follows deleted* 'a terrible example of Pygmy vengeance!'

229.16   calculated] 'u' *over wiped-out possible* 'a'

229.17   ancestors] 'anc' *possibly altered from* 'ain'

229.25   us] *over wiped-out possible* 'th'

229.27   enemy —] *dash deletes comma*

229.32   or] *over wiped-out* 'or', *then interlined above for clarity*

229.34   hands] 's' *added, deleting comma*

230.1   crimson] *interlined with a caret above deleted* 'bloody'

230.11   vulgarly] *interlined with a caret above deleted* 'commonly'

230.28   stranger's] *over wiped-out* 'club'

231.2   were] *over wiped-out possible* 'acting', *then interlined above for clarity*

231.5   intended] *over wiped-out possible* 'dec'

231.7   inasmuch] 'i' *over wiped-out possible* 't' *or* 'b'

231.16–17   brought together] *over wiped-out* 'collected [thousand]', *then partially wiped out and interlined above for clarity*

231.23–24   roast the enemy] *over wiped-out* 'burn the enemy q', *then interlined above for clarity*

232.8   shrill] *over wiped-out possible* 'many'

232.9   putting] 'p' *over wiped-out* 'q'

232.10	could] 'c' *altered from* 's'
232.27	big] 'g' *over wiped-out possible* 'd', *followed by wiped-out mark*
232.27	words] 'w' *over wiped-out letter, possibly* 'g'
233.11	injury] *interlined with a caret*
233.18	acknowledges] 'dges' *over wiped-out* 'ges'
233.27	whatever] 'w' *altered from* 'a'
234.15	Cilix] 'C' *altered from* 'E'
235.7	Brother Cadmus!"] *over wiped-out* 'Cadmus!" '; *initial quotes retained*
235.14	garlands.] *precedes wiped-out* 'Neverth'
235.15	which] 'wh' *over wiped-out possible* 'wit'
235.19	a particularly] 'a' *altered from* 'h'
235.25	capered] 'ca' *over wiped-out possible* 'sp'
236.31	child!"] *quotes intended to delete original dash*
237.7	children] *over wiped-out* 'of them', *then interlined above for clarity*
237.22	softly!"] 's' *over wiped-out* 'p'
238.1	while] 'w' *over wiped-out* 'l'
238.5	pretending] 'pr' *over wiped-out possible* 'as'
238.6	distant journey] *over wiped-out* 'long journey, a', *then interlined above for clarity*
238.14	snowy] 'y' *over wiped-out* 'ey'
238.21	likewise, and] *over wiped-out* 'and ran to t'
238.24	the treacherous] 'the' *over wiped-out possible* 'was'
239.6	swum with] *over wiped-out* 'swam with', *then* 'swum' *interlined above for clarity*
239.14	flashed] 'a' *altered from* 'u'
239.21	came] *over wiped-out* 'and'
239.23	dark; and] '; and' *over wiped-out* 'and'
239.30	likewise] *over wiped-out* 'als'
239.32	sea-] 'e' *altered from* 'a'
240.10	Remember] *second* 'em' *over wiped-out* 'b'
240.12	sobbed Queen] *over wiped-out* 'answered Queen', *then* 'sobbed' *interlined above for clarity*
241.2	roaming] 'ro' *over wiped-out* 'w'
241.11	wildernesses] 'es' *added after following word was written*

241.18	forehead] 'a' *possibly altered from* 'r'
241.23	wore.] *period altered from comma*
241.27	their] 'ir' *altered from* 'm'
241.28	men] 'm' *possibly mended from* 'w'
241.31	assistance] 'as' *over wiped-out* 'he'
241.33	done no work, in her] *over wiped-out* 'nothing in her palace', *then interlined above for clarity*
242.6	his back] *over wiped-out* 'i[ ]ba'
242.28	helped] 'l' *over wiped-out possible* 'p'
242.30	boughs.] *altered from* 'bowers', *and period added*
242.30–31	Inside, there were two] *over wiped-out* 'and containing two plea', *then interlined above for clarity*
243.11–12	grown up there] 'own up there' *over wiped-out* 'own up th'
243.16–17	decree of state] *over wiped-out* 'command which', *then interlined above for clarity*
243.18	arrive] 'ar-/' *over wiped-out* 'pass'
244.7	my] *over wiped-out* 'our' *then interlined above for clarity*
244.12	in seeking] 'in' *over wiped-out* 'and'
244.17	Telephassa; although] 'alth' *over wiped-out* 'alth' *and semicolon added*
244.21	ago.] *period altered from exclamation*
244.22	forgotten] 'f' *over wiped-out* 'g'
244.26	mother] 'mo' *over wiped-out* 'Mo'
245.8	abundance] *over wiped-out* 'plenty', *then interlined above for clarity*
245.13	a long] 'a' *over wiped-out* 'lo'
245.22	mind] 'ind' *over wiped-out* 'nd'
245.32	asking] *over wiped-out* 'beg [ ], *then interlined above for clarity*
245.32	if] 'i' *over wiped-out* 'f'
245.34	away] *second* 'a' *over wiped-out* 'y'
246.7	hobble] 'bl' *over wiped-out* 'll'
246.8	delay you] 'you' *follows deleted comma*
246.9	trouble] 'u' *over wiped-out possible* 'b'
246.11	may."] *period precedes wiped-out exclamation*
246.15	we] 'w' *over wiped-out possible* 'l' *or* 'h'

247.1	here, in] 'in' *over wiped-out possible* 'was'; *comma probably added*
247.1	the course] 'the' *over* 'a'
247.3	palace] 'p' *over wiped-out* 'pl'
247.10	King] *over wiped-out* 'Thasus', *then interlined above for clarity*
247.16	a lengthened] 'a' *over wiped-out possible* 'a w'
247.17	sat] 'sa' *over wiped-out possible* 'sh' *or* 'sp'
247.18	nevertheless] 'never' *over wiped-out* 'however'
247.18–19	remembrance] *second* 'em' *interlined with a caret*
247.24	by] *follows deleted* 'it' *or* 'at'
248.30	discern] 'dis-/' *over wiped-out* 'see' *and* 'cern' *interlined above* 'ern'
248.33	repressed] *initial* 'r' *over wiped-out* 'f'
248.33	his] 'i' *altered from* 'e'
249.12	now!] *exclamation deletes comma*
250.13	of his pilgrimage] *over wiped-out* 'of his p'
250.22	for] *over wiped-out* 'of'
250.32	discern] *apparently altered from* 'descry', *the* 'y' *wiped-out and the* 'i' *left undotted*
251.9	the most] *over wiped-out* 'more'
251.12	search] 's' *over wiped-out* 'q'
251.15	like] 'l' *over wiped-out* 'v'
251.33	there] 'r' *over wiped-out* 'e'
251.35	whisper] *precedes wiped-out comma*
252.34	this] *interlined with a caret*
252.34	she] *interlined with a caret*
253.9	if she] *over wiped-out* 'whether'
253.14	slowly] *over wiped-out possible* 'softl'
253.16	went] *interlined with a caret above deleted* 'when'
253.23	behind.] *period altered from semicolon*
253.25	path] *over wiped-out* 'road', *then interlined above for clarity*
254.2	if] *interlined with a caret above deleted* 'whether'
254.3	whether] *over wiped-out* 'whether', *then interlined with a caret for clarity*
254.28	supposed] *over wiped-out* 'thought'
255.3	I'm] 'm' *over wiped-out* 'l'
255.6–7	took so] 'k' *over wiped-out* 's'

255.25	laying] *over wiped-out* 'plan'
256.18	door] *precedes wiped-out comma*
256.19	of] *over wiped-out* 'a'
256.30	being] *over wiped-out* 'a[s] they'
257.20	his] 'h' *over wiped-out* 'f'
257.29	dragon's] *over wiped-out* 'serpe'
257.33	Cadmus] 'Ca' *altered from* 'so'
257.34	his] 'h' *over wiped-out possible* 't' *or* 'h' *or* 'b'
258.2	Thus] *over wiped-out* 'And' *then interlined above for clarity*
259.9	as great] 'as' *interlined with a caret;* 'g' *over wiped-out* 'g'
259.17	stalks of] 'stalks' *over wiped-out possible* 'steel'; 'of' *over wiped-out* 'of'
259.27	before] *follows wiped-out comma*
260.14	neighbor] 'ne' *altered from possible* 'm'
260.15	the fallen] 'the' *over wiped-out* 'hi'
261.18	happened] *over wiped-out* 'chanced', *then interlined above for clarity*
261.20	which] 'ich' *over wiped-out* 'h'
261.25	whole,] *comma replaces wiped-out semicolon*
262.16–17	enjoyment] 'en' *over wiped-out* 'ej'
262.24	it] *interlined with a caret*
262.35	and rose] 'and' *over wiped-out* 'with'
263.12	five] *altered from* 'fai'
263.15	Halting] 'H' *over wiped-out possible* 'A'
263.16	gazed] 'g' *over wiped-out* 'l'
263.22–23	long-lost] 'lost' *over wiped-out* 'sister'
263.24	sweet] *over wiped-out* 'sisterly', *then interlined above for clarity*
263.30	Cadmus advanced] *over wiped-out* 'Cadmus drew nearer', *then* 'advanced' *interlined with a caret for clarity*
264.5	So] 'S' *possibly altered from* 's'
264.5	King Cadmus dwelt in the] *over wiped-out* 'Cadmus dwelt in the palace'; *then* 'King . . . in' *interlined above for clarity*
264.8	many] *over wiped-out* 'a grea', *then interlined above for clarity*
264.15	old] *over wiped-out* 'sons', *then interlined above for clarity*
264.18	penny] *second* 'n' *over wiped-out possible* 'p'

265.10	part] 'art' *over wiped-out possible* 'at'
265.15	a valuable] 'a' *interlined with a caret above deleted* 'some'
265.20	like air out of a blown bladder,] *interlined with a caret*
266.2	Scudding before the] *over wiped-out* '[Being] driven by the', *then* 'Scudding before' *interlined above for clarity*
266.7	cliffs] 'iffs' *over wiped-out possible* 'ifs'
266.18	sought] *over wiped-out possible* 'look', *then interlined above for clarity*
266.20	they] 'th' *over wiped-out* 'h'
266.21	King] 'Ki' *over wiped-out* 'Ul'
266.31	take] *interlined with a caret*
267.7	stretched] *over wiped-out* 'exte'
267.20	tell] *interlined with a caret above deleted* 'inform'
267.20	poor] *over wiped-out* 'ship', *then interlined above for clarity*
267.27	Pleasing himself with] *over wiped-out* 'With this idea in his head', *then interlined above for clarity*
267.32	its] *interlined above deleted* 'his'
267.32	little] *over wiped-out* 'bird'
267.35	catch] 'c' *over wiped-out possible* 'b'
268.4	the bird] *over wiped-out* 'it flew'
268.10	elsewhere] *second* 'e' *squeezed in between* 's' *and* 'w', *then the entire word deleted and interlined above for clarity*
268.11	known] *over wiped-out* 'met'
268.16	and over] *(second in line)* 'and' *over wiped-out possible* 'ag'
268.32	and repeated] 'and' *over wiped-out* 're'
269.7	swine's] *apostrophe added to* 'swines'
269.8	very much] *interlined with a caret*
269.12	of drift-wood] 'of drift-' *over wiped-out* 'to cook it'
269.26	stood] *interlined with a caret above deleted* 'stands'

269.26–27	appeared to be] 'red to be' *over wiped-out* 'rs to be'
269.27	had] 'd' *possibly altered from* 's'
270.2	at his] 'at' *over wiped-out* 'for'
270.4	middle] *over wiped-out possible* 'centre'
270.22	beg] *over wiped-out* 'ask'
271.1	other] *follows deleted* 'the'
271.33	tuft] *final* 't' *over wiped-out* 'f'
272.3	chirped] *over wiped-out* 's[aid] the'
272.5–6	some mighty] *over wiped-out* 'the secr', *then interlined above for clarity*
272.8	for he] *interlined with a caret above deleted* 'who'
272.23	said] *over wiped-out* 'that w'
272.24	mere] *interlined with a caret*
272.25	shape] *over wiped-out* 'for'
272.29	between the] *over wiped-out* 'in the mouth'
272.33	'Peep,] *over wiped-out possible* 'f'
273.2	us] *interlined with a caret*
273.3	cried his] *over wiped-out* 'said his'; *then* 'cried' *interlined above for clarity*
273.15	in the] 'in' *over wiped-out* 'to'; 'the' *over wiped-out* 't'
273.20	wasted] *interlined with a caret*
273.25	to flavor] 'to' *interlined with a caret*
274.1	they] *interlined with a caret*
274.21	answered] *over wiped-out* 'said'
274.22	palace-kitchen] 'p' *possibly altered from* 'k'; 'tc' *of* 'kitchen' *over wiped-out* 'th'
274.22	now] *over wiped-out* 'ver'
274.24	big] *interlined with a caret above deleted* 'tall'
274.25	huge] *over wiped-out* 'Poly', *then interlined above for clarity*
274.25	one] 'e' *over wiped-out* 'l'
274.26	Cyclops] 'c' *over wiped-out* 'l'
275.18	fondled] 'ed' *possibly altered from* 'y'
275.18	beef-bone.] *precedes wiped-out* 'B'
276.5	plainly] 'ly' *over wiped-out* 'gly'
276.8	or a wolf] 'or' *over wiped-out* 'a'

276.12	forms] *over wiped-out* 'shapes'
276.15	in another] 'in' *possibly altered from* 'an'
276.19	harmony] 'har' *over wiped-out possible* 'mu'
276.33	buzz of the loom] *over wiped-out* 'household buzz of', *then interlined above for clarity*
277.8	which] 'c' *over wiped-out* 'h'
277.20	while] *over wiped-out* 'or two'; *comma added before* 'while'
277.22	meet] 'm' *altered from possible* 'w'
277.33	left] *a possible* 'ing' *wiped off end of word*
278.9	four] *over wiped-out possible* 'girl'
278.11	Eurylochus] 'yl' *over wiped-out* 'ol'
278.13	feast.] *precedes beginning of new paragraph,* 'But we will leave the prudent Eurylochus, waiting in the outer parlor,' *which is deleted; the remainder of the previous line following* 'feast.' *is then filled in with* 'Chancing to cast his eyes'; *this sentence continues after the deletion*
278.28	faces] *interlined with a caret above deleted* 'aspects'
279.2	while] *over wiped-out* 'and'
279.17	prepared.] *precedes deleted* 'for you.'
279.19	be served] *over wiped-out* 'serve up'
279.25	with] *over wiped-out word, possibly* 'to'
279.26	fire] *over wiped-out* 'fuel', *then interlined with a caret for clarity*
280.2	and fringed with gold cord.] *interlined above deleted* 'with golden fringe.'
280.11	of] *over wiped-out word, probably* 'of'
280.20	on royal thrones,] *interlined with a caret*
280.23–24	far more] *interlined with a caret*
280.25	be!] *precedes deleted* 'Bu'
280.32	sparkled as it] *over wiped-out* 'bubbled as [if] (or [it])' *then interlined above for clarity*
280.33	throat] 'ro' *over wiped-out* 'ir'
281.31	guzzlers and] *interlined with a caret; a wiped-out* 'a' *follows* 'and'
282.5–6	as sharp] 'as' *interlined with a caret*
282.11	bore] *over wiped-out* 'brought', *then interlined above for clarity*

282.12	all] *interlined with a caret*
282.18	it] *over wiped-out possible* 'h'
282.19	smile] 's' *over wiped-out* 'f[ ]'
282.29–30	exercise] *over wiped-out* 'touch'
282.32	begone] 'b' *over wiped-out* 'g'
283.1	at] *altered from* 'it'
283.1	comrades] 'r' *over wiped-out* 'p'
283.3	as he] 'he' *over wiped-out* 'sup'
283.20	ear-piercing] *initial* 'e' *over wiped-out* 'p'
283.24	your] 'y' *over wiped-out possible* 'th'
283.29	save the] *over wiped-out* 'but the rig', *then interlined above for clarity*
283.29	in accordance] *over wiped-out* 'accord'
284.3	bit] *over wiped-out word, probably badly-formed* 'bit'
284.4	trough] 'u' *over wiped-out possible* 'th'
284.4	and gobbled] 'and' *interlined with a caret*
284.4–5	in a] *over wiped-out* 'with'
284.6	they] *interlined with a caret*
284.6	among] *interlined with a caret above deleted* 'on'
284.8–9	when they should be slaughtered, and] *interlined with a caret*
284.10	Meantime] 'M' *over wiped-out* 'In'
285.14	drenched] *interlined with a caret above deleted* 'wet'
285.15	by] *altered from* 'in'
285.18	frowned] *over wiped-out* 'looked'
285.25	'Peep] *single quote over wiped-out double quotes*
285.29	head] *over wiped-out* 'hed'
286.6	wore] 'w' *over wiped-out* 'h'
286.16	are] *over wiped-out* 'you'
286.26	Picus] *altered from* 'Circe'
286.31	resembling] *over wiped-out possible* 'similar'
287.16	; he went] 'he we' *over wiped-out* 'and s'; *semicolon may have been altered from comma*
287.24	the whole earth over] *over wiped-out* 'through the whole earth', *then interlined above for clarity*
287.25	Keep] 'K' *over wiped-out* 'A'

287.27	are talking] 'are' *interlined with a caret*
287.28	of wine] *interlined with a caret*
287.28	out] *over wiped-out* 'of'
288.11–12	came bounding to meet him,] *interlined with a caret*
288.18	and glared at him,] *interlined with a caret*
289.3	courtesy] *over wiped-out* 'low'
289.17	and my] *over wiped-out* 'have b', *then interlined with a caret for clarity*
289.29	since] 's' *over wiped-out* 's'
290.8	was] *interlined with a caret*
290.10	studded] 'st' *altered from* 'su'
290.14	dazzling] *over wiped-out* 'glisten'
290.18	royal] *interlined with a caret*
290.22	butler was gone] *over wiped-out* 'wine was coming', *then interlined above for clarity*
290.32	a beast] 'a' *interlined with a caret*
291.25	instead] 'in' *over wiped-out* 'is'
291.29	clashing] 'shing' *over wiped-out* 'nging'
292.6	The chief-butler] 'The' *over wiped-out* 'She'
292.7	golden] *interlined with a caret*
292.10	royal] *over wiped-out* 'noble', *then interlined above for clarity*
292.20	nearly] *over wiped-out* 'almost', *then interlined above for clarity*
292.27	her] *interlined with a caret*
293.17	with] 'wi' *over possible* 'ny'
293.23	certainly] *over wiped-out* 'be m', *then interlined above for clarity*
293.33	and their] 'and' *over wiped-out* '(and'
294.17	they] *over wiped-out possible* 'Th'
295.4	a long] 'a' *over wiped-out* 'l'
296.1	exceedingly] *interlined with a caret above deleted* 'very'
296.8	harvest] *interlined with a caret above deleted* 'crops'
298.3	found] 'f' *altered from* 's'
298.7	and] 'd' *over* 'y'
298.16	behold?] *query over wiped-out* 'but'
298.23	beauty was] *over wiped-out* 'appearance was', *then interlined above for clarity*

298.27	was] *interlined with a caret*
298.28	lustre on] 'on' *over wiped-out possible* 'in'
298.31	she was] *over wiped-out* 'she [al]'
298.32	silly] *interlined above deleted* 'foolish'
299.1	with] *interlined above deleted* 'in'
299.8	Did] *interlined with a caret before wiped-out* 'Could' *which was written over wiped-out* 'The'
299.10	childish] 'c' *over wiped-out* 'f'
299.11	stem] *interlined above deleted* 'shrub'
299.21	smoke] *over wiped-out* 'fire'
299.30	rather] *over wiped-out* 'hand', *then interlined for clarity*
300.20	chariot] 'ch' *over wiped-out possible* 'sh'
300.24	pleasant vale] *over wiped-out* 'pleasant fi', *then* 'pleasant' *interlined above for clarity*
300.31	ears] 'e' *over wiped-out possible* 'h'
301.5	a garden] 'a' *over wiped-out* 'g' *or* 'a'
301.11	and iron] 'and' *over wiped-out* 'iron'
301.32	which] *over wiped-out* 'that', *then interlined above for clarity*
302.12	whom] *over wiped-out* 'what do', *then interlined with a caret for clarity*
302.21	reverberated] *second* 'er' *interlined with a caret above* 'reverbated'
303.11	pulled at] *over wiped-out* 'drew up the', *then interlined with a caret for clarity*
303.19	been] *interlined with a caret*
303.26	, while] *over wiped-out* ', although', *then deleted and interlined with a caret for clarity*
304.2	here] *interlined with a caret*
304.4	went] 'w' *over wiped-out* 'th'
304.11	which] 'w' *over wiped-out* 'h'
304.20	either] *interlined with a caret*
305.10	large] *interlined with a caret above deleted* 'great'
305.20	he] *over wiped-out* 'had'
305.20	have] *interlined with a caret*
305.23	upper] *precedes deleted* 'of the upper'
305.24	was as] 'as' *over wiped-out* 'if'
305.31	neither] *over wiped-out* 'eith'

306.14	child] *interlined with a caret*
306.17	considered] 'co' *over wiped-out possible* 'th'
306.20	the smell] 'the s' *over wiped-out* 'which'
307.23	wet] *interlined with a caret*
307.33	said] 'sa' *over wiped-out possible* 'cr'
308.23	it may be] *over wiped-out* 'probably', *then wiped out and interlined above, then wiped out again and interlined with a caret for clarity*
309.23	dimly through] *over wiped-out possible* 'all day and', *then interlined above for clarity*
309.31	customs] 'c' *over wiped-out possible* 'l'
310.12	mother] 'm' *over wiped-out* 'sh'
310.22	grew as] *over wiped-out* 'looked', *then interlined above for clarity*
310.29–30	How unkind of those ugly satyrs!] *interlined with a caret*
310.35	how,] *interlined with a caret*
311.14	though] *a final* 't' *wiped from the word*
311.24	woman] 'w' *over wiped-out* 'it'
312.10–11	are made in such] *over wiped-out* 'are of such a kind' *then interlined above for clarity*
312.13	making] *over wiped-out* 'feeling'
312.17	a dragon] 'a' *interlined above deleted* 'some'
312.17	some] *interlined with a caret*
312.26	abode] *over wiped-out possible* 'res'
313.3	did] *follows deleted* 'of going abroad into the sunny world.'
313.8	as if she were] *over wiped-out* 'if not better'
313.9	set out] *over wiped-out* 'both set', *then interlined above for clarity*
313.11	the people] 'the' *interlined with a caret*
314.9	had] *over wiped-out* 'held'
314.9	chords] 'ch' *over wiped-out* 's[w]'
314.15	wreath] 'w' *over wiped-out possible* 's'
314.17	she] *over wiped-out* 'sh'
315.3	dominions] *over wiped-out* 'palace'
315.25	harp] *interlined with a caret above deleted* 'lyre'
316.19	beloved] *over wiped-out* 'dark'
316.23	all] *second* 'l' *over wiped-out* 'o'

316.30	put] 'p' *over wiped-out* 'f'
317.8	and gaze] 'and' *interlined with a caret above deleted* 'at'
317.15	they do] *over wiped-out possible* 'my li'
318.9	do] *over wiped-out possible* 'be'
319.21	may] *interlined with a caret*
319.26	of live] 'of' *over wiped-out* 'li'
319.29–30	the child's] *interlined with a caret above deleted* 'his'
321.14	first grow] *over wiped-out* 'grow along'
321.19	again] *over wiped-out possible* ', by'
321.26	king's] 'k' *over wiped-out* 'K'
321.32	may] *interlined with a caret above deleted* 'will'
322.8	Proserpina;] *semicolon deletes comma*
322.14	have] *interlined with a caret*
322.23	was] *over wiped-out* 'were', *then interlined for clarity*
322.24	flamed] *interlined with a caret above deleted* 'burned'
323.12	as kind] 'as' *interlined with a caret*
323.13	Perhaps] 'haps' *over wiped-out* 'pap'
323.31	was] 'a' *over wiped-out* 'er'
323.31	little Proserpina] *over wiped-out* 'Proserpina, [when]'
324.4–5	bending his dark face] *over wiped-out* 'stooping down to kiss her', *then* 'bending his dark' *interlined above for clarity*
324.9	besides] *over wiped-out possible* 'with [ ]'; *comma before* 'besides' *probably added after alteration*
324.16	roasting] 'asting' *over wiped-out possible* 'lling o'
324.18	liking.] *interlined with a caret above deleted* 'taste'
324.19	poor fat little man that he is!] *interlined with a caret which deletes a period, and a comma added after* 'trouble'
324.33	King] *over wiped-out* 'Plu'
325.8	the pomegranate] 'the' *over wiped-out possible* 'it'

325.10	shall] 'all' *over wiped-out* 'ould'
325.11	never think] *over wiped-out possible* 'not have thoug'
325.15	left the room] *interlined with a caret above deleted* 'withdrew'
326.5	a little] 'a' *over wiped-out possible* 'con'
326.9	said the king] *interlined with a caret*
326.13	I myself] 'I my' *over wiped-out* 'I my'
326.21	ah] 'a' *altered from* 'A' *which is possibly over another letter*
326.27	dusky] *over wiped-out* 'p[rison]'
326.30	food.] *period over wiped-out exclamation*
327.7	many] 'ma' *over wiped-out letters* ['ma'?]
327.9	away.] *precedes deleted* 'In a very short time, they were on the sur-/face of the earth.'
327.14	great] *over wiped-out* '[i]'
327.22	sprout] *interlined above deleted* 'grow'
327.24	after their long] *over wiped-out* 'and ate enorm', *then* 'after their' *interlined above for clarity*
327.31	Mother] *over wiped-out* 'Ceres had', *then interlined above for clarity*
327.33	had] *over wiped-out* 'was'
328.1	mean?] *query deletes comma*
328.14	mutual transport] *over wiped-out* 'transport was not', *then interlined above for clarity*
328.27	left] *interlined with a caret*
329.8	certainly] 'cer' *over wiped-out* 'did'
330.7	Chiron] 'Ch' *over wiped-out* 'ch'
330.18	suspected] *interlined with a caret*
331.2	grandchildren] *first* 'd' *interlined with a caret above* 'granchildren'
331.7	often] *interlined with a caret above deleted* 'sometimes'
331.12	horse] *over wiped-out* 'white'
331.23	above] 'v' *over wiped-out* 'b' *or* 'l'
331.34	being] *over wiped-out* 'f[in]d'
332.23	heavy] 'he' *over wiped-out* 'ra'
333.5	Or] *over wiped-out* 'or'
333.19	she] *over wiped-out* 'asked'
333.21	great brown] *over wiped-out* 'large brown', *then interlined for clarity*

333.22	or] *over wiped-out* 't[o]'
333.23	peacock] 'o' *over wiped-out possible* 'k' *then entire word interlined above for clarity*
333.31	peacock] *second* 'c' *over wiped-out* 'k'
334.1	if] *over wiped-out* 'I'
334.6	off] *interlined with a caret above deleted* 'from'
334.25	remarked.] *period replaces wiped-out comma*
334.34	the old dame's] *interlined with a caret above deleted* 'her'
335.13	hundred] *over wiped-out* 'arms'
335.27–28	Speaking Oak] *interlined with a caret above deleted* 'oracle'; 'O' *altered from* 'o'
335.29–30	the Speaking Oak] *interlined with a caret above deleted* 'oracle'; *a preceding* 'the' *inadvertently undeleted*
335.33	Instead] *over wiped-out* 'He gath', *then interlined above for clarity*
335.33–34	he went] 'he' *interlined with a caret*
335.34	struggling] 'strug-/' *over wiped-out* ', at last,', *then interlined above for clarity*
336.11	go] *interlined with a caret*
336.15	roundabout] *over wiped-out* 'around her', *then interlined above for clarity*
336.16	fancied] 'ied' *over wiped-out* 'ing'
336.18	rheumatic] *over wiped-out* 'hobble', *then interlined above for clarity*
336.20	peacock] 'o' *over wiped-out* 'k'
337.1	Iolcos] 'I' *altered from* 's'
337.21	come?] *query altered from exclamation*
338.23	Speaking Oak] 'S' *altered from* 's' *and* 'O' *altered from* 'o'
338.29	them] 'th' *altered from* 'w'
338.31	thrown] *interlined with a caret above deleted* 'put'
339.20	said] 's' *over possible* 'a'
340.17	home] *over wiped-out* 'him,'
341.11	a gentle] *over wiped-out* 'there were'
341.12	other] *over wiped-out* 'r[ ]an'
341.15	confusedly] *over wiped-out* 'indistin', *then interlined above for clarity*
341.20	leafy] 'y' *over wiped-out* 'ty'

341.27	again] *initial 'a' over wiped-out 'g'*
341.30	not] *interlined with a caret*
341.32	tree.] *precedes wiped-out and deleted* 'But, on inquiry among the peop'
342.2	should] *'s' over wiped-out 'it'*
342.18	a while] *originally* 'awhile' *but 'a' wiped out and reinscribed to the left as a separate word*
343.4	from beneath] 'from b' *over wiped-out* 'beneath'
343.7	arm] 'ar' *over wiped-out possible* 'wa'
343.10	perhaps] 'ha' *over wiped-out* 'pa'
343.10	the mouth] 'the' *over wiped-out* 'its'
343.22	advice, you] 'y' *wiped out and reinscribed to the right, perhaps in order to insert comma after* 'advice'
343.33	odd] *interlined with a caret above deleted* 'strange'
344.4	wondrous] 'rous' *over wiped-out* 'erful'
344.4	Jason—"(Since] *dash deletes comma*
344.7	youths] *'s' over possible* 'es'
344.8	have] *over wiped-out* 'be'
344.10	oaken] *possibly inscribed* 'oken', *then 'o' changed to 'a' and new 'o' added before 'a'*
344.28	they] *interlined with a caret*
345.6	Hercules] 'H' *over wiped-out possible* 'h'
345.18	grove] *over wiped-out* 'fore'
345.23	fair damsel] 'fair d' *over wiped-out* 'young d'
345.30	blustering] *interlined above deleted* 'boisterous'
346.10	Lynceus] *interlined above deleted* 'he'
346.14	him] 'im' *altered from* 'an'
346.27	rot] *precedes wiped-out comma*
346.34	answered] *'s' over wiped-out possible* 'ag'
347.1	for the question to be put,)—"Seat] 'for' *interlined with a caret above deleted* 'to'; *on next line,* 'the . . . put' *interlined above deleted* 'be asked'; 'put' *covers quotes before* 'Seat', *which were re-inscribed below*
347.13	strain of] *over wiped-out* 'piece of m' *then* 'strain' *interlined above for clarity*
347.14	billows] *over wiped-out* 'g[ ]'
347.29	his] *interlined with a caret above deleted* 'the'

347.33   who] *interlined with a caret above deleted*
          'which'
347.34   he] *altered from* 'it'
348.6   any of] *interlined with a caret above deleted*
          'all'
348.11   hospitably] 'hos-/' *over wiped-out* 'rec-/' *and*
          'pit' *over wiped-out* 'ei'
348.16   subjects] 'b' *over wiped-out* 'j'
348.18   people] *interlined with a caret*
348.19   it] *interlined with a caret*
348.32   Cyzicus] 'z' *altered from* 'c'
349.5   by] *over wiped-out* 'on all'
349.5   himself;] *semicolon deletes comma*
349.6   wield] 'e' *over wiped-out* 'l'
349.6–7   with another] 'with' *interlined with a caret;*
          'an' *over wiped-out* 'and'
349.9   him] *interlined with a caret*
349.12   had] *precedes deleted* 'had as many arms'
349.17   have] *interlined with a caret*
349.19   voyagers] *interlined with a caret above deleted*
          'adventurers'
349.26–27 were in the habit of] *over wiped-out* 'snatched
          away his fo' *then* 'were . . . habit' *inter-
          lined above for clarity*
349.31   the victuals] 'the' *over wiped-out* 'their'
349.32   out;] *semicolon over comma*
349.33   set] *precedes deleted* 'out'
350.12   reposing] *precedes deleted* 'themselves'
350.14   them] 'em' *over wiped-out possible* 'eir'
350.16   fifty] 'fif' *over wiped-out possible* 'her'
350.21   aloft] 'o' *over wiped-out possible* 'f'
350.27   not] 'n' *over wiped-out* 'w'
350.30   Daughter] 'D' *altered from* 'd'
350.30   Oak,] *comma over wiped-out exclamation*
350.32   peril] *over wiped-out* 'trouble'
350.33   their] *interlined with a caret*
351.10   this] *altered from* 'their', *then interlined above
          for clarity*
351.16   were] 'ere' *over wiped-out* 'as'
351.19   do] *over wiped-out* 'y'
351.19   imagine] 'a' *over wiped-out* 'g'

351.24	born] *over wiped-out* 'broug', *then interlined above for clarity*
351.26	which] 'c' *over wiped-out* 'h'
351.30	understood] *over wiped-out* 'heard', *then interlined above for clarity*
352.4	is not this] *over wiped-out* 'are not t', *then interlined above for clarity*
352.6	nine-and-forty] 'a' *over wiped-out* 'f'
352.8	I do] *over wiped-out* 'you'
352.10	fear] *mended from* 'fare' *or badly-formed* 'fear' *then interlined above for clarity*
352.11	awe] *over wiped-out* 'terror' *then interlined above for clarity*
352.23	Orpheus] *precedes wiped-out comma*
353.6	my] *altered from* 'cou'
353.8	him] *interlined with a caret*
353.23	Prince] *over wiped-out* 'Jason' *then interlined above for clarity*
354.8	cinder!] *exclamation precedes wiped-out exclamation*
355.6	other] *interlined above deleted* 'most'
355.7	which] *follows deleted* 'of'
355.15	persons] *over wiped-out* 'peop'
355.17	as into a deep well, yet can never be certain] *over wiped-out* 'yet can never be certain whether you see into'; *then* 'as . . . well' *and* 'yet . . . certain' *interlined above for clarity, the comma after* 'well' *inserted clearly within the line*
355.28–29	Circe, my father's sister, taught me to be one.] *interlined with a caret*
355.33	galley] *over wiped-out* 'vess'
356.19	The young] 'The' *over wiped-out* 'Jason', *then interlined above for clarity*
356.24	gave] *over wiped-out* 'h[ ]', *then interlined above for clarity*
356.31	After entering] 'After e' *over wiped-out* 'After g'
357.12	afraid—" said] *right hand quotes altered from left hand quotes*
357.22	At some distance] *over wiped-out* 'He now perceived', *then interlined above for clarity*

357.23	regularly] 'a' *possibly altered from* 'r'
357.26	which was] *interlined with a caret*
357.30	and] 'a' *possibly altered from* 'w'
358.4	flash.] *over wiped-out* 'gleam.'
358.9	down] *over wiped-out* 't[ow]'
358.21	fancied] 'f' *over wiped-out possible* 'th'
358.24	an iron] 'an' *interlined with a caret*
358.30	danger] *over wiped-out* 'about to', *then interlined above for clarity*
358.31	the bull] *over wiped-out* 'by' *which is over wiped-out* 'the bull'; *then interlined above for clarity*
358.32	gripe] *interlined with a caret above deleted* 'take'
358.33	it.] *precedes wiped-out beginning of quotes*
359.27–28	These bright objects] 'se' *of* 'These' *possibly over wiped-out* 'y'; 'bright objects' *interlined with a caret*
359.30	beneath] *interlined with a caret*
360.1	Next were seen their] 'Next were' *over wiped-out* 'Then were' *and* 'seen their' *over wiped-out* 'seen their'; *then all four words interlined above for clarity*
360.14	possess] *over wiped-out* 'have', *then interlined above for clarity*
360.14	which] 'w' *over wiped-out* 'th'
360.21	flourishing] 'fl' *over wiped-out* 'br'
360.32	Guard] 'u' *altered from possible* 'ol'
361.8	discern] 'd' *over wiped-out* 'se'
361.14	him] *interlined with a caret*
361.15	been] *interlined with a caret*
361.23	behold] *interlined with a caret above deleted* 'see'
362.21	palace] *first* 'a' *over wiped-out* 'la'
363.24	march] 'm' *over wiped-out* 'g'
363.29	as Jason was] *over wiped-out* 'as he was hast', *then interlined above for clarity*
363.34–364.1	only the night before, he was by no means] *over wiped-out* 'he was by no rights very sure that she would not', *then interlined above for clarity, the comma after* 'before' *retained within the line*

364.1   certain] *interlined with a caret above deleted* 'sure'

364.13   tomorrow's] *over wiped-out* 'nightfall', *then interlined above for clarity*

364.19   seen] *interlined with a caret*

364.23   While they] *over wiped-out* 'While cros', *then interlined above for clarity*

364.24   heads] *over wiped-out* 'thr[ea *or* us]', *then interlined above for clarity*

365.9   a glimmer] 'a' *over wiped-out* 'th'

365.10   or, now-and-then] 'or now' *over partially wiped-out* 'or else' *then* 'or now-' *interlined above for clarity*

365.24   glitters] 'glit-/' *over wiped-out* 'hangs' *and* 'ters' *over wiped-out* 'be' *then both parts of the word interlined above for clarity*

366.7   radiance] *over wiped-out* 'lig'

366.9–10   there was a frightful hiss, and] *interlined with a caret*

366.12   tree] *interlined with a caret*

366.13   him] *interlined with a caret*

366.15   within] *over wiped-out* 'nigh'

367.1   dragon] 'd' *over wiped-out letter, possibly* 's'

367.2   hissing] *over wiped-out* 'darting'

367.8   it] *over wiped-out possible* 'th'

367.9   full] 'fu' *altered from* 'le'

367.12   outright.] *period precedes wiped-out exclamation*

367.13   You] 'Y' *over wiped-out lefthand quotes*

367.19   helped] 'h' *over wiped-out* 'c', *then entire word interlined above for clarity*

367.20   clapped] 'cl' *altered from* 'ca'

367.21   trees] *precedes deleted* 'Meanwhile, Lynceus, with his sharp eyes, had already caught a glimpse of Jason, bringing the Golden Fleece, although several stone-walls, a hill, and the black shadows of the Grove of Mars, all intervened between. By his advice, the nine-and-forty heroes had seated themselves'

367.22   Espying] 'n' *over wiped-out* 'g'

367.22   winged] *interlined with a caret*

367.22   North Wind] 'Wind' *over wiped-out* 'wind' *which was possibly combined with* 'North' *as one word*

367.22–24   (who . . . aloft,)] *parentheses added after phrase inscribed; closing parenthesis over wiped-out* 'in'

367.24   Jason] 'J' *over wiped-out* 't'

367.24   bade] *over wiped-out* 'shouted', *then interlined above for clarity*

367.29   heroes] *over wiped-out* 'nine-'

COMPOSITORIAL STINTS

A Wonder Book
(First Edition of 1852)

Note: This table lists (in order) the compositor's name, written on the MS at the start of his stint; Centenary page-lines included; within square brackets the first and last words of the stint; MS page references followed by the notations (l) identifying links, and (t) identifying texts, each chapter being numbered separately; the 1852 first-edition (I) page-line references; and, within parentheses, the number of first-edition lines of type set in the stint.

Nichols	5.1–38.16	[Beneath . . . stories."] MS 1–5 (l), 1–19 (t), 6–8 (l). I, 7.1–58.24 (1214)
Stevenson	38.17–50.21	[Cousin . . . parlor.] MS 9–10 (l), 1–8(t). I, 58.25–77.25 (449)
Nichols	50.21–60.20	[No . . . felt!] MS 8–13 (t), 11–12 (l). I, 78.1–92.16 (361)
Nichols	61.1–67.22	[The . . . idea] MS 13–15 (l), 1–2 (t). I, 93.1–101.25 (201)

Stevenson	67.22–83.17	[of . . . besides.] MS 2–14 (t) 16 (l). I, 102.1–127.4 (599)
Stevenson	85.1–89.31	[The . . . mantel-piece.] MS 17–20 (l). I, 128.1–135.7–8 (176)
Nichols	90.1–94.22	[Did . . . this] MS 20 (l), 1–4 (t). I, 136.1–142.25 (168)
Stevenson	94.22–99.29	[was . . . disheartened,] MS 4–8 (t). I, 143.1–150.24 (199)
Nichols	99.29–104.25	[and . . . in] MS 8–12 (t). I, 151.1–158.25 (199)
Stevenson	104.25–109.28	[a voice . . . certainly] MS 12–16 (t). I, 159.1–166.25 (199)
Ware	109.28–113.20	[a very . . . rhymes.] MS 16–17 (t), 21–22 (l). I, 167.1–172.19 (121)
Nichols	115.1–121.12	[And . . . prince.] MS 23–25 (l), 1–3 (t). I, 173.1–181.24 (209)
Ware	121.13–124.14	[So . . . remark-] MS 3–5 (t). I, 181.25–186.18 (119)
Stevenson	124.14–131.23	[ably . . . it] MS 5–10 (t). I, 186.19–197.25 (279)
Nichols	131.23–134.32	[with . . . gone!] MS 10–13 (t). I, 198.1–203.5 (129)
Nichols	134.33–143.26	["Alas!" . . . follows.] MS 13–15 (t), 26–29 (l). I, 203.6–213.26 (245)
Stevenson	144.1–149.9	[Once . . . often] MS 1–5 (t). I, 214.1–221.25 (193)
Nichols	149.9–171.19	[laugh . . . Tanglewood.] MS 5–20 (t), 30–32 (l). I, 222.1–256.9 (831)

TANGLEWOOD TALES
(*First Edition of 1853*)

NOTE: This table lists (in order) the compositor's name, written on the MS at the start of his stint; Centenary page-lines included; within square brackets the first and last words of the stint; MS page references, each chapter being numbered separately; the 1853 first-edition (I) page-line references; and, within parentheses, the number of first-edition lines of type set in the stint.

(unknown)	175.1–180.9	[A short . . . made.] MS 1–5. I, 7.1–15.14 (207)
Marvin	180.10–185.26	[Eustace . . . world.] MS 5–6, 1–3. I, 15.15–23.12 (186)
Manning	185.27–190.30	[It . . . lips.] MS 3–6. I, 23.13–32.6 (219)
Marvin	190.31–199.15	[So . . . again.] MS 6–13. I, 32.7–47.4 (374)
Manning	199.16–201.32	[Theseus . . . do.] MS 13–15. I, 47.5–51.15 (111)
Marvin	201.33–209.24	[No . . . hands.] MS 15–20. I, 51.16–65.4 (340)
Squire	209.25–218.24	["Thanks . . . them.] MS 21–23, 1–5. I, 65.5–80.20 (367)
Marvin	218.25–221.9	["Ho! . . . up!"] MS 5–6. I, 80.21–85.5 (111)
Manning	221.10–231.11	[But . . . war.] MS 7–15. I, 85.6–102.21 (442)
Marvin	231.12–242.8	[After . . . hereabouts!"] MS 15–17, 1–7. I, 102.22–121.16 (444)

Manning	242.9–250.17	[At . . . going.] MS 7–13. I, 121.17–135.20 (355)
Marvin	250.18–254.34	[This . . . down!"] MS 13–17. I, 135.21–143.15 (195)
Manning	255.1–257.8	["Nor . . . saw!] MS 17–18. I, 143.16–147.10 (95)
Marvin	257.9–260.6	[Running . . . sow!] MS 18–20. I, 147.11–152.12 (127)
Manning	260.7–262.21	["Cadmus . . . teeth!] MS 21–22. I, 152.13–156.23 (111)
Marvin	262.22–268.7	[And . . . forward.] MS 23–24, 1–3. I, 156.24–166.7 (217)
Manning	268.8–270.16	["Have . . . afterwards!"] MS 3–5. I, 166.8–170.7 (100)
Marvin	270.17–277.4	["That . . . up?"] MS 5–10. I, 170.8–181.13 (281)
Manning	277.5–281.12	["Tush! . . . dainties.] MS 10–13. I, 181.14–188.19 (181)
Marvin	281.13–283.16	[And, . . . noses!] MS 13–15. I, 188.20–192.7 (89)
Manning	283.17–285.22	[But . . . return.] MS 15–16. I, 192.8–196.3 (97)
Marvin	285.23–291.9	[It . . . him!] MS 16–21. I, 196.4–205.20 (243)
Manning	291.10–305.30	["Drink, . . . plate.] MS 21–24, 1–7. I, 205.21–230.16 (611)
Marvin	305.31–312.7	["I . . . cavern?"] MS 7–11. I, 230.17–241.15 (274)
Manning	312.8–317.32	["No," . . . good.] MS 11–15. I, 241.16–251.12 (247)

Marvin	317.33–321.12	["Will . . . inexorable.] MS 15–17. I, 251.13–257.10 (148)
Martyn	321.13–324.2	["Never," . . . his.] MS 17–19. I, 257.11–261.24 (114)
Manning	324.3–326.32	["I . . . mother!"] MS 19–21. I, 261.25–266.25 (127)
Marvin	326.33–335.17	[Now, . . . sandals.] MS 21–22, 1–5. I, 267.1–280.26 (329)
Manning	335.18–337.23	[At . . . man?"] MS 5–6. I, 281.1–284.21 (96)
Martyn	337.24–340.6	[Poor . . . power.] MS 7–9. I, 284.22–289.4 (108)
Marvin	340.7–342.21	[Therefore, . . . rest.] MS 9–11. I, 289.5–293.7 (103)
Martyn	342.22–345.20	["Cut . . . dance!] MS 11–13. I, 293.8–298.6 (124)
Manning	345.21–347.25	[One . . . horizon.] MS 13–15. I, 298.7–301.25 (94)
Marvin	347.26–350.8	[In . . . again.] MS 15–17. I, 302.1–306.9 (109)
Manning	350.9–352.22	[Then . . . him!"] MS 17–18. I, 306.10–310.16 (107)
Marvin	352.23–358.18	[And . . . asbestos!] MS 19–23. I, 310.17–320.17 (251)
Manning	358.19–363.13	[Greatly . . . fleece.] MS 23–27. I, 320.18–328.25 (208)
Martyn	363.14–368.6	["You . . . wings!] MS 27–30. I, 329.1–336.25 (205)

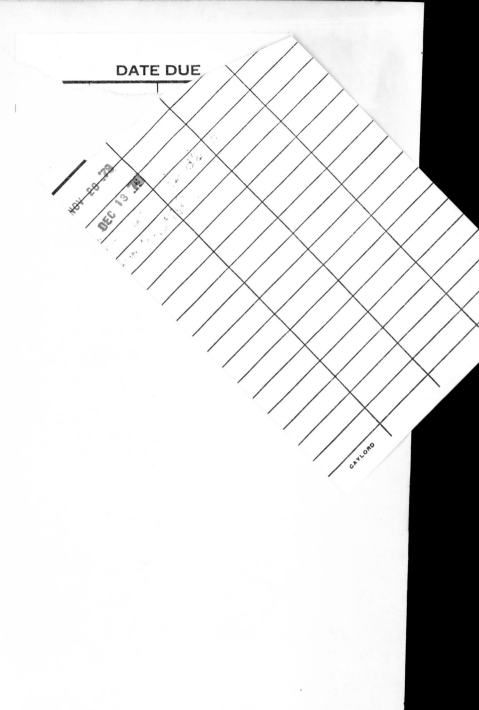